POINTS OF CONTACT

Science, Religion, and the Search for Truth

GLENN SAUER

Maryknoll, New York 10545

Founded in 1970, Orbis Books endeavors to publish works that enlighten the mind, nourish the spirit, and challenge the conscience. The publishing arm of the Maryknoll Fathers and Brothers, Orbis seeks to explore the global dimensions of the Christian faith and mission, to invite dialogue with diverse cultures and religious traditions, and to serve the cause of reconciliation and peace. The books published reflect the views of their authors and do not represent the official position of the Maryknoll Society. To learn more about Maryknoll and Orbis Books, please visit our website at www.orbisbooks.com.

Published by Orbis Books, Box 302, Maryknoll, NY 10545-0302.

Manufactured in the United States of America

Library of Congress Cataloging-in-Publication Data

Names: Sauer, Glenn, author.
Title: Points of contact : science, religion, and the search for truth / by Glenn Sauer.
Description: Maryknoll, NY : Orbis Books, 2020. | Includes bibliographical references and index. | Summary: "A Catholic scientist offers a proposal for reconciling the historically evolving divide between science and religion"—Provided by publisher.
Identifiers: LCCN 2019048249 (print) | LCCN 2019048250 (ebook) | ISBN 9781626983731 (paperback) | ISBN 9781608338375 (ebook)
Subjects: LCSH: Religion and science. | Catholic Church—Doctrines.
Classification: LCC BL240.3 .S28 2020 (print) | LCC BL240.3 (ebook) | DDC 261.5/5—dc23
LC record available at https://lccn.loc.gov/2019048249
LC ebook record available at https://lccn.loc.gov/2019048250

For Debra

Contents

Introduction ix

Acknowledgments xiii

PART I. Foundations **1**

1. Enemies or Friends? **3**
Ian Barbour's Four Typologies of Science and Religion 5
Conflict 5
Independence 7
Dialogue 8
Integration 12
Christian Responses to Darwin 14
The Nature of Reality 19

2. Humility **26**
Faith and Reason 31
Knowledge and Belief 33
Repetition and Revelation 37
Spirituality 40
Critical Realism 43
Paradigms 46
Hubris 51
Humility in Science and Religion 54

3. The Voice of God **57**
Our Disciplinary Education 59
Shift toward Science 60
Beyond the Sciences 63

Teilhard de Chardin's Life of Science and Faith 67
Early Sparks of Interest 67
Mining the Secrets of Fossils 68
Teilhard the Theologian 70
A New Theology 72
Cosmic Significance of Human Evolution 73
The Inevitability of Consciousness? 77
Listening to the Voice of God 79

PART II. Big Questions **85**

4. Creation **87**
Models of the Cosmos 88
Aristotle 88
Galileo 91
Isaac Newton 98
The Big Bang 100
Albert Einstein 101
Edwin Hubble 103
Georges Lemaître 103
Confirmation of the Big Bang 106
The Anthropic Principle 109
The Multiverse 111
The Theory of Everything 112
How Can We Be Sure? 115
Ultimate Explanations 117

5. Life **122**
Stardust 123
There's No Place like Home 125
The Water of Life 127
The Vital Element 129
The Secret of Slime 130
Origins of Life 130
Thermodynamics 134
Forms of Life? 135

The Search for the Last Universal Common Ancestor (LUCA) 139
Life Energy 142
A Living Planet 143
Why Can't We Just Live Together? 145
Our Interconnected World 148
Is There Anybody Out There? 151

6. Evolution **158**
Charles Darwin 157
The HMS Beagle 160
Natural Selection and Population 165
On the Origin of Species 167
Collateral Damage 170
Darwinism Gone Wrong 174
Creationism and Its Descendants 177
The Scopes Trial 177
Laws and Specific Types of Creationism 179
Intelligent Design 180
Lasting Effects on Science Education 185
Wonderful Life 186
These Old Bones 192

7. Humans **196**
The Secrets of Inheritance 198
Biology Grows Up 201
Let's Go for a Walk 204
Apocalypse and Opportunity 207
Theodicy 209
And the Meek Shall Inherit the Earth 211
Human Evolution 214
Body 216
Mind 222
Spirit 226
Becoming Human 229

Index 233

Introduction

When I was a young boy in the small town of Wernersville, Pennsylvania, I was outside all the time. My friends and I were always running through the cornfields behind my house, exploring the small creek that wound its way under several bridges along Furnace Road, hiking or biking up South Mountain, or playing endless games of backyard baseball. My personal favorite was the raucous summer games of flashlight hide and seek with the thirty-plus kids from the Franklin and Pearl streets neighborhood. On Saturday afternoons, my father would load my brother Gregg, my best friend Tony, and me into the car and take us to our Catholic religious education classes at the nearby St. Isaac Jogues Jesuit Novitiate where we were taught the Baltimore Catechism of the time. I happened to be very good at memorizing and reciting the catechism and at least one of the Jesuit Brothers who taught us there suggested to my father that I might consider a vocation to the priesthood. Whether we actually liked our classes or not is difficult to recall. But we loved going to the novitiate: 240 acres of rolling hills, expansive lawns, hidden trails, cornfields, and religious shrines. Those grounds were the site of many childhood adventures and misadventures.

My family moved away from Wernersville when I was in the sixth grade. I went on to high school, college, and graduate school and began my professional life as a research scientist. While doing postdoctoral work at the University of South Carolina in Columbia during the 1990s, I became vaguely aware of occasional conflicts between scientific and religious points of view, most commonly centered around the teaching of evolution in public school curricula. I read the newspaper accounts with some interest but was too busy with my research on bone formation and with teaching biochemistry to think much about it. In 2000, I moved to Connecticut with my wife, Debra, four children, and two dogs to begin a faculty position at Fairfield University, one of twenty-seven Jesuit colleges and universities in the United States. Shortly after arriving at Fairfield, my first dean, Dr. Beverly Kahn, sent me information about applying for the Science and Religion Course Award program administered by the Center for Theology and the Natural Sciences (CTNS) in Berkeley, California, with support from the John Templeton Foundation. To this day I don't know why Dean Kahn suggested that I consider applying. I can only guess that the fact that I was raised Catholic might have come up during my job interview with her.

My application to CTNS for the course award was successful, and I developed a course called "God and Modern Biology," which I have been teaching annually at Fairfield for the past twenty years. My biggest surprise in starting this project was that science and religion is an academic discipline, like biology or theology. The field has its own literature, professional journals, and annual conferences. My CTNS course award led to several other projects, including a Fairfield University faculty and staff discussion group supported by the Metanexus Institute in Philadelphia, a delightful trip to Mexico for the Science and Transcendence Advanced Research Series (STARS) program from CTNS, and finally a parish outreach project also named "God and Modern Biology" with the Catholic Diocese of Bridgeport, Connecticut. In all of this work, I have been generously supported by the John Templeton Foundation. The many years of discussions, arguments, and shared insights among students, faculty colleagues, community partners, and participants in these projects has led to this book. It is intended to serve as an introduction to the broad interdisciplinary field of science and religion. It is thus written for nonspecialists, though I hope it will be of interest to faculty colleagues of many disciplines and specialties. This book might serve as the text for an introductory course in science and religion like mine, as a starting point for adult discussion groups in churches, synagogues, and Catholic parishes, or even as a change of fare for science or theology discussion groups at colleges and universities around the world.

This volume is organized into two main parts. In part I (Foundations), chapter 1 serves as a general introduction to science and religion using the pioneering work of Ian Barbour as a starting point to frame the discussion. Chapter 2 considers the virtue of humility as it applies to terms like knowledge, faith, and reason. Too often, one side or the other in the science vs. religion wars will seize one of these terms as their exclusive domain on which to plant their battle standards—I hope to find a way past that type of exchange. Chapter 3 explores why people are drawn to science either as a career, like I was, or as interested members of our larger community. Here the life of the French Jesuit Pierre Teilhard de Chardin can serve as an illustration. I will also explore why in our modern era, science and religion are viewed by some as oppositional fields. In part II (chapters 4–7) we will examine some of the big questions in the science-and-religion conversation using the lives and ideas of the key historical figures who have shaped this dialogue over the past two centuries. These chapters will tell two stories. First, they will recount the history of our universe and Earth from the Big Bang to modern-day humans as we presently understand it. And second, they will lay out the historical development of the scientific fields that have contributed to our cosmic story, along with the ways in which science has intersected with religion and theology over the centuries. The stories will be framed by the topics of Big Bang cosmology (chapter 4), the origin of life (chapter 5), Darwin and evolution (chapter 6), and the history of life on Earth to the evolution of humans (chapter 7). I hope to provide enough depth on these topics to whet the appetite of you, my readers, for further exploration. However, I do not provide a comprehensive analysis of the scientific fields or detailed theological arguments, as a complete consideration of any of these fields could fill multiple volumes. Finally, interspersed throughout the book, I hope to offer you some guidance on how you might begin to reflect on these topics at a spiritual level. As a spiritual director in the Murphy Center for Ignatian Spirituality at Fairfield University, I am interested in developing and encouraging spiritual growth. The discussions I have had on these topics with students, friends, and colleagues over the years have helped to mold and shape my spirituality. I hope they will do the same for you.

The St. Isaac Jogues Novitiate in Wernersville is now the Jesuit Center for Spiritual Growth. The Jesuit novices are long gone, and the Jesuit, religious, and lay spiritual directors who work there now provide individual and group retreats for priests, religious sisters, spiritual directors, and anyone else interested in self-exploration and spiritual growth. On the final evening of my first retreat at the Jesuit Center several years ago, I sat on the front lawn looking across the valley at nearby Cushion Peak, where my family would often hike on crisp fall days. As I sat there contemplating the mountain, I imagined my childhood self staring down at the present-day me from the peak and across the years. A flood of memories washed over me—my family, my friends, my mentors, and colleagues who have filled my life with so many blessings and so many gifts. Tears of joy filled my eyes, and I thanked God for all that I have experienced in my life. This sacred place was the start of that journey. I am grateful to you now, my readers, for the opportunity to share a part of my journey with you.

Wernersville, Pennsylvania
July 29, 2019

Acknowledgments

This work was made possible through many years of financial support from the John Templeton Foundation of West Conshohocken, Pennsylvania, and their collaborators at the Center for Theology and the Natural Sciences in Berkeley, California, and the Metanexus Institute of Philadelphia, Pennsylvania. I am also indebted to the many students, faculty colleagues, and community friends who have participated in these programs—especially the members of the Catholic Diocese of Bridgeport, Connecticut, and of the following parishes in Connecticut: St. Pius X (Fairfield), St. Luke (Westport), St. Mary (Ridgefield), St. Francis of Assisi (Weston), St. Aloysius (Darien), and Assumption (Fairfield).

I thank my many faculty friends and colleagues at Fairfield University, especially Professors Nancy Dallavalle and Paul Lakeland of the Religious Studies Department, who have contributed so much to my knowledge of theology and religion, worked with me as co-teachers, and been gentle guides and reviewers as I developed this work over many years. Thanks to my deans of the College of Arts and Sciences: Dr. Beverly Kahn, Dr. Timothy Law Snyder, Dr. Robbin Crabtree, and my current mentor and friend, Dr. Richard Greenwald. They have always provided their enthusiastic support whenever I had an idea for a new project or needed some time to finish an old one. I also thank my mentors in Fairfield's Spiritual Direction Formation Program: Maria Decsy, Eileen Crusan, Deborah Delano, Maria Tattu Bowen, and Sister Karen Doyle, SSJ; and my longtime spiritual director Patricia Brennan. Their caring and patient efforts over the years have taught me what spirituality is really all about, helping me to grow in surprising new ways. Of all my colleagues at Fairfield University, I owe my deepest thanks to Rev. James Bowler, SJ. Jim has at various times been a teacher, a mentor, a spiritual director, my supervisor, a collaborator, and most of all a dear, dear friend. His many subtle thoughts, insights, and inspirations flow throughout these pages. To my newest colleague, my editor at Orbis Books, Jill O'Brien, many thanks for your patience, wisdom, and guidance in helping me prepare this, my first book-length manuscript.

Thanks to my family for sharing our journey together, especially Debra, who has reviewed, discussed, and inspired all of this work; and my children, Christian, Maria, Gabrielle, and Teresa, who are always there to comfort, love, and support me in all that I do. And lastly, to my dog, Mina, my constant and loyal companion throughout all the days of writing that went into this volume.

PART I
Foundations

1

Enemies or Friends?

I like books. I have hundreds of them lining the shelves of both my home and university office. So, on most weekends I like to spend a little time browsing the *New York Times Book Review*. On any given weekend, one might come across books on the *Times*' bestseller non-fiction list with titles such as *God: The Failed Hypothesis* by physicist Victor Stenger, *The God Delusion* by evolutionary biologist Richard Dawkins, or *God Is Not Great: How Religion Poisons Everything* by popular author and journalist Christopher Hitchens. Many of the writers in this so-called new atheist genre of contemporary literature use modern scientific explanations of the natural world to argue that God almost certainly does not exist and that (at best) religious belief in modern times is irrelevant. On the other side of the coin are religiously inspired books such as *Intelligent Design* by mathematician William Dembski, *Darwin's Black Box* by biochemist Michael Behe, or *Darwin's Doubt* by Discovery Institute senior fellow Stephen Meyer. These writers often misrepresent or trivialize modern science, especially evolutionary biology, in favor of more traditional interpretations of natural history and human origins.

For well over a century, the relationship between science and religion has been portrayed as a perpetual state of warfare.[1] Many times, popular print media are all too eager to play up this notion.[2]

1. Andrew Dickson White, *A History of the Warfare of Science with Theology in Christendom* (New York: Appleton, 1896). Reprinted by Astounding Stories, 2015.

2. Ronald L. Numbers, *The Creationists: From Scientific Creationism to Intelligent Design* (Cambridge, MA: Harvard University Press, 2006), 396–98.

For example, a cover story in *National Geographic* raised the question "Was Darwin Wrong?"[3] Meanwhile, *Time* magazine ran a cover feature on "The Evolution Wars."[4] In a *New York Times* op-ed piece, biologist David Barash describes giving his students "The Talk," in which he points out to them the "intellectual instability" of religious belief.[5] In the warfare model, one must choose either science or religion. More specifically, this model presents us with a choice between an atheistic, materialist worldview and a worldview filled with superstition and fantasy where scientific fact can be conveniently ignored. Both sides of the warfare model promote narrow mindedness and offer ignorance and divisiveness at a time in Western history when reliable knowledge and inclusiveness are sorely needed.

When I visit Catholic parishes or other religious communities to discuss science and religion, it is the warfare mindset that community members expect to dominate our discussions. This expectation exists despite the fact that, for the most part, religious communities like these are not antagonistic to science and are actually quite interested in learning about recent scientific advances in cosmology, health-related fields, the history of life on Earth, and environmental concerns. Contrary to the claims of the warfare proponents, such discussions do not lead to a polarizing rejection of either religion or science, but to intellectual and spiritual growth, a deepening sense of community, and a greater solidarity with the natural world. In my experience, "warfare" does not come anywhere close to describing how most people think about science and religion. New frameworks are needed for addressing questions arising from the interactions between scientific knowledge and religious faith. The tedious ping-pong match between the "new atheists" and the science deniers in our culture ought to be ignored in favor of a humbler, more inclusive, and life-affirming conversation.

---

3. David Quammen, "Was Darwin Wrong?" *National Geographic* 207 (November 2004): 2–35.

4. Claudia Wallis, "The Evolution Wars," *Time* 166 (August 15, 2005): 5–15.

5. David P. Barash, "God, Darwin and My College Biology Class," *New York Times Op-Ed*, September 27, 2014.

Ian Barbour's Four Typologies of Science and Religion

Ian G. Barbour was a scientist and theologian who taught both physics and religion for many years at Carleton College in Northfield, Minnesota. In the 1960s Barbour published a groundbreaking book entitled *Issues in Science and Religion*, which is widely regarded as the foundation of a new interdisciplinary academic field of the same name, that is, science and religion.

Conflict

Despite popular media portrayals that focus on conflict, Barbour did not see warfare between science and religion everywhere he looked, either historically or in the present. He saw science and Christian theology developing hand in hand over the centuries, with some of science's biggest breakthroughs made by devoutly religious people such as Isaac Newton (who first quantified gravity), and Gregor Mendel (the father of modern genetics). From Barbour's perspective, warfare—or, as he describes it, conflict—is only one of several possible ways, or typologies, in which science and religion might interact in the human imagination.[6] Barbour refers to the warfare model as an example of what he calls the "Conflict" typology, a highly selective and narrow view of science and religion that includes both *scientific materialism* and *biblical literalism*.[7] While this certainly describes a small but outspoken number of scientists as well as some fundamentalist Christian communities, the majority of people, according to Barbour, would fall into one of three other typologies that he names "Independence," "Dialogue," and "Integration."

At the outset, I would like to simply state that I agree with Barbour. Advocates of the conflict thesis are promoting a false dichotomy that negates the great richness of both scientific knowledge and religious thought. Just by picking up the newspaper we can see the

6. Ian G. Barbour, *Religion and Science: Historical and Contemporary Issues* (San Francisco: HarperCollins, 1997).

7. Ian G. Barbour, *When Science Meets Religion* (San Francisco, HarperOne, 2000).

sharp divisions in our world as polarized viewpoints dominate public conversations. But science and religion do not need to be cast as antagonists, adding to the discord. It just might be possible that these realms of human thought and experience could be seen as partners that could begin working together to help heal the divisiveness in our world. In order to do this, we need only to stop focusing on conflict and begin looking for places of fruitful interaction. Barbour's 2014 newspaper obituary focused on his work in bridging the "science–religion divide,"[8] and his life's work has provided some tools for achieving this, if only we look past conflict.

As an introductory exercise, I would like to take a look at Barbour's other, lesser-known typologies as they relate to a few recent points of contact between science and religion. My perspective is that of a scientist, a practicing Roman Catholic, and a spiritual director. The religious viewpoints I will explore throughout this book are predominantly informed by a Christian understanding of nature and our greater reality but will hopefully be of interest to persons of other faith traditions, agnostics, atheists, and those with no stated position or tradition. Regardless of one's scientific background or religious views, I believe integration of these realms of thought is not only possible; it is necessary. Many of the young people I encounter as a spiritual director describe themselves as "seekers" who are not firmly attached to any religious affiliation. They take the findings of science very seriously, but they also embrace the notion that there is a spiritual aspect of reality that they want to understand in order to become more fully human, truer to their own individual natures. This quest for individual meaning is a primary focus of spiritual direction. It is for the seekers in our midst that I hope this book will be of special interest, for it is in working with them that I find the greatest hope for moving past the deadening confines of conflict. We will now briefly examine Barbour's other typologies (independence, dialogue, and integration) and look at some recent examples of each.

8. Elaine Woo, "Ian Barbour Dies at 90; Academic Who Bridged Science–Religion Divide," *Los Angeles Times*, January 1, 2014.

Independence

In his 1950 encyclical *Humani generis*, Pope Pius XII addressed several issues emerging from mid-twentieth-century thought in the areas of theology, philosophy, and science that had been challenging the traditional Roman Catholic doctrine of that time.[9] On the topic of evolution, and to the surprise of many, Pius XII's stance was essentially neutral. He neither agreed nor disagreed with the science of evolution but allowed for this field of inquiry to unfold into the future. He warned, however, of materialist philosophies, based in part on biological evolution, that challenge the existence of God or God's participation in the process of creation.[10]

Many years later, evolutionary biologist Stephen J. Gould coined the term NOMA, or "non-overlapping magisteria," to describe his own position regarding science and religion. Gould described himself as an atheist, but he found much agreement with Pius XII.[11] To Gould, science and religion were two completely independent realms of human activity, and neither yielded information that was useful in any way to the other. In Gould's poetic terms, "Science is about the age of rocks, religion tells us about the rock of ages."[12] This certainly seems to be a better model than one of perpetual conflict as adhered to by many of the new atheist writers. If nothing else, the independence typology advocates for having tolerance for those with different viewpoints. In my own experience, independence describes the way many people, including most of the young adults I encounter in my classes at Fairfield University, engage with science and religion. Neither field, it seems to most, has much to do with the other.

The academy is oftentimes a world where disciplines are extremely compartmentalized. At many universities, students never encounter

---

9. Pope Pius XII, *Humani Generis*, "Concerning Some False Opinions Threatening to Undermine the Foundations of Catholic Doctrine" (Vatican City, 1950).

10. Ibid., nos. 36–38.

11. Stephen J. Gould, "Non-overlapping Magisteria," in *Leonardo's Mountain of Clams and the Diet of Worms: Essays on Natural History* (New York: Harmony Books, 1998), 269–84.

12. Stephen J. Gould, *Rocks of Ages: Science and Religion in the Fullness of Life* (New York: Ballantine Books, 1999).

religion as an academic subject—it is seen instead as a somewhat discretionary activity that is practiced by some people one day a week, and by others perhaps twice a year. But from a practical standpoint, can we always keep science and religion in separate intellectual and experiential boxes? Over the course of modern history many technological developments, themselves rooted in discoveries made in scientific laboratories, have raised profound ethical questions. The atomic bomb, the Vietnam War–era defoliant Agent Orange and other harmful synthetic chemicals, artificial intelligence, and a wide variety of reproductive technologies quickly spring to mind. Science alone is poorly equipped to answer ethical questions. And although ethical considerations are often rooted in religious traditions, religion alone cannot provide an answer to these complicated dilemmas either. According to Francis Collins, director of the National Institutes of Health, "One of the strongest motivations of humankind is to seek answers to profound questions, and we need to bring all the power of both the scientific and spiritual perspectives to bear on the understanding of what is both seen and unseen."[13] Although it may ease tensions, the independence model of interaction between science and religion does not resolve differences. We thus need to look toward other models of interaction.

Dialogue

Pope John Paul II would have agreed with Francis Collins that an ongoing "dialogue" between science and religion is essential. In a letter written to Vatican Observatory director George Coyne, SJ, which was read at the outset of a 1988 conference commemorating the tercentennial of Isaac Newton's *Principia Mathematica,* John Paul II wrote, "Science can purify religion from error and superstition; religion can purify science from idolatry and false absolutes. Each can draw the other into a wider world, a world in which both can flourish."[14] One area of scientific investigation in which a dialogue

---

13. Francis S. Collins, *The Language of God: A Scientist Presents Evidence for Belief* (New York: Free Press, 2006), 6.

14. John Paul II, *Letter of his Holiness John Paul II to Reverend George V. Coyne, S.J. Director of the Vatican Observatory* (Vatican City: Libreria Editrice Vaticana, 1988).

between science and religion has certainly played a key role is the field of developmental biology—specifically, the biology of human embryonic stem cells. A human being is a large, multicellular organism whose various systems are comprised of 210 different types of cells. Despite our eventual cellular complexity, every one of us begins life as a single fertilized egg, called a zygote. Exactly how the single-celled zygote gives rise to so many different cell types in a mature individual has been a fundamental question in biology for centuries.

In 1998, Dr. James Thomson of the University of Wisconsin developed a technique for extracting what he called "human embryonic stem cells" (hES cells) from very-early-stage embryos, called blastocysts, which had been donated from fertility clinics.[15] The work by Thomson and others showed that hES cells could be used in the laboratory to produce virtually the entire range of adult cell types. Thomson's breakthrough technique for procuring hES cells thus opened vast new avenues for biological research. Even more intriguing than the use of hES cells in basic research was their potential application for producing replacement cells and tissues. Biomedical researchers saw the potential for curing a host of degenerative disorders such as Parkinson's disease, cardiovascular disease, arthritis, and even diabetes.[16] But such great potential did not come without its ethical costs. Harvesting hES cells from blastocysts requires the chemical dissection and destruction of these early human embryos. Many people both inside and outside the scientific community warned of the serious religious and ethical implications of this work. Referring to the fact that the harvesting of hES cells resulted in the destruction of human embryos, for a utilitarian use by others, Pope John Paul II called this a practice that would "devalue and violate human life."[17] From this perspective, one could thus view these practices as tantamount to a new form of slavery.

---

15. James A. Thomson et al., "Embryonic Stem Cell Lines Derived from Human Blastocysts," *Science* 282 (1998): 1145–47.

16. Thomas B. Okarma, "Human Embryonic Stem Cells: A Primer on the Technology and Its Medical Applications," in *The Human Embryologic Stem Cell Debate*, ed. Karen Lebacqz, Laurie Zoloth, and Suzanne Holland (Cambridge, MA: MIT Press, 2002), 8–25.

17. Allesandra Stanley, "Bush Hears Pope Condemn Research in Human Embryos," *New York Times*, July 24, 2001.

In August 2001, President George W. Bush, after consulting with scientists and a wide range of ethicists and religious leaders including John Paul II, issued a presidential policy decision restricting hES cell research to the sixty-four cell lines that existed at that time.[18] According to the Bush directive, federal funds could not be used to derive cells from new donor embryos or cloned embryos. At the time, almost no one was completely happy with the new policy decision. Scientists were relieved that some of the ongoing research would be permitted but warned that sixty-four cell lines were not enough and that US national research interests would soon be eclipsed by other nations. Catholics and many other Christian groups were relieved that there was not an expansion of activities but continued to insist that any research at all in this area was unacceptable. Patient advocacy groups were angered by what they saw as a roadblock to the development of therapies that could potentially benefit themselves or loved ones.

The Bush policy announcement triggered a variety of state funding initiatives, extensive political squabbling, and a number of failed legislative efforts aimed at either broadening or further limiting federal funding for hES-cell research. The Catholic Church referred to the harvesting of hES cells for scientific research and/or clinical purposes as a "gravely immoral act," although it was highly supportive of using umbilical cord blood and adult stem cells as alternatives.[19] As many in the scientific community pointed out, however, emerging research showed that such alternatives lacked the potency of hES cells and were costlier and more difficult to procure.

The ongoing controversy prompted some scientists to look for better alternatives to hES cells. In 2007, a Japanese research group described a procedure for producing "induced pluripotent stem cells (iPSC)."[20] In this method, viruses are molecularly engineered into

---

18. George Bush, Executive Order 13455, "Expanding Approved Stem Cell Lines in Ethically Responsible Ways," *Federal Register* 72 (2007): 34591–93.

19. US Conference of Catholic Bishops, *On Embryonic Stem Cell Research* (Washington, DC: USCCB Publishing, 2008).

20. Kazutoshi Takahashi, Keisuke Okita, Masato Nakagawa, and Shinya Yamanaka, "Induction of Pluripotent Stem Cells from Fibroblast Cultures," *Nature Protocols* 2 (2007): 3081–89.

carriers for introducing stem cell–associated human genes into normal adult cells. The introduced genes then "reset" the developmental clock of the recipient cells, causing them to revert to a stem cell–like stage. Following the reset, the iPSC can then be experimentally manipulated as one would an hES cell. Although stem cells produced in this way appear to have more potency than umbilical cord or adult stem cells, they have also been found to age abnormally or show a tendency to produce tumors. So while this technology has provided a powerful new research tool, the application of it to patient care appears to be limited at this time.

Another emerging area of research called "transdifferentiation" is one in which normal adult cells are transformed directly from one cell type into another.[21] For example, a skin cell could be transformed into a nerve cell, or a liver cell could be transformed into an insulin-producing pancreas cell. Transdifferentiation is achieved by exposing laboratory-cultured cells to a regimen of signaling molecules called transcription factors, which turn specific genes on or off. Transdifferentiation methodologies are actually a much older technique than the derivation of hES cells. Dating originally to research done in the 1980s, work in this area has been dramatically revived in recent years in light of the ongoing controversies and/or scientific problems with using hES cells or iPSC. If either the iPSC or transdifferentiation method proves to be effective clinically, the need for hES cells could be dramatically reduced or perhaps even eliminated.

It is too early to tell if any of the hES-cell alternatives will ever have clinical relevance. However, the United States Food and Drug Administration gave clearance in early 2019 for clinical testing using IPSCs to treat retinal macular degeneration—and if President Bush's policy had not prevented the widespread use of hES cells in 2000, perhaps none of the alternatives (like IPSCs) might have been pursued to their present state of development. Scientists working with the alternative methods often point to the religious and ethical controversies surrounding hES cells as one of the motivating factors in their research. In the case of Bush's hES-cell decision, the politi-

21. Thomas Graf, "Historical Origins of Transdifferentiation and Reprogramming," *Cell Stem Cell* 9 (2011): 504–26.

cal dialogue between science and religion encouraged the opening of new avenues of inquiry. Even if hES cells ultimately become the preferred technique for clinical applications, the knowledge gained about cell development and cell fate determination from the alternative methods will continue to be beneficial to scientific progress in developmental biology. The dialogue between science and religion, even if heated at times, and even if some are not completely satisfied with the outcomes, can thus be beneficial.

Of the Barbour typologies considered so far, this case illustrates that dialogue is certainly preferable to conflict and more fruitful than independence. And sometimes, perhaps a simple dialogue between science and religion is enough. But tackling global problems like climate change, environmental pollution, and habitat destruction will require much more than just dialogue if we wish to pass on a gentler, more sustainable world to future generations. The integration model provides a more compelling motivation for a sustained interaction between the two fields.

Integration

Moving beyond dialogue is Barbour's typology of "integration." In this model, the relationships between religious doctrines and scientific theories are more direct than in the other models. This may require a reformulation, to some extent, of traditional religious or theological concepts, but this can be accomplished, if it is done well, in a way that is entirely consistent with both religion and science. One of the scientific disciplines that calls us to integration is the field of evolutionary biology. This might be a surprise to some readers, given the ongoing "evolution wars" between religious fundamentalists and some members of the scientific community. We will explore this conflict in greater detail later, but for now let's just say that the term "evolution wars" is a misrepresentation of science and religion by both sides of the "war," with each having a vested interest in self-promotion, the selling of headline-grabbing books, and/or the promotion of ideological agendas.

The protagonists in the evolution wars could not be more wrong—the science of evolution is not divisive. If one drops the stereotypes and religious bigotry that characterize this war of words, the science of evolution could turn out to be quite unifying. Growing numbers of both scientific and religious scholars, such as Arthur Peacocke, Kenneth Miller, John Haught, and Elizabeth Johnson, CSJ, to name a few, suggest that evolution might provide a path by which differing worldviews might be integrated. And through this long-overdue integration, perhaps we can help advance understanding and eventual solutions to global climate change and other seemingly intractable problems.

Charles Darwin published the culmination of his life's work as a naturalist in 1859. His book, *On the Origin of Species by Means of Natural Selection*, revolutionized the science of biology.[22] Since its original publication, *On the Origin of Species* has never been out of print and has been translated into over one hundred different languages. It is often said that after the Bible, it is the next most widely read and influential book in all of human history. At the time Darwin's epic work was first published, the idea of evolution, that is, that life on Earth has changed over time, was not new. Naturalists looking at fossils found anywhere in the world could identify all sorts of species from ages past that are no longer around today, though they frequently showed features and characteristics resembling those of existing species. In other cases, fossils revealed the long-ago existence of ancient organisms for which no living examples were known. Well before Darwin was born, natural philosophers and other intellectuals of Western Europe had begun to challenge the historical notion that each and every living species arose as a unique and special creation by God. The fossils suggested that over Earth's history, plants and animals in any locale were replaced by other living forms. What Darwin did in *On the Origin of Species* was to provide a naturalistic mechanism for evolutionary change. He called that mechanism *natural selection*.

Darwin proposed that the natural world "selected" which individuals would produce more offspring in a way analogous to how a farmer selects which of his cattle or sheep are bred to improve his livestock herd. As the favored traits accumulate within a population

---

22. Charles Darwin, *On the Origin of Species by Means of Natural Selection* (London: John Murray, 1859).

over many generations, the newest generations become distinct enough from their forebears that the population is now recognized as a new species. Darwin and his contemporaries referred to this gradual process of change as the "transmutation of species." We now call it evolution. *Natural selection* is defined as the differential success in reproduction within any natural population that over time originates new species. It is important to keep in mind that the product of natural selection is the gradual adaptation of the population, not the individual, to its environment. As we look around us in the present day, we see many other species inhabiting the planet simultaneously with us. But as we look back in time, we see a continuity of life, with new forms springing forth and emerging from ancestral populations in what Darwin saw as a continually branching "tree of life." Darwin's idea, at the core, was very simple. It was also very elegant in its explanatory power, and it turned out to be revolutionary.

"Darwin's Theory," as the theory of natural selection is often called, was quickly embraced by the scientific community. However, it has been resisted by some parts of society, usually on religious grounds, even to this day. It might be asked, "Why has the scientific community overwhelmingly accepted evolution by natural selection as a fundamental truth about the natural world?" Contrary to some fundamentalist claims, all scientists are not atheists. The primary reason for widespread scientific acceptance of Darwinian theory is that it has been tested and verified in countless ways since it was first proposed over a century and a half ago. But also, and more simply, it just makes sense! It unifies essentially everything that was known about the biological world in Darwin's time as well as everything that has become known since then. It is to biology what Newton's gravitational theory and later Einstein's relativity theory are to physics. Although the theory continues to be debated and refined, very few biologists today dispute the broadest implications of Darwinian thought.

Christian Responses to Darwin

Pope John Paul II summarized how scientists view Darwinian theory by saying, "the theory has been progressively accepted by researchers" and that "the convergence (of data), neither sought nor fabricated of the results of work that was conducted independently is in itself a significant argument in favor of this theory."[23] It was surprising to many religious believers as well as many scientists that these words came from the leader of the largest Christian community on Earth, the Roman Catholic Church. Even more surprising was John Paul II's further assertion that the science of evolution is entirely consistent with the teachings of the Catholic Church.

The scientific evidence for evolution is abundant, in virtually any place you look, and in every subdiscipline of biology. Nowhere is this more apparent than in the study of genetics, a field, incidentally, that Darwin knew virtually nothing about. One of the implications of Darwin's work is that all living organisms are related through some distant ancestor. Evolutionary genetics has verified this fact, over and over again. Human DNA is 98.5 percent identical to that of the chimpanzee, an organism with whom we share a relatively recent (in geological terms) common ancestor. The further back in time you go to the many evolutionary divergences in the tree of life, the more our DNA differs from other life forms, but the overall relationship is still very close. For example, some human developmental genes are virtually identical to genes that are found in fruit flies! It is very hard to argue that this is simply a coincidence. So how do we make sense, religiously, of scientific facts such as these? By way of introduction here are just a few ideas:

> God acts in evolution *precisely because of* and within genetic variation.[24]

> This vista compels us, more than ever before, to regard God as *continuously creating*, as *the eternal Creator*, for God continues to give existence to processes that are inherently creative and producing new forms.[25]

---

23. John Paul II, "Evolution and the Living God," in *Science and Theology: The New Consonance*, ed. Ted Peters (Boulder, CO: Westview Press, 1998), 149.

24. Robert John Russell (United Church of Christ minister and founder of the Center for Theology and Natural Science), "Does the 'God Who Acts' Really Act in Nature?" in *Science and Theology: The New Consonance*, ed. Ted Peters (Boulder, CO: Westview Press, 1998), 77.

25. Arthur Peacocke (biochemist and Anglican priest), *Paths from Science towards God: The End of All Our Exploring* (Oxford: Oneworld Publications, 2001), 67.

And from a Roman Catholic perspective, the idea that God suffers along with nature's suffering in the process of evolution:

> In the symbol of the cross, Christian belief discovers a God who participates fully in the world's struggle and pain.[26]

Christians believe that in the person of Jesus Christ, God became flesh. Human flesh, yes, but since scientific evidence shows that we are related to all living creatures, progressive Catholic theologians such as Elizabeth Johnson argue that through his death and resurrection Christ redeems not just humankind but all of creation.[27]

Over the course of Earth's 4.6–billion-year history there have been five periods of mass extinction of plants and animals. The most famous of these was a large meteor impact 65 million years ago that brought about the extinction of the dinosaurs along with many other forms of life. We are currently living in the midst of Earth's sixth mass extinction event. The name that has been given to this new era of Earth's history is "the Anthropocene," or "The Age of Man."[28] The causes of the new wave of extinction sweeping Earth are many: habitat destruction, deforestation, ocean acidification, agricultural pesticides, environmental pollution, greenhouse gases and global warming, to name a few. But ultimately humankind is at the root of all these disruptions. In the words of Pope Benedict XVI, "Preservation of the environment, promotion of sustainable development and particular attention to climate change are matters of great concern to the entire human family."[29]

In March 2013, the College of Cardinals of the Roman Catholic Church elected a new pope. Jorge Mario Bergoglio of Argentina was the first South American and the first Jesuit to become pope. Cardinal Bergoglio selected the papal name Francis, in honor of the much

---

26. John Haught (Roman Catholic theologian), *God after Darwin: A Theology of Evolution* (Boulder, CO: Westview Press, 2001), 46.

27. Elizabeth Johnson, *Ask the Beasts: Darwin and the God of Love* (London: Bloomsbury Publishing, 2014), 222–27.

28. Paul J. Crutzen, "Geology of Mankind," *Nature* 415 (2002): 23.

29. Pope Benedict XVI, *Letter to the Ecumenical Patriarch of Constantinople on the Occasion of the Seventh Symposium of the Religion, Science, and the Environmental Movement* (Rome: Libreria Editrice Vaticana, 2007).

beloved St. Francis of Assisi. In his statements and actions during the first year of his papacy, Pope Francis made it clear that one of his main focuses would be concern for the poor and disenfranchised of the world. In June 2015, Pope Francis released the much-anticipated encyclical letter *Laudato si'* ("praise be to you"), whose title was taken from a well-known prayer by St. Francis of Assisi.[30] The primary focus of *Laudato si'* is climate change and the other environmental disruptions that are being caused by the activity of Earth's dominant species, *Homo sapiens*.

In the third millennium of the Common Era, humankind finds itself to be the primary cause of environmental catastrophe, in direct opposition to scriptural calls for responsible stewardship, which are central to the Abrahamic religions. In Pope Francis's view, all poverty and most human suffering are the direct consequence of the various environmental disruptions we have brought forth on Earth. As an encyclical, the pope's letter spells out Catholic doctrine regarding the current environmental crisis, but the document is really an appeal to all of Earth's people to seriously address our destructive behaviors in a constructive way before our gift of creation is irrevocably harmed. Catholic social teaching has, for many years, focused on the plight of the poor and marginalized peoples of the world. Inspired by St. Francis, who spoke of the living creatures of the Earth as our brothers and sisters, Pope Francis would have our concern for the poor and disadvantaged extend beyond our own species to all of creation.

A church hymn based on Matthew 25 begins, "Whatsoever you do for the least of my people, that you do unto me." If only we, as a species, could start thinking of other species as our brothers and sisters, as siblings that need our protection and concern. To Native Americans and other indigenous peoples of the world who are closely connected to the environment, this is a way of life. But much of our society, especially in the Western world, has lost this deep connection to the natural world. We tend to view other species as irrelevant, as inconveniences that we can simply ignore, or as commodities that we can do with as we wish for our own advantage or selfish purposes.

---

30. Pope Francis, *Laudato Si', "On Care for our Common Home"* (Vatican City: Libreria Editrice Vaticana, 2015).

The real challenge of Pope Francis's message is that he places the roots of our current ecological crisis squarely at the foot of our global consumer economy, which is dominated by greed and self-interest. Historically, the largest economies of the world, such as the United States, China, and other industrialized nations, have brought about the most ecological destruction. Shortly after the publication of *Laudato si'*, the nations of the world came to an agreement to start taking steps toward heading off catastrophic global climate change.[31] The Paris Accord was met with fierce resistance by some, especially in the United States, where climate-change denial found an inexplicable political appeal. Some politicians, like President Donald Trump, unapologetically denied the reality of climate change. Shortly after Trump took office, the United States pulled out of the Paris Accord.[32] Many on the political right, even those who are not outright deniers, try to avoid the issue altogether by claiming that they are "not scientists." But as Pope Francis clearly demonstrates, and as most of the world realizes, one does not have to be a scientist to accept the overwhelming evidence on climate change that has been provided by the scientific community.

Pope Francis called into question the motives and the integrity of those who would block concerted national or international efforts to combat climate change.[33] *Laudato si'* was a call to all citizens of the Earth to try to think differently about our planet and its health. There are, of course, those with vested financial or political interests who will continue to deny the overwhelming evidence that full-scale environmental change is upon us. And there are others who accept the facts about what is happening to our world but say that it is just not possible or just too late for humans to do anything about it. But to this, I would encourage all to keep working despite the odds, as St. Francis of Assisi always expected of his followers:

> Those brothers to whom the Lord has given the grace of working should do their work faithfully and devotedly so that,

---

31. United Nations Climate Change Conference, *Final Agreement—Paris 2015* (New York: COP 21, 2015).

32. Michael D. Shear, "Trump Will Withdraw U.S. from Paris Climate Agreement," *New York Times*, July 1, 2017.

33. Pope Francis, *Laudato si'*, 122–23.

> avoiding illness, the enemy of the soul, they do not extinguish the Spirit of holy prayer and devotion to which all other things of our earthly existence must contribute.[34]

Pope Francis illustrates the wisdom and power of Barbour's integration typology. He accepts the findings of modern science, which irrefutably show that the Earth is warming because of human activities. In *Laudato si'*, he realistically considers the various scientific and technological challenges the world faces in constructively addressing this issue. And he responds to these challenges out of his religious convictions of love for all people, including our nonhuman brothers and sisters. His response is based on a theological understanding of Earth and all of creation as a gift from God, a gift for which Jewish and Christian scripture instructs us to exercise good stewardship. By integrating his religious beliefs with the findings of science, Pope Francis lays out a roadmap for addressing this very real threat to the future not only of humankind but all of Earth's creatures. Rather than locking humankind into an unhealthy war with nature, he invites peace and healing through global cooperation. Through integration, Pope Francis encourages an opening of hearts and minds in order to fully appreciate the complexity and richness of the reality in which we live.

The Nature of Reality

It seems that in order to reverse humanity's course toward global environmental destruction, humankind needs to become more integrated in our scientific, social, political, and religious worldviews. Divisiveness and polarization, while profitable perhaps to a self-interested few, will not contribute to a more sustainable future. Like Pope Francis, we need to approach the problems of our modern age with open hearts and minds, embracing the diversity of human cultures and the great variety of ideas and insights they provide. As we will explore further in chapter 3, some of our misunderstandings come from a hyperspecialization of human activities that has split

---

34. From the *Rule of 1223*. See Adrian House, *Francis of Assisi: A Revolutionary Life* (Mahwah, NJ: HiddenSpring, 2001), 303–4.

knowledge and thought into isolated academic and professional disciplines, especially in the West. People have become so locked into their own points of view that they cannot consider, or often are not even aware of, the ideas and experiences of others. The vocational specialization of our modern age is an unfortunate consequence of the inexorable growth and globalization of the human population. In order to re-establish holistic and unifying approaches to addressing common problems, efforts must be made to overcome the atomization of human activities forced upon us by relentless growth economies.

In terms of science and religion, we might be able to achieve a more fruitful conversation if we recognize that there are two basic statements that can be made about the fundamental nature of reality. First, there is the physical reality that can be empirically described by science; second, there is a spiritual or transcendent reality that has traditionally been the realm of religion. Together, these two realities make up what physicist Michael Dennin describes as the "fullness of reality" or, in other words, all that exists.[35] We might also call the combined material and transcendent realities the "greater reality" that includes an actual Divine or nonmaterial existence that is behind, beneath, and beyond that which we can physically describe.

From a practical standpoint, no one can reasonably deny that physical reality exists. We live in it. This is the world in which science operates. Scientists attempt to provide accurate descriptions of physical things as they really are. Now there are many lines of philosophical argument, dating back to Plato's famous cave analogy, which suggest that our perceptions of reality are inherently limited or flawed. We can never be entirely sure of what is real and what only seems to be real. The shadows seen on the wall of Plato's cave are not real; they are but one perception of the true reality. Still, they are shadows, cast upon the wall of the cave by real objects moving in front of a fire. And so, even when our empirical perceptions are in error or incomplete, they do at least tell us something about our physical reality. One of the goals of science is to continually revise

35. Michael Dennin, *Divine Science: Finding Reason at the Heart of Faith* (Cincinnati, OH: Franciscan Media, 2015), 16–38.

those empirical impressions so that we can come up with truer descriptions of physical reality.

Religious faith looks beyond physical reality to include that which cannot be empirically detected because it does not have a physical or material presence. For many religions, the transcendent reality sought through religious or spiritual experience includes a creator God. As difficult as it may be to accurately describe physical reality, describing God is much more difficult—many would say it's impossible. Since God is immaterial, our five senses alone are of little use. One can thus only come to know God through indirect means such as intuition, prayer, and reflection on experience. Nonsensory aspects of our mental processes must be brought to the inquiry. Furthermore, describing God through our indirect experience of God is made more difficult because our language is often inadequate to this task. We must rely on metaphor, allegory, and emotion to express what God is "like" or how God "appears" to us. Understandings of God vary, therefore, from person to person and from age to age. They are always in flux because the true nature of God is impossible to know with the same kind of certainty with which we can describe physical reality. Transcendent reality is not verifiable by means of physical methods of science and therefore is not given the same degree of acceptance by all people, at least in modern times.

It might be helpful to look at Barbour's typologies once again with the underlying assumptions of science (physicality) and religion (transcendence) in mind. If we assign a simple circle to encapsulate the kinds of knowledge and experience described by each of these fields of human experience, we can attempt to visualize the strengths and weaknesses of each of Barbour's typologies. In the *conflict* typology, each circle is invisible to the other. There is a refusal to accept that either physicality or transcendence exists in a meaningful way, and any claim from the other domain is ignored. Of course, the refusal to even acknowledge the ideas, viewpoints, or concerns of those who differ from you is a recipe for disaster. Human history is full of examples where the views, rights, or even the humanity of one group is denied by another. Much of the political discourse in the United States and elsewhere in recent years is characterized by this kind of rhetoric. This is not a path toward reconciliation and harmony; it is a path toward tyranny and oppression. In the conflict typology, progress is hindered in both science and religion. Advocates of this type of polarized conflict should have their motives questioned—if they are not helping to advance their fields or humankind, they must then only be interested, really, in advancing themselves. We wind up with celebrity scientists on the one hand and megachurch pastors on the other. A perpetual atmosphere of mistrust and ongoing ignorance are the unfortunate outcomes.

In the *independence* model, both circles are visible on the page, but they are not in contact with each other.[36] One might acknowledge that the other domain *may* exist; but that even if it does, it is not relevant in any way to one's preferred view of reality. This is far better than the denial of each other's existence because some appeals can be made across the gulf that separates the views. Sociobiologist E. O. Wilson, the author of *Consilience*[37] and *The Creation: An Appeal to Save Life on Earth*,[38] recognizes that there are people who have underlying assumptions about reality that differ from his own and that it is important to engage with them in some way. Wilson reaches out to those with whom he disagrees in order to find common ground so that the interests of both—in Wilson's case, saving the Earth's biodiversity—can be advanced. Although Wilson attempts to engage with religious believers, he implies that scientific approaches are the only way to achieve progress. He advocates for a change of mind, but what is also needed, from both sides, is a change of heart.

In Barbour's *dialogue* typology, the circles of physical and transcendent reality do contact each other, and there is some overlap of common concern. Progress, for both science and religion, is possible as a result of this interaction. If the moral and ethical implications of scientific advances can be considered, it is possible that such a conversation could result in new fields of scientific inquiry. New path-

36. As noted earlier in the chapter, this model bears some resemblance to Gould's notion of NOMA.

37. E. O. Wilson, *Consilience: The Unity of Knowledge* (New York: Alfred A. Knopf, 1998).

38. E. O. Wilson, *The Creation: An Appeal to Save Life on Earth* (New York: W. W. Norton, 2007).

ways for scientific investigation can emerge, as we saw in the stem cell case. New religious understandings might also follow. Through the shaded areas of overlap, both fields are enriched by contact with each other, even though many of their individual concerns may remain outside of the intersection. Dialogue is thus certainly preferable to either conflict or independence, but in my opinion, it is only through *integration* that meaningful sustained progress can be achieved.

In Barbour's *integration* model, the circles of physicality and transcendence are concentric. The realm of science, with its defined limits to investigation of physical phenomena, and religion, with more open conceptions of reality, can both contribute in a meaningful way to an understanding of our greater reality. While it could be debated as to which realm is contained within which, progress in the understandings provided by each realm of activity can mutually support and inform the other. Knowledge is never static; it is always provisional, always moving forward. No one is excluded from the conversation and everyone has a role to play. This is reminiscent of St. Paul's appeal to the Corinthians, "for as the body is one, and has many members, all the members of the body, being many, are one body" (1 Cor 12:12). Not everyone has to believe the same thing about the nature of reality or one's place in it. But everyone has ownership in a common purpose; anyone and everyone can positively affect the status and future conditions for humanity and the world.

An integrative perspective on science and religion is the stance that Pope Francis emphasizes in *Laudato si'*, and it is the strategy that will inform much of this book. Along the way we will see examples of where integration has not yet been achieved and the various misunderstandings that result. Some of this is historical; some is ongoing. I want to emphasize again that not everyone can or even should have the same religious, philosophical, or scientific perspectives on reality. Richness comes through a diversity of views. The perspectives of scientists and nonscientists, religious believers and nonbelievers, and seekers of all types are all important if we keep our hearts and minds respectfully open to the others in our midst.

In my experience, I believe that most people are open to this type of approach to personal exploration, whether they are religious or not. But because we cannot *directly* see, hear, or otherwise empirically sense or measure God or transcendent reality in a material way, there are those who might say that these greater realities do not exist. Those who accept this view likely think that the typologies of Barbour and any conversation about science and religion are irrelevant or, at best, a harmless distraction. The material world is really all that exists and all that matters, physical evidence is the only kind of evidence that is meaningful, and empirical data is the only kind of information that can be considered.[39] There are many in the scientific community who may feel this way, even though, for the most part, they do not openly advocate conflict with religious believers. And this viewpoint is fine, if one is only trying to explain a material process operating within the natural world.

But materialistic thinking cannot be used to discuss the Divine nature or any aspect of transcendent reality. If only empirically verifiable physical data are deemed acceptable, then the denial of God is a foregone conclusion. The main assumption underlying a purely materialist position, that is, that the physical world is all that exists, places limits on any attempt to understand a greater reality that includes the fullest range of human experience. These self-imposed limits on the acceptability of data are, it seems to me, somewhat arbitrary. They are used mainly to deny the existence of God or to invalidate religious experience rather than to promote a fully robust knowledge of reality. For example, modern string theory predicts that there are fully eleven distinct dimensions to reality.[40] Humans are only able to detect and measure four of these (height, width, depth, and time) in the physical world that we inhabit. Many scientists, I think, trust that the calculations of the string theorists are valid, and that the seven other dimensions, imagined or inferred, by physicists quite possibly exist even though they are not empirically verifiable. Therefore, a denial of the existence of God that is based upon the lack of empirical verifiability, it seems to me, must have more to do with a restrictive atheistic definition of reality than it

39. Jerry A. Coyne, *Faith vs. Fact: Why Science and Religion Are Incompatible* (New York: Viking, 2015), 65–89.

40. Brian Greene, *The Elegant Universe: Superstrings, Hidden Dimensions, and the Quest for the Ultimate Theory* (New York: W. W. Norton, 2003), 187–211.

does to any claimed philosophical commitment to logic, reason, and the methods of science. Proponents of the empiricism argument thus contradict themselves when they then turn around and are willing to accept the tenets of string theory.

We are spiritual beings as well as physical ones. Throughout the history of humankind, so far as we know, there has always been a call to the human mind and spirit to understand what lies beyond the physical world and our limited capacities to understand it. The world of religion is where we find possible answers to some of these questions. Surely, the answers change over time and new ways of looking at the reality in which we find ourselves emerge. But the provisional nature of knowledge does not invalidate religion just as it does not invalidate science. Both science and religion are enlivened by our insatiable desire to know and to understand by asking questions. Central to these inquiries should be a high regard for the virtue of humility. A humble acceptance of the limits of both the scientific method and religious doctrine can open us up to a more inclusive and optimistic future. It is in the spirit of humble and open inquiry that I begin this exploration. I hope to show that through an open, yet critical approach to both scientific knowledge and religious understanding, integration is possible, and a greater appreciation of the fullness of reality can be achieved. The result of this integration is not only satisfying personally—it is, I believe, important for coming to grips with the future that God calls us to. Science and religion have historically contacted each other in many ways; sometimes in opposition, sometimes in collaboration, but the interaction is always fascinating. And through a humble acceptance of each field by the other, it is my hope that a more fruitful partnership might still be achieved.

2

Humility

> If it seems to you that you know many things and that you are an expert in them, recognize nevertheless that there are many things that you do not know. Do not be high-minded but admit your great ignorance.[1]

This small piece of advice from the fifteenth-century text *The Imitation of Christ*, attributed to the English monk Thomas à Kempis, is every bit as applicable today as it was so many years ago. The word *humility* is derived from the Latin root *humilitas,* or humus, the earth beneath our feet. Humility therefore signifies lowliness. Humility is the characteristic ascribed to a person who does not think of himself or herself as being above others. A humble person is modest and unpretentious. Humility is a form of temperance or self-restraint, one of the four cardinal virtues. The Christian attitudes concerning humility are rooted in its foundational text, the Bible. In the Sermon on the Mount, Jesus of Nazareth extols the virtue declaring the meek (or humble) "blessed" (Matt 5:5). Hubris or pride, the opposite of humility, is to be resisted at all costs:

> Whoever exalts himself will be humbled;
> but whoever humbles himself will be exalted. (Matt 5:12)

In Christianity, humility is not only a desirable personal characteristic, it is a virtue that is foundational to the faith. According to

1. Thomas à Kempis, *The Imitation of Christ*, trans. William C. Creasy (Notre Dame, IN: Ave Maria Press, 1986), 31–32.

St. Teresa of Avila, humility is the root of prayer.[2] In this context, humility includes submission to God's will, obedience to superiors, and recognition of the talents of others. Another important aspect of humility is recognizing one's own limitations. According to St. Thomas Aquinas, humility "consists in keeping oneself within one's own bounds, not reaching out to things above one, but submitting to one's superior."[3]

It is not only the Christian religious tradition that extols the virtue of humility. A call to humility can be found throughout the texts of many of the world's religions, including Judaism, Buddhism, Hinduism, Islam, and Native American traditions. For example, from Islam:

> Successful indeed are the believers
> Who are humble in their prayers,
> and who shun vain conversation,
> and who are payers of the poor-due,
> and who guard their modesty.[4]

Similar sentiments can be sited by Hindi worshipers:

> Be humble, be harmless,
> Have no pretension,
> Be upright, forbearing;
> Serve your teacher in true obedience,
> Keeping the mind and body in cleanness,
> Tranquil, steadfast, master of ego,
> Standing apart from the things of the senses,
> Free from self;
> Aware of the weakness in mortal nature.[5]

It seems that the characteristic of humility is encouraged, sought after, and thought of as "holy" throughout the world, regardless

2. Harvey D. Egan, SJ, *An Anthology of Christian Mysticism*, 2nd ed. (Collegeville, MN: Pueblo Books, 1991), 438–51.

3. Thomas Aquinas, *Summa Contra Gentiles,* trans. Charles J. O'Neil (Notre Dame, IN: University of Notre Dame Press, 1956), book 4, chap. 55.

4. Qur'ān 23.1–5

5. *Bhagavad Gita* 13.7–8

of religious tradition. Descriptions of humility can also be found throughout the writings of secular groups. For example, as expressed in the *Humanist Manifesto*:

> Reason and intelligence are the most effective instruments that humankind possesses. There is no substitute: neither faith nor passion suffices in itself. The controlled use of scientific methods, which have transformed the natural and social sciences since the Renaissance, must be extended further in the solution of human problems. But reason must be tempered by humility, since no group has a monopoly of wisdom or virtue.[6]

For humanists, the virtue of humility derives not from religious principles but rather from ethical consideration of how people should treat one another. Many prominent scientists were among the original signees of the *Humanist Manifesto*, and many of the friends I have made during my career in science describe themselves as secular humanists.

The very nature of science inspires awe and humility at the vast complexity of the natural world. Well-known scientists such as Francisco Ayala,[7] Ursula Goodenough,[8] and others have written at length on their profound sense of wonder at nature's majesty. It does not take an astrophysicist to recognize the smallness of our Earth within the vast expanses of the universe. Experts within any scientific discipline and subdiscipline will not hesitate to wonder about what remains unknown in their own research field. After all, any scientific discovery always brings a host of new questions to be explored. We can never know everything about even the most fundamental natural processes on our Earth, much less the vast complexities of interacting processes beyond our world. We can proudly (and rightly) proclaim the great leaps of scientific understanding that we humans have achieved in the past few hundred years. We can marvel at the accelerating rate at

6. Paul Kurtz, *Humanist Manifestos I and II* (Amherst, NY: Prometheus Books, 1984).

7. Francisco J. Ayala, *Darwin's Gift to Science and Religion* (Washington, DC: Joseph Henry Press, 2007).

8. Ursula Goodenough, *The Sacred Depths of Nature* (New York: Oxford University Press, 1998).

which these scientific breakthroughs occur. We can even dream of a time, perhaps even soon, when genetically based cures for disease, bio-engineered replacement tissues, and even interplanetary travel become not only possible, but routine. Yet, despite our vast and ever-expanding knowledge, when we compare "all that we know" with "all that could be known," we will forever remain ignorant. Most scientists are admittedly humbled by their own ignorance.

If scientists are willing to admit their ignorance regarding the natural universe that we know, why do many seem unwilling to acknowledge or entertain ideas that emanate from outside our scientific disciplines? A number of evolutionary psychologists have suggested that belief in God or gods had some survival benefit such as cooperativity or group cohesiveness for early humans.[9] According to this argument, believing groups would be favored over those that were not believers, so religious belief would then spread throughout a population. Other authors, like evolutionary biologist Richard Dawkins, insist that religious belief has no adaptive value at all but is simply a by-product of something else in human nature. He compares human religious belief to moths flying into a candle flame, that is, a harmful behavior that results from the moth's normal nighttime navigational abilities.[10] Dawkins suggests that for humans the "something else" may have to do with the tendency of children to believe what they are told by adults, but his implication in *The God Delusion* is clear: the sooner humans discard the by-product of religious belief, the better off everyone will be. Psychologist Pascal Boyer, in *God Explained*, similarly suggests that religion is an evolutionary by-product, in this case from a human tendency to attribute cause and effect to otherwise unexplainable circumstances.[11]

To these authors, it seems, the "myths" of religion are rendered obsolete by the emerging "truths" of the scientific enterprise. In all fairness, there may be validity to some of these theories. The trouble is,

---

9. E. Fuller Torrey, *Evolving Brains, Emerging Gods: Early Humans and the Origins of Religion* (New York: Columbia University Press, 2017), 219.

10. Richard Dawkins, *The God Delusion* (New York: Houghton Mifflin, 2006), 172–79.

11. Pascal Boyer, *Religion Explained: The Evolutionary Origins of Religious Thought* (New York: Basic Books, 2001).

however, that theologians or scholars of religion are rarely consulted in constructing these hypotheses, or if they are, it is simply to supply amusing anecdotes about the foolishness of religious belief. The scientific method is viewed as the supreme arbiter over all questions of existence, meaning, and purpose. As ignorant as scientists might be willing to admit they are about the natural world, some feel justified in claiming that their scientific lens alone is enough to disprove that any reality exists beyond our physical one. The certitude with which some of these "expert" authors claim that the scientific method is the only way of viewing reality is both intellectually and personally arrogant.[12] They show the same lack of wisdom in their blind trust in science as modern-day creationists place in literal readings of the Bible.

But scientists are by no means the only ones who can come across as arrogant in their views. In the course of human history, wars have been fought between rival religious groups, each claiming that it is absolutely right and the other is absolutely wrong. The most famous examples, of course, are the Crusades of the twelfth and thirteenth centuries, which were fought between the Christian Church of Europe and Middle Eastern Muslims over possession of the holy sites in Jerusalem. It is thought that the demise of the ancient Mesopotamian civilization was the result of warfare between rival cities, each claiming allegiance to one or another of their gods.[13] Religious conflicts continue to fuel discord and violence in many parts of the world today. The September 11, 2001, terrorist attacks on New York and Washington, DC, by Muslim religious fanatics had far-reaching consequences both socially and politically.

In the United States, some evangelical Christian groups have adopted a "warfare" approach in their opposition to the science of evolutionary biology.[14] When Christian fundamentalists dismiss evolution as "only a theory,"[15] as in recent court cases involving the

---

12. Jerry A. Coyne, *Faith vs. Fact: Why Science and Religion Are Incompatible* (New York: Viking, 2015), 197–201.

13. Torrey, *Evolving Brains, Emerging Gods*, 174–76.

14. Bradley J. Gundlach, "Protestant Evangelicals," in *The Warfare between Science and Religion: The Idea that Wouldn't Die*, ed. Jeff Hardin, Ronald L. Numbers, and Ronald A. Binzley (Baltimore, MD: Johns Hopkins University Press, 2018), 163–83.

15. Kenneth R. Miller, *Only a Theory: Evolution and the Battle for America's Soul* (New York: Viking, 2008), 1.

teaching of evolution in public schools, they have completely lost sight of the doctrine of humility as a virtue. Creationist textbooks like the *Exploring Creation* series by Jeannie Fulbright are scrubbed of all mention of evolutionary theory, a chief cornerstone of modern biology. Others like *Of Pandas and People* by Percival Davis and Dean Kenyon discuss Darwin and evolutionary theory but only as a badly flawed alternative to creationistic accounts. These authors conveniently overlook the fact that "Darwin's theory" has been tested, retested, and confirmed in numerous scientific disciplines for over 150 years and by scientists numbering in the thousands if not hundreds of thousands. The hubris that they display by rejecting a central tenet of the biological sciences is alienating to almost everyone in the scientific community. It is no wonder that they receive strong pushback from most scientists.

Regardless of one's religion, background, or personal worldviews, humility is generally considered to be a positive personality trait while hubris is viewed as a negative characteristic. It strikes me that both sides in the recent polarized public debates on evolution are undermining themselves. Scientists who seek to negate the existence of God through their application of the scientific method only make science, and themselves, look smaller. Religious believers, eager to extol the grandeur of God, only succeed in diminishing God by insisting that evolution and other scientific theories are antithetical to religious doctrine. Why do so many in this conversation seem unable or unwilling to approach those outside of their own discipline or life experience with humility? In this chapter I will explore the virtue of humility as it is exhibited in the practice of science and in the exercise of religious faith. I will suggest that a humbler approach by both sides might improve the ongoing contact between science and religion.

Faith and Reason

Our human drive to know is at the roots of both science and religion. Before we move on specifically to scientific and religious studies and practices, we should address a frequent mischaracterization of how knowledge is advanced in these areas of human understanding. Science is sometimes portrayed as the domain of *reason* while religion is seen as the domain of a "lesser" human activity called *faith*.[16] In common usage the word *faith* usually refers to a strong personal adherence to a religious belief system such as Catholicism or Islam. But this is an incomplete definition of faith. In the broadest sense, faith, as defined by the *Oxford English Dictionary*, is "complete trust or confidence in someone or something." This is certainly an accurate definition of faith for many people who profess to have a strong belief in God. But one could also say that it is true for those who have full confidence in the scientific method for discovering truth about the natural world. They have a *faith* in science. Faith in God and faith in science are not mutually exclusive. One can have faith in both.

There is also a tendency to think that *reason*, defined as "the intellectual power of the human mind to form valid judgments by a process of logic," is a property of science but not of religious belief. Scientists pride themselves, as they should, on the application of rational thought to organize, analyze, and draw conclusions from the empirical data they collect in order to explain natural events or phenomena. But just as faith does not apply solely to religion, reason does not apply only to science. The various doctrines of religious belief systems that have been passed down through the ages were developed by theologians and philosophers through the application of rational thought, or reason, to make sense of the core teachings of sacred texts in light of the contemporary situations the living community of believers found themselves in. Therefore, reason applies to religion as well as science. Any characterization of the interaction between religion and science as a battle between faith and reason is a false dichotomy.

There are many ways in which humans come to know and understand the world in which we live. *Faith* and *reason* are two of them. Other ways of knowing are language, emotion, memory, intuition, imagination, and sense perception. Some of these may be more frequently applied in some areas of human experience than others, but all can be applicable to both science and religion. Sense perception, or empiricism, is the principle way in which scientists gather the

16. Coyne, *Faith vs. Fact*, 9–25.

physical data they use to test hypotheses about the natural world. But the physical senses also enhance the religious experiences of, for example, members of a Roman Catholic community participating in the Eucharist at a Christmas Eve Mass. An emotional outpouring of joy and excitement as experienced by churchgoers at a baptismal ceremony might also be found in a paleontologist who suddenly uncovers the fossil remains of a new species of dinosaur. The claim that certain ways of knowing are universally superior to others undermines a humble approach to conversation with those who have differing views and circumvents the advancement of knowledge.[17]

Such a claim also falsely elevates some disciplinary fields of knowledge over others in perceived importance. Each field of knowledge has a greater reliance on some ways of knowing than others. Scientists use their physical senses; theologians rely on faith; poets and musicians draw on their emotions; and politicians must trust their intuition. Specialists in one area should not presume that methodologies utilized by their disciplines are automatically the best ones to use in other fields. The acquisition and implementation of knowledge are never complete; one can always know more and know better.

Knowledge and Belief

When I ask my introductory science students on the first day of class to describe what the word "science" means, a common response is that it is "a collection of known facts about the world." The facts that these students are thinking about relate to processes that are physical, chemical, or biological occurring in the natural world—in other words, to how things work. But this is not a particularly good definition of science. Science is not merely about collecting facts. Science is a *process* of discovery that uncovers new facts as we gain knowledge about how the natural world works. Scientific knowledge is *empirical knowledge* gained by direct observation or experience. Thus, scientists seek to acquire new knowledge about the natural world by using the five human senses and the extensions of these senses provided by scientific instruments such as microscopes, spectrophotometers,

17. Ibid., 185–96.

seismometers, sonar, voltmeters, electrochemical detectors, and various other technological devices. The data that scientists collect is therefore empirical, that is, directly observable or experienced by taking physical measurements. The confirmation of these observations by others is critical to something becoming a "known fact." Scientific knowledge advances through the combined observation and consensus of a scientific community.

I think that almost any professional scientist, young or old, will tell you that uncovering new knowledge through the scientific process is an exhilarating and at the same time humbling experience. One experiences great joy in making a new discovery. New discoveries come through hard work and much trial and error as hypotheses are formulated, tested, revised, and retested. Paths to discovery that once seemed promising often turn out to be dead ends, and new paths must be explored. Scientists learns to live within the limits of their knowledge and ability while engaging in a field of exploration that they have come to love. And so, scientists seldom work alone. Teams of graduate students, postdoctoral researchers, and lead investigators must work together to overcome problems, collect data, test new ideas, and analyze the results of experiments. These collaborative efforts require the humble recognition of each team member's strengths and weaknesses. The shared sense of accomplishment when a new discovery is made or when a research article is ultimately published magnifies the excitement and fosters a sense of gratitude for the work of others. A good scientist is also aware that his or her work is but one small part of the overall research efforts that are happening in labs and field stations around the world to advance the knowledge in any scientific discipline. A humble recognition of the efforts, and opinions, of others is essential to a successful career in science.

Scientists learn to trust and believe in the work of their colleagues in the scientific community. For any scientist, the new discoveries that he or she can make in a lifetime are a small fraction of the total number of scientific facts with which they will become familiar through learning from the works of other scientists. Many times, facts are learned not through the firsthand accounts of scientists published in scientific journals but through secondary descriptions in textbooks or review articles. Because the primary literature contains a description of the methodologies used to collect original data, it is possible that any published work could be repeated in order to satisfy personal curiosity or confirm a reported finding. But in practice this is rarely done. The prospect of repeating, step by step, all the prior studies that are relevant to a research project would be expensive and time consuming. Scientific progress would be glacially slow. A successful career as a research scientist requires making new observations and discovering new facts, not simply confirming what others have done previously. In order to make any use of empirical facts generated by others one first must assent to them being true. In other words, a scientist must *believe* in the work of others.

A *belief* is a statement that a person accepts as true or factual even though the individual did not directly observe or experience the phenomenon themselves. Belief is typically thought of as being part of the realm of religion, but as I argued above, belief also plays an important role in science. Each religious tradition has a core set of beliefs that are foundational to that tradition. Fundamental to Catholicism is a belief in God who is the creator of the universe, in God as Holy Spirit who animates the hearts and minds of believers, and in God in the form of Jesus Christ who appeared on Earth two thousand or so years ago. But many religious beliefs are also supported by empirical facts that can be confirmed through historical research. Most biblical scholars agree that Jesus of Nazareth was a historical figure who lived, preached, and died in the Middle East in the area located within modern-day Israel.[18] We also know that Jesus was viewed as a prophet by many of the Jewish people of the time. Jesus established a band of followers who, as disciples, spread his teachings and ultimately set the foundations for the Christian religions. Jesus was a highly controversial figure in the time and place in which he lived. He was an outspoken critic of the ruling Roman Empire as well as of the priests and other Jewish leaders in and around Jerusalem. Many of Jesus's teachings were radical departures

---

18. Kristin Romey, "The Search for the Real Jesus," *National Geographic* 232 (2017): 30–69.

from the sacred texts that were foundational to the Hebrew people. Jesus was ultimately killed for the views he expressed, and his followers were persecuted during their lifetimes. These are the historical facts about Jesus's life that were assembled from eyewitness accounts in the four Gospels of the New Testament.

The New Testament narratives convey the historical testimony of Jesus's earliest followers. They are part of what Jesuit priest Christopher Mooney describes as the threefold database that Christian theologians utilize to advance the knowledge of or framework for understanding God and the Christian religion. The other parts of this database are the traditions and worship practices in Christian churches over the centuries and the lived experiences of contemporary Christian believers.[19] The knowledge that theologians seek to attain extends beyond the physical facts of history and science to the consideration of a transcendent creator God. The facts that one needs in order to understand a transcendent God are not exclusively sensory based, as in science, but they are experiential. They include the religious experiences of the individual believer as well as the collective experiences of the religious community.

The task of a theologian who is seeking to better understand God is, in my opinion, a courageous and humbling undertaking since, in the end, God is unknowable. Saint Thomas Aquinas (1225–1274) is widely considered to be one of the Catholic Church's greatest philosophers and theologians. He was certainly one of its most prolific writers. Near the end of his life, while working on the multivolume *Summa Theologiae*, he is reported to have stopped dictating to his scribe, and when asked why simply stated, "because all that I have written seems like straw to me."[20] Such humble acceptance of the limits of one's own work and life strikes me as inspirational. Every year during the administration of ashes on Ash Wednesday, Catholics are reminded, "Remember you are dust, and to dust you will return." Other religious traditions have their own practices of fasting

---

19. Christopher F. Mooney, SJ, *Theology and Scientific Knowledge: Changing Models of God's Presence* (Notre Dame, IN: University of Notre Dame Press, 1996), 11–12.

20. Brian Davies, *The Thought of Thomas Aquinas* (Oxford: Oxford University Press, 1993), 9.

and penance in preparation for important holy days. These practices encourage believers to be humble before God so that they might live a better, more fulfilling life. Knowledge about God and oneself cannot be gained without at least a modicum of humility.

Similarly, according to some, scientists are also called to a deep sense of humility before the natural world that they study. Cell biologist Ursula Goodenough describes the humble stance of a scientist:

> We are called to acknowledge our dependency on the web of life both for our subsistence and for our countless ascetic experiences: spring birdsong, swelling tree buds, the dizzy smell of honeysuckle. We are called to acknowledge that which we are not: we cannot survive in a deep-sea vent, or fix nitrogen, or create a forest canopy, or soar 300 feet in the air and then catch a mouse in a spectacular nosedive.[21]

The history of human life, which we will explore in chapter 7, makes us realize how fortunate humankind is to simply occupy this Earth, let alone understand it. Our living ancestors of the past 500 million years have survived at least five mass extinctions. Our species *Homo sapiens* came close to its own extinction some 70,000 years ago in our ancestral African homeland. As we will see in chapter 5, even life on Earth itself may be unique in the vast universe in which we live. Who among us cannot look at what we know, realize how very much we do not know, and contemplate how miraculous our lives are, without a deep and abiding sense of humility?

Repetition and Revelation

Much of the above discussion has focused on the similarities that I see between science and religion. But clearly there are important differences between how scientists and religious scholars advance their fields of knowledge. One key distinction is that science is much more dependent on empirical observation than is religion. Empirical observations of the natural world can be confirmed by others through

21. Ursula Goodenough, *The Sacred Depths of Nature* (New York: Oxford University Press, 1998), 86–87.

repetition. They are verifiable by others. The process by which scientific observations become facts is by other scientists repeating the observations. Religious experiences are harder to pin down and difficult to verify in any agreed-upon and reliable way. The verification of a religious experience, for an *individual*, happens through continued prayer or extended conversations with a spiritual director or religious leader. Someone else cannot repeat and verify the experience. Religious experiences are unique to each person. Since scientific facts are immediately verifiable by others using standardized and agreed-upon methods, scientific claims are usually afforded a much greater degree of credence than are religious claims.

A second key difference is the mathematical nature of scientific data. Science relies on controlled and quantitative measurements. In a controlled experiment, scientists can make sure that there are repeated measurements for the same subject or group of subjects so that the mathematical data can be analyzed statistically. Quantitative measurement and statistical repetition are great strengths of the scientific method. A spiritual or religious experience, on the other hand, cannot be quantified. Religious experience is highly qualitative and not subject to repetition and statistical comparison, even though certain themes or similarities frequently emerge among religious believers. The sample size for a religious experience is only ever one. Single data points in science are not useful for comparisons. Critics of religion sometimes cite the lack of quantitative and statistical rigor as a primary failing of religious belief, but this is an unjustified attempt to hold religion to scientific standards.[22] Religious experience is relational in nature and therefore uniquely singular to each individual person. Since no two human relationships are identical, it is not reasonable to suggest that an individual person's relationship with God would be any more open to statistical analysis than would a person's relationship with a spouse, siblings, or friends.

A third difference between science and religion is in the role played by *revelation* in religious experience and theology. In religion, revelation refers to the disclosure of new knowledge to humans by

22. Coyne, *Faith vs. Fact*, 36.

God. There is no real counterpart to revelation in science. A historical metaphor for understanding how humans come to know about God is "the two books."[23] According to this tradition, God's self-disclosure, or revelation, comes to us through "the book of nature" as well as the "book of scripture." Natural theologians of the Middle Ages and onward firmly believed that the works of nature revealed God's power, goodness, and interconnectedness with reality, while God's plans, guidance, and hopes for humanity could be found in the sacred scriptures. Knowledge coming from nature was viewed as complementary to knowledge gleaned from scripture, not as antagonistic to it.

The fundamentalist Christian movement that insists on the literal reading of biblical texts is a relatively recent phenomenon that emerged in the late-nineteenth century in response to American Protestant concerns about the science of evolution.[24] Prior to that time, scriptural texts were rarely read for the literal meaning only. The events and stories of scripture were not meant to be read like a science or history textbook, but as a record of personal experiences that metaphorically reveal God's message to humanity. Literal readings of scripture overlook the much larger spiritual meanings of the texts. This understanding of scripture as having both a *literal sense* and a *spiritual sense* has been a key to Christian theology throughout most of its history.[25] An ancient medieval verse summarizes the literal and spiritual meanings of sacred texts:

> The meaning of the letter gives information about events;
> Allegory teaches that one should believe;
> The moral meaning about what we should do;
> The anagogic about what we should strive for.[26]

23. Peter Hess, "God's Two Books: Special Revelation and Natural Science in the Christian West," in *Bridging Science and Religion*, ed. Ted Peters and Gaymon Bennett (Minneapolis, MN: Fortress Press, 2003), 123–40.

24. Ronald L. Numbers, *The Creationists: From Scientific Creationism to Intelligent Design* (Cambridge, MA: Harvard University Press, 2006), 46–50.

25. *Catechism of the Catholic Church* (Vatican City: Libreria Editrice Vaticana, 1994), 115.

26. Wilfred Stinissen, *Nourished by the Word: Reading the Bible Contemplatively* (Liguori, MO: Liguori Press, 1999), 42.

Although the literal meanings of scripture can be valuable, they should not be considered as the most important. It is the spiritual meanings, that is, the allegorical, the moral, and the anagogic or ultimate meaning, that have the greatest value for religious believers.[27] The spiritual meanings are the ones that seek the transcendent. They are the meanings that lie beyond the literal reports of actual events in the physical world. These are the meanings in scripture that reveal the presence of God to religious believers. Scripture scholars have long agreed that it is the spiritual meanings of biblical texts, not a word-by-word historical account, that is important for God's revelation.

The various books of the Bible were written at different times and for different target audiences. They convey what the early peoples who told these stories thought to be their most important messages or teachings. Providing historically accurate descriptions of events or people was of secondary or even no importance. The Gospels of the New Testament, for example, were written down only as Jesus's original apostles began to die and could no longer personally provide the oral testimony to Jesus's teachings and life that were foundational to the earliest Christian communities.[28] The lives and times of the early Christians were very different than ours are today. Scripture scholars would likely agree that the original meanings of these texts were probably different in many respects from what they are today. The ongoing discussion, debate, and re-interpretation of scripture, using historical study, reason, and prayer for the discernment of meanings is what makes the Bible and other religious texts living documents for the faithful. Scripture is important not as a book of rules that must be followed but as a revelation of God's presence in the world to God's people, both historically and today.

Spirituality

Scripture, while important for revealing something about God and God's relationship to the world, is not the only source of spiritual

27. Ibid., 43–59.

28. Jaroslav Pelikan, *Whose Bible Is It? A Short History of the Scriptures* (London: Penguin Books, 2003), 102–3.

information. Much more important to many people are their own personal religious or spiritual experiences. These experiences arise out of an individual person's yearnings for God or knowledge of God's call to them. They are, for the believer, a direct encounter with the Divine, from which he or she gains personal affirmation, a greater insight on key life situations, or assistance in discernment of life choices. Spiritual experiences can come to an individual through private prayer, group worship experiences, or suddenly through an unexpected event or synchronicity among several events. Religious or spiritual people view these events as a direct intersection of the Divine with the progress of their daily lives. It is very possible that such an experience will take on a deep meaning in the way in which a believer lives out his or her life. Some people share their experiences openly with their faith communities through "witnessing" stories. Others keep spiritual or religious experiences very private, discussing them only with a spouse or very close friend, a priest or another religious leader, or sometimes a spiritual director.

Spiritual direction, sometimes called spiritual companionship, has a long history of practice in each of the major monotheistic religions.[29] One of the best-known forms of spiritual direction in the Christian tradition is the *Spiritual Exercises of St. Ignatius of Loyola.*[30] In spiritual direction, the director listens as a person describes a prayer or other experience relating to his or her spirituality. Through questioning and assistance in guided reflection, the director helps their companion deepen the experience so that God's message or hopes for him or her can be more fully revealed. Through spiritual direction, directors are trying to help people to gain a better understanding of the transcendent reality that exists behind the physical prayer experience. For religious believers, it is through spiritual direction that encounter with God is deepened and relationship

---

29. William A. Barry and William J. Connolly, *The Practice of Spiritual Direction* (San Francisco: HarperOne, 2009).

30. George E. Ganns, SJ, *The Spiritual Exercises of Saint Ignatius* (Chicago: Loyola Press, 1992).

developed.[31] Often these transcendent experiences are more intense, more meaningful, or seem more "real" to the person having them than are purely sensory encounters with physical reality. Because these individual experiences are so unique, they are not subject to scientific verification. Once again, the transcendent cannot be quantified. For many people, these unique experiences become central organizing events in their lives and play a large part in who he or she is and will become as a person. Spiritual direction is a practice that relies on the deep humility of both the director and the person seeking direction.[32] God is revealed, in a unique way, to each person who takes the time to humbly pray and reflect on the messages coming to him or her through scripture and personal experience.

Sometimes when I am meeting with a young person interested in beginning spiritual direction, I am told, "I am spiritual but not religious." This is a sentiment that is being expressed more frequently in recent years, not just in the United States but around the world, and by people of many ages and backgrounds.[33] Psychologist David Tacey offers a number of explanations for this growing trend; many have to do with disillusionment over outdated theologies and the general failings of institutional churches and clergy.[34] Organized religions, for many, seem to be external entities that are imposed from without by some artificial hierarchical structure, while spirituality is viewed as being a more integrated or internal part of the personality. Even new atheist author Sam Harris suggests that there are aspects of spiritual practice that are worthy of pursuing, though he is characteristically harsh about linking the benefits to any of the world's religions, most especially Christianity.[35] Harris views spirituality as an aspect of human consciousness that can be developed and improved upon through meditation and other practices. His "guide to spirituality" is

31. William A. Barry, SJ, *Spiritual Direction and the Encounter with God* (New York; Paulist Press, 2004), 59–72.

32. Barry and Connolly, *The Practice of Spiritual Direction*, 143–64.

33. David Tacey, *The Spirituality Revolution: The Emergence of Contemporary Spirituality* (London: Routledge, 2004), 30–46.

34. Ibid., 36–37.

35. Sam Harris, *Waking Up: A Guide to Spirituality without Religion* (New York: Simon & Schuster, 2014).

inwardly directed and aimed at self-improvement. In contrast, most spiritual experiences that I am aware of, either for myself or with the people I direct, are really more about the relational aspects and connectedness of their lives. The relationships that are encountered and deepened through prayer may be with God, other people, the "mystery" of creation, or with the Earth and nature. But regardless of the focus, it strikes me that spirituality may be one of the areas of contact between science and religion where a more fruitful dialogue might take place, as long as that dialogue is approached with a humility that respects and honors the great range of religious and spiritual expressions seen in our human family.

Critical Realism

Very late on a Saturday night in the fall of 2001, I was returning to my home in Connecticut from a conference in Oxford, United Kingdom. The conference was an international gathering of theologians and scientists sponsored by the Center for Theology and Natural Science in Berkeley, California, to discuss the topic of *critical realism*. As I boarded the shuttle van that would take me home from JFK airport in New York, the driver, a middle-aged man by the name of Jim, informed me that we were the last shuttle out that night and so we would have to pick up the late passengers from several more flights. I was tired from a long day of travel, but there appeared to be little I could do but settle into the front passenger seat next to Jim and resign myself to a long ride home.

On each loop around the airport that night we picked up one or two additional passengers with whom Jim politely shared the same news he had given me. Some accepted the news with the same sense of resignation that I had, while others bristled with anger over what they perceived as the gross inconvenience or injustice of the situation. At one point, as we were nearing our departure from the airport, a young couple returning from a vacation trip to Italy became so irate that they insisted they be let out of the van immediately so they could get a cab. Jim explained that the only way he could do that would be to re-enter the airport's ground transportation loop one more time, thereby delaying the home arrival of everyone else in the van by another forty-five minutes. One of the two loudly proclaimed, "We don't care about anyone else in the van; we just want to get out of the van and into a cab!" Despite the protests and icy glares from the other passengers, Jim complied with their wishes, and we all took yet another spin around the airport. It was poetic justice, as Jim explained after the unhappy tourists disembarked, that the cab would ultimately need to follow the same route as our shuttle van, so they were in fact only prolonging their own travel and misery as well.

The incident with the young vacationers got Jim talking. He explained to me that in his decade or so driving for the shuttle company he had become a student of human nature. At the time he started driving, after losing his job in a manufacturing company, Jim said that he had a hard time understanding people, especially the boss who had fired him. But he decided to approach his life optimistically and try to learn from the variety of people he met each day in his new job. He went on to say that he now understood people to a much greater degree than he had ten years before and began to relate a series of stories of the people he remembered and the lessons he had learned from them over the years. Some of these stories taught about arrogance or selfishness, like the experience with the young couple that night. But, more often than not, they were stories that revealed the human capacity for kindness and generosity. Each of Jim's stories ended with a statement about what that experience had taught him about human nature. Each story would be immediately followed by a new story that had caused him to revise or reconsider that knowledge. I mostly sat and listened while offering an occasional question to keep the conversation going. Jim was only too happy to continue with his tales for the next two hours, either to pass the time or to keep himself awake. Perhaps both. Finally, just before pulling up in front of my house, Jim's last stop of the night, he concluded, "You know? I figure that if I learn just one thing new about people each day, it was a day worth living." Jim then unloaded my suitcase from the back of the van, thanked me for my patience and his tip, and was on his way.

Over the next couple of days, as I thought about the conference I had attended, I was struck by the realization that what we had been discussing in Oxford for a week was the same thing that Jim was describing in his personal "study of human nature," namely, the provisional nature of knowledge. Our knowledge in any field of study, whether it be science, religion, or human nature, is always open-ended and incomplete; it is subject to constant revision and refinement as new information and/or new experiences come our way. Philosophically, this mode of knowledge advancement through the progressive revision of existing models was named *critical realism* by British philosopher Roy Bhaskar.[36] By *realism*, Bhaskar meant that we are trying to describe the world as it *really* is. By *critical*, he meant that any of our descriptions are open to thorough examination and subject to revision or rejection through the application of our powers of observation and reason.

According to Ian Barbour, whose typologies we visited in chapter 1, it is through the application of the critically realistic scientific method that scientists are trying to make truth claims about the physical essence of the natural world.[37] These truth claims are made by creating models that use the empirical data that is available to date. As new data become available or as new concepts emerge from related scientific fields, the model is refined or tweaked so that a "truer" description of reality emerges. Over the years, our understanding of any natural process might become very good, perhaps even excellent, to the point where we can begin to predict outcomes in a reliable fashion, but our understanding will never be total. A critically realistic approach to science is also a humble approach.

Barbour proposed that theologians, scholars of religion, and individual religious believers are also in a constant state of refinement and revision of their understanding of God and their religious communities as new information and new experiences, religious or otherwise, come to light.[38] In *The Evolution of God,* Robert Wright describes how the human understanding of God has progressed gradually over time from the capricious and competitive multiple

---

36. Roy Bhaskar, *A Realist Theory in Science* (London: Verso, 1975).

37. Ian Barbour, *Religion and Science: Historical and Contemporary Issues* (New York: HarperCollins, 1997), 106–10.

38. Ibid., 110–15.

gods of ancient Greece and Rome, to the vengeful God of the early Hebrews, to the forgiving and loving God of modern Christians.[39] In the brief time that humans have walked the Earth, it is unlikely that God has changed, but humankind's understanding of God, mediated by the lived experiences of religious believers, has developed over time. The understandings that human communities have about God and the greater realities of our universe are far different today than they were two thousand years ago. They will be far different again two thousand years from now. Just as science is never static, neither is religion. Acknowledging that our religious ideas and models of God are subject to change, as are our scientific concepts and models of nature, is a humble acceptance of the limits of human knowledge. Let us now examine how developments in science and religion have played out in the history of science and religious belief by considering the nature of the broad theoretical frameworks that support these beliefs.

Paradigms

In *The Structure of Scientific Revolutions,* historian of science Thomas Kuhn called the major conceptual changes that have occurred in the history of science *paradigm shifts.*[40] A *paradigm,* according to Kuhn, is a fundamental set of assumptions, principles, and theories that guide the work in any scientific field at a particular time.[41] A paradigm shift occurs when accumulating data that do not support the prevailing model reaches a critical mass. This prompts a wholescale re-evaluation of the old paradigm and the formulation of a new one that is better supported. A paradigm shift can be large, affecting an entire scientific discipline such as Einstein's *theory of relativity* or Darwin's *theory of natural selection,* or it can be smaller and noticed only by those working on a specific research problem. In my research field, bone and cartilage development, such a shift occurred in the early 1990s with the general acceptance that matrix vesicles were the

39. Robert Wright, *The Evolution of God* (New York: Little, Brown, 2009).

40. Thomas Kuhn, *The Structure of Scientific Revolutions*, 3rd ed. (Chicago: University of Chicago Press, 1996), 147–59.

41. Ibid., 43–44.

initial sites of bone mineral formation in calcifying cartilage and other hard tissues.

Matrix vesicles are tiny microscopic structures derived from cell membranes that were first identified in electron micrographs of the growing ends of bones in the late 1960s.[42] Such analyses frequently showed that what appeared to be calcium phosphate crystals, the hard mineral material that gives bone its rigid strength, usually appeared first within the central lumen of the matrix vesicles. At the time, the accepted view of how mineral formation begins in calcified tissues was that it was triggered and controlled by collagen, the dominant protein of the extracellular matrix.[43] Matrix vesicles were largely dismissed as artifacts of the tissue fixation process or as inconsequential, cell-derived structures with no significant function. Nevertheless, a handful of investigators continued their studies on these structures, often meeting at small conferences devoted entirely to matrix vesicle biochemistry. One of the leaders of the small matrix vesicle research community was Professor Roy Wuthier of the University of South Carolina, who became my postdoctoral advisor. The matrix vesicle researchers were, in a sense, a small fringe community within the larger field of bone research. At bone research conferences they were not always treated warmly by many who accepted the collagen-dominant paradigm for bone mineral formation. After I joined the Wuthier lab I heard many stories of frequent, sometimes heated, arguments between Dr. Wuthier and other researchers at research conferences during the 1970s and early 1980s. Chief among Dr. Wuthier's antagonists was Professor Melvin Glimcher of Harvard University.

Doctor Glimcher was a well-known pioneer in the study of bone collagens and one of the chief architects of the prevailing collagen-centered paradigm. He led a large and well-funded research group at

42. Clarke Anderson, "Vesicles Associated with Calcification in the Matrix of Epiphyseal Cartilage," *Journal of Cell Biology* 41, no. 1 (1969): 59–72.

43. Melvin J. Glimcher, Alan J. Hodge, and Francis O. Schmitt, "Macromolecular Aggregation States in Relation to Mineralization: The Collagen-Hydroxyapatite System as Studied in Vitro," *PNAS USA* (*Proceedings of the National Academy of Sciences of the United States of America*) 43, no. 10 (1957): 860–67.

Harvard University, and he was one of the most prolific and influential figures in bone research at the time. Many of the leading bone scientists of that era spent at least a part of their careers, either as graduate students or as postdoctoral associates, in Professor Glimcher's laboratory. The underlying assumption of the collagen-centered group led by Glimcher was that since collagen was by far the major organic component of mineralized tissues, it must control the mineralization process. Scientific and medical texts from the 1970s and early 1980s commonly stated, as a fact, that the mineralization process of bone was controlled by collagen. The suggestion by Dr. Wuthier and his matrix vesicle colleagues that a quantitatively minor, cell-derived fragment of membranes might be responsible for initiating mineralization was looked at by some as scientific heresy. Contributing to the reluctance of the broader bone research community to accept an alternative hypothesis was that the challenge to Dr. Glimcher and his Harvard colleagues was led by a lesser-known scientist. Dr. Wuthier was soft-spoken, had a gentler, less dominating personality than Dr. Glimcher, and was from a less prestigious university. The collagen-dominant view persisted, despite the accumulating evidence favoring a role for matrix vesicles from Dr. Wuthier's lab as well as from other investigators, even some who had originally trained in the Glimcher lab.

By the time I joined the Wuthier lab in the late 1980s, Dr. Wuthier and his students had been successful in isolating functional matrix vesicles from cartilage tissue.[44] When incubated in a solution designed to mimic the composition of cartilage fluids, the isolated vesicles accumulated calcium and within a few hours would precipitate calcium phosphate crystals just as had been observed microscopically in intact cartilage. Subsequent studies in our lab included the kinetics of matrix vesicle mineralization,[45] the physical characterization of

---

44. Roy E. Wuthier et al., "Isolation and Characterization of Calcium-Accumulating Matrix Vesicles from Chondrocytes of Chicken Epiphyseal Growth Plate Cartilage in Primary Culture," *Journal of Biological Chemistry* 260, no. 29 (1985): 15972–79.

45. Brian R. Genge et al., "Correlation between Loss of Alkaline Phosphatase Activity and Accumulation of Calcium during Matrix Vesicle-Mediated Mineralization," *Journal of Biological Chemistry* 263, no. 34 (1988): 18513–19.

the mineral crystallites that formed,[46] the identification of key vesicle proteins that mediate the process,[47] and the various components of the core complex that triggers initial mineral formation.[48] These investigations led to the eventual, widespread acceptance of matrix vesicle-mediated mineralization by the bone research community. At the same time, other investigators working on bone found that there was a variety of soluble acidic proteins present in association with collagen that were also involved in bone mineralization.[49] Thus, the picture that emerged was that collagen is important as an overall organizer and for providing tensile strength to bone tissue, in a manner analogous to the iron rebar that is used when pouring concrete building foundations. But collagen is not the primary mediator of bone mineralization. Instead, it is a passive recipient of a calcification process that is controlled by other cellular and macromolecular components of the tissue. The facts laid out in the medical texts changed as new empirical data challenged the existing assumptions underlying the static, collagen-dominated paradigm. A new paradigm on bone mineralization emerged that was built on this new data but contextualized to update and improve on the previous model.

The point of this story is not to vindicate any particular research group or to criticize another but to illustrate the way in which science works. The story portrays a paradigm shift that occurred in my research field of bone biochemistry in the early 1990s. I have no doubt that scientists in virtually any other field of research could relay a similar story about their experiences at one time or another. Most of the time, these shifts are noticed only by those who are working in the area that is affected by the new conceptualization.

---

46. Glenn R. Sauer and Roy E. Wuthier, "Fourier Transform Infrared Characterization of Mineral Phases Formed during Induction of Mineralization by Collagenase-Released Matrix Vesicles in Vitro," *Journal of Biological Chemistry* 263, no. 27 (1988): 13718–24.

47. Brian R. Genge, Licia N. Y. Wu, and Roy E. Wuthier, "Identification of Phospholipid-Dependent Calcium-Binding Proteins as Constituents of Matrix Vesicles," *Journal of Biological Chemistry* 264 (1989): 10917–21.

48. Licia N. Y. Wu et al., "Characterization of the Nucleational Core Complex Responsible for Mineral Induction by Growth Plate Cartilage Matrix Vesicles," *Journal of Biological Chemistry* 268 (1993): 25084–94.

49. Paul A. Price et al., "Primary Structure of the γ-Carboxyglutamic Acid-Containing Protein from Bovine Bone," *PNAS USA* 73, no. 10 (1976): 3374–75.

Sometimes the change is recognized by researchers in other fields and transforms those areas of investigation as well. In the field of bone biochemistry, the original data concerning collagen's role in bone mineralization had not changed, but the interpretation of that data had. It was recontextualized and refined. Our understanding of the cellular and biochemical mechanism of bone formation became more resolved and enriched.

Scientific paradigms can be thought of as the lens through which scientists in that field or community view the world at a given moment in time. Theologians have used the concept of paradigm shifts in science to illustrate that these kinds of broad conceptual changes occur in religious communities as well.[50] As with science, the framework for understanding God is not static but continually evolves over time. Christian theology, for example, has progressed through a series of paradigm shifts over the course of its history. Swiss Catholic theologian Hans Küng has traced the major Christian paradigm shifts from the apocalyptic paradigm of early Christianity, through Greek, Augustinian, and Thomistic paradigms to the paradigms of the Protestant Reformation and Catholic Counter-Reformation, concluding with the Enlightenment paradigm.[51] At the time of his analysis, Küng proposed that Christian theology was entering a new period of what he called the Ecumenical paradigm. Included in this newer, postmodern religious paradigm were the changes to the Mass coming out of the Second Vatican Council (1962–1965).[52] Although still grounded in the fundamental beliefs of Catholicism, the Vatican II changes affected billions of Catholics worldwide, not all of whom were happy with the changes. Resistance to paradigm shifts occurs in religion, just as it does as in science. Recently, there has been some movement away from traditional organized religious practice to more open and expressive forms of religion. David Tacey refers to these changes as a "spirituality revolution."[53] Religious writer Richard Rohr goes further, suggesting that changes in reli-

50. Mooney, *Theology and Scientific Knowledge*, 17–19.

51. Hans Küng, *Theology for the Third Millennium* (New York: Doubleday, 1988).

52. Ibid., 102–6.

53. Tacey, *The Spirituality Revolution*, 11–29.

gious and spiritual practice, coupled with the findings of science, are leading to another paradigm shift for the Christian religions. He speaks of these changes as a rediscovery of the "Universal Christ," which includes the recognition of the sacred nature of every person and everything.[54]

These "faith paradigms" are not unlike the scientific paradigms that they are modeled after. Both types of paradigm provide viewpoints for perceiving and interpreting observed events or phenomena. Both faith paradigms and scientific paradigms are influenced by the culture in which they exist and color the lenses through which theologians, scientists, and the general population interrogates the world in which we live. As paradigms, both are subject to change as old ideas are called into question or even disproved by new findings. Paradigm shifts in religion and science both function to advance knowledge toward a "truer" understanding of reality. If we can humbly accept that these changes have happened in the past, are happening now, and will continue to happen into the future, both science and religion might give each other room to grow.

In modern times, scientific paradigm change is much more rapid than what is observed in religion or theology. But that was not always the case. Prior to the Enlightenment, changes in theology happened at a greater pace than the advancement in knowledge of the natural world. That our scientific worldview currently changes rapidly is one of the challenges that faces modern-day theologians and is perhaps a contributing factor in tensions between science and religion. But if both scientists and theologians could remain humble about what they know, acknowledging the certainty of change in their own fields while remaining open to knowledge from disciplines outside their own, a renewed sense of cooperation between science and religion might emerge.

Hubris

In the spring of 2009, newly elected president of the United States Barack Obama nominated Francis Collins to be the director of

54. Richard Rohr, *The Universal Christ* (New York: Convergent, 2019), 46–48.

the National Institutes of Health, the primary biomedical research agency of the United States government. In an op-ed piece published in the *New York Times*, neuroscientist Sam Harris objected to the Obama nomination based on Dr. Collins's publicly expressed belief in God.[55] Prior to his nomination as NIH director, Collins led the Human Genome Project, which in 2003 completed its goal of determining the full sequence of human DNA. Under Collins's direction, the Human Genome Project was completed ahead of schedule and under budget. In his column, Harris conceded that Collin's scientific credentials were beyond reproach. What Harris found objectionable was Collins's open expression of religious faith.

During his years at the helm of the Human Genome Project, Collins received many questions concerning how a scientist can maintain his/her religious faith in the face of scientific progress. Those questions were frequently prompted by the writings of Harris and others in the new atheist camp. In response to these critiques, Collins delivered a series of lectures on his religious views and published *The Language of God*, which argued that science and religious beliefs are fully compatible.[56] From Collins's perspective, scientific progress can inform one's religious belief system and vice versa; science's ongoing interrogations of the natural world can draw inspiration from a belief in God. In this view, Collins is simply applying a philosophy of *critical realism* to both his scientific and religious thought and, in doing so, gains what is to him a deeper and richer perspective on both. The open-mindedness and humility of Francis Collins are attributes that President Obama and many others believed made him well suited to lead the NIH. But open-mindedness, especially when it comes to religion, is not a characteristic of the new atheist writers. In his op-ed piece, Harris implies that only one who believes as he does is qualified to lead the NIH. So much for humility.

Some writers today, like Harris, automatically assume that their particular worldview (atheistic materialism) is intellectually, morally, ethically, and in all other ways superior to the worldviews of religious believers. To these authors, religion is in the realm of naïve thinking,

---

55. Sam Harris, "Science Is in the Details," *New York Times*, July 27, 2009.
56. Francis Collins, *The Language of God* (New York: Free Press, 2006).

outdated philosophies, and superstition that should be discarded and replaced by their own materialistic philosophies. These writers have conflated the methodological naturalism of science with their own philosophical commitment to atheism. The result is a form of scientific materialism in which any mention of God or other possibility of nonmaterial reality is automatically rejected without consideration. Historian of science Michael Ruse has observed that many of these critics of religion have elevated science to a form of secular religion.[57] For example, regarding Richard Dawkins:

> Finally, and most importantly, there is the fact that Dawkins is engaged in a moral crusade, not as a philosopher trying to establish premises and conclusions, but as a preacher, telling the ways to salvation and damnation. *The God Delusion* is above all a work of morality. . . . Dawkins is on a mission to crush religious belief in the name of science, in the name of Darwinian evolution.[58]

Writers like Harris and Dawkins invariably refuse to acknowledge that their materialistic atheism is not science at all but a philosophical commitment, and in some sense, a faith commitment.

Neither is open-minded humility a characteristic seen in conservative Christian groups that are opposed to science. In the late 1990s, a well-funded effort sponsored by the Discovery Institute of Seattle, Washington, was mounted to introduce "Intelligent Design" as an alternative to Darwinism into the public schools of the United States. On the surface, the intelligent design movement was a continuation of fundamentalist Christian efforts to block and/or undermine the teaching of evolution that dates back to Tennessee's famous Scopes Monkey Trial of 1925.[59] We will examine these fundamentalist responses to the science of evolution more fully in chapter 6. But, as it turns out, intelligent design was only one part of a more comprehensive "wedge strat-

57. Michael Ruse, *Defining Darwin: Essays on the History and Philosophy of Evolutionary Biology* (Amherst, NY: Prometheus Books, 2009), 215–41.

58. Ibid., 237.

59. Thomas Dixon, *Science and Religion: A Very Short Introduction* (New York: Oxford University Press, 2008), 81–103.

egy" to undermine science and its perceived materialistic ideologies so that it could eventually be replaced by a type of science that is more consistent with traditional Christian teachings.[60] Although the intelligent design initiative eventually failed in the courts, public distrust of science continues to be stirred up by self-serving politicians, most notably today in response to climate change. For the most part, these are the same politicians supported by conservative Christian groups. But the Christian virtue of humility is nowhere in the conversation.

Humility in Science and Religion

Until his retirement in 2008, Richard Dawkins was the Simonyi Professor for Public Understanding of Science at Oxford University. This title was indeed appropriate for Dawkins's professional work as an evolutionary biologist. Dawkins is a gifted writer with a passion for explaining evolutionary theory, and his many books offer a wide range of intriguing and instructive examples of evolution from the biological world.[61] His first book, *The Selfish Gene* (1976), which I first read as an undergraduate, was foundational to my understanding of biology. Unfortunately, it is Dawkins's aggressive and dismissive stance toward religion in his later writings that have earned him the enmity of many religious believers. Stephen Meyer and other conservatives behind the intelligent design controversy frequently cite Dawkins as a primary example of science's unending attack on religion[62]—an allegation to which Dawkins, happily and inevitably, responds and returns the volley. Enough already!

If scientists and religious believers would indeed practice the humility that they are so eager to advocate for within their own spheres of activity, perhaps a more meaningful dialogue could begin to emerge in the public arena. It may surprise some to find that meaningful dialogue *is* already occurring, and has been for some

60. Miller, *Only a Theory*, 174–76.

61. See, for example, *Richard Dawkins, The Ancestor's Tale: A Pilgrimage to the Dawn of Life* (New York: Houghton, 2004).

62. Stephen C. Meyer, *Darwin's Doubt: The Explosive Origin of Animal Life and the Case for Intelligent Design* (New York: HarperCollins, 2013), 409–13.

time, in the interdisciplinary field of science and religion.[63] Scientists and theologians who are willing to listen seriously to one another to gain deeper understandings from the other field are advancing the case for cooperative action in addressing some of the world's most pressing issues. While some might dismiss such efforts as the misguided work of "accommodationists,"[64] I would challenge such critics to come up with a better way of engagement than the tedious and polarizing ping-pong match of the past couple of decades. Fortunately, as noted in chapter 1, a model for productive engagement has been put forward by Pope Francis in his encyclical on the environment, *Laudato si'*.[65] This document, grounded in the teachings of Pope Francis's Catholic faith, accepts at face value the findings of science on climate change and environmental degradation caused by human activity. Pope Francis humbly defers to the expertise of scientists on the evidence and possible technical solutions for these problems, while pulling from his faith to build the moral and ethical arguments to confront them. His purpose is to advance conversation and global cooperation on these issues before our Earth is irreparably harmed. This broad and ambitious goal is something that both science and religion ought to be able to agree on.

Both science and religion can each be portrayed as a search for truth. Scientists and religious scholars should be appreciated for the passion and enthusiasm they bring to finding truth in their respective fields. But when scientists like Harris and Dawkins use oversimplified stereotypes to portray religious believers essentially as dunces, they are not being truthful. There are many forms of religious expression within Christianity, Islam, Judaism, and the Eastern religions that are richer, more nuanced, more inclusive, and more empowering than the religious fundamentalists they would like to lump together with all religious believers. Similarly, when conservative religious organizations like the Discovery Institute support initiatives to discredit science by exploiting perceived gaps in evolu-

---

63. Dixon, *Science and Religion*, 13–17.

64. Coyne, *Faith vs. Fact*, 99–119.

65. Pope Francis, *Laudato si', "On Care for Our Common Home"* (Vatican City: Libreria Editrice Vaticana, 2015).

tionary theory and by typecasting science as antagonistic to religion, they are not being truthful. There are thousands upon thousands of research papers in the scientific literature that broadly support Darwinian evolution. And these papers make virtually no mention of religion.

The two disciplines ought to humbly accept the truths that each has to offer, whether they can find full agreement on all issues or not. One of the primary ways of dealing with overly arrogant people is to avoid engaging with them. Hence, those who absolutely "know" themselves to be right on matters outside of their own areas of expertise trivialize not only their arguments but also the discipline that they would describe themselves as representing. Such a stance does not produce effective contributions to the science-and-religion conversation or to society at large. Religious leaders should recognize the authority of scientific experts in describing processes that affect and/or control the natural world. At the same time, scientists need to recognize that there are ways of knowing outside of science, and that religious teachings can open windows on deep knowledge and truth that is not accessible to scientific analysis. For according to the great Indian and Hindu leader Mahatma Gandhi, "Truth without humility would be an arrogant caricature."[66]

---

66. Promod Kumar Sharma, *Mahatma: A Scientist of the Intuitively Obvious* (India: Partridge Publishing, 2014), 76.

3

The Voice of God

During my childhood, my family spent two weeks every summer at the southern New Jersey shore. Our days were spent building sand-castles on the beach, rafting in the ocean surf, or fishing off the jetties surrounding the Barnegat Bay lighthouse. But it was in the late afternoon as the beaches emptied out for the day and the sun began to set behind the saltmarshes that our family vacations had their most enduring impact on me. Looking out over the ocean as the sky changed colors in the fading light, my bare feet sinking into the soft sand with the water lapping around my ankles, I felt an unmistakable longing to know more. Exactly what I wanted to know would be difficult for me to say now. Were there sharks in the water out there? Why do fish come in so many shapes and sizes? What kind of creatures are on the sea bottom just beyond where I can stand? Why is the sea so calm today, when yesterday the waves were so large and violent? During the rest of the year, Jacques Cousteau television specials fed my imagination. I wanted to be a marine biologist so I could answer all those questions. But I realize now that scientific answers were not all that I wanted to know. In those precious summer days, my consciousness was drawn outside of myself, merging with the sea and the sky and the fish, yes, but moving far beyond what I could see and touch and feel. I was being called, in a most personal way, by God.

Few can fail to be moved by the beauty of a windswept coastline, a mountain vista, the movement of animal herds across the African savannah, or even the blooms on a pepper plant in a backyard garden. The natural world calls to us in a visceral way. Through our

DNA we are related to all living things on this planet. Nature speaks to us in ways that we do not deny yet cannot fully understand. We find it hard to put words to the feelings that nature stirs within us. Awe, wonder, marvel, respect, gratitude are some of the words that come to mind yet don't fully capture the depths of the thoughts or feelings moving through us. Though we can seek to understand the biochemistry of photosynthesis, the physiology of large mammals, or the intricate dynamics of a coastal ecosystem, we are nonetheless dumbstruck by the abundant miracles of the natural world. Nature captures our attention and pulls us outside of ourselves; our human spirit seeks to find union with the world around us. What is that aspect of nature that tugs at our heartstrings, and that we yearn to be joined to? Where does the spiritual power with which nature calls to us come from?

To the French Jesuit paleontologist Pierre Teilhard de Chardin (1881–1955), it is the Spirit of God dwelling in the very heart of the physical matter that makes up the universe and upon which all life is based that calls to us:

> Steep yourself in the sea of matter, bathe in its fiery waters, for it is the source of your life and your youthfulness.
>
> Oh the beauty of spirit as it rises up adorned with all the reaches of the earth!
>
> . . . Bathe yourself in the ocean of matter; plunge into it where it is deepest and most violent; struggle in its currents and drink of its waters. For it cradled you long ago in your preconscious existence; and it is that ocean that will raise you up to God.[1]

It is through our contact with the natural world that we might find God. As a Jesuit, Teilhard embraced the notion of St. Ignatius of Loyola, founder of the Jesuit order, that God was present in everyone and everything. The presence of the Spirit in the world is what calls to us, seeks us out, and beckons us forward. Any scientist is eager to speak of the wonder he or she may find in their own pur-

1. Pierre Teilhard de Chardin, *The Heart of Matter* (New York: Harcourt Brace & Jovanovich, 1978), 71–72.

suit of nature's secrets, whatever their scientific discipline or mode of inquiry. Yet most would be reluctant to admit any religious or spiritual significance, at least publicly, to their life's work. This, to me, is incredibly unfortunate and terribly sad. Young people go off to college in search of answers, and find them they do, but often with a loss of the innocence and wonder that drew them to their subjects in the first place. God disappears.

Our Disciplinary Education

The modern university had its origins in medieval Europe. Medieval universities were associations of teachers and students, with instruction based largely on the writings of Aristotle. The Latin-based curriculum was organized systematically into the *trivium* (grammar, rhetoric, and logic), which had to be completed satisfactorily before students could proceed to the mathematically based disciplines of the *quadrivium* (arithmetic, geometry, music, and astronomy). What we would call science today was not a part of the ancient curriculum. It had not been invented yet. Most, though not all, of the European universities either grew out of or were related to institutions associated with the Catholic Church.[2] As these universities developed into the early modern period (1500–1800), studies in natural philosophy, that is, science, theology, law, and medicine also became central to the research and teaching activities of faculty and students. Students were thus exposed to a wide range of subject matter and ways of thinking over the course of their formal education.[3]

American liberal arts universities, which are based on the European university model, have traditionally maintained this broad exposure to academic disciplines in order to foster the intellectual growth and personal maturity of their graduates.[4] In a liberal arts education, students are encouraged to reflect on how the material

2. Paul F. Grendler, "The Universities of the Renaissance and Reformation," *Renaissance Quarterly* 57 (2004): 1–42.

3. Paul F. Grendler, *The Universities of the Italian Renaissance* (Baltimore, MD: Johns Hopkins University Press, 2002).

4. John R. Thelin, *A History of American Higher Education* (Baltimore, MD: Johns Hopkins University Press, 2004).

they are learning in a particular class or major touches on and integrates with their learning in other disciplines. This holistic, reflective approach to learning recognizes that there is more than one way of knowing ourselves and our world and is, traditionally, a central hallmark of Jesuit colleges and universities.

Shift toward Science

Over the past century, higher education has moved away from education of the whole person to a discipline-centered and often vocationally driven menu of specialties in which students must choose between different ways of knowing. In the 1960s, largely as a result of the escalating Cold War between the United States and the Soviet Union, there was a shift in focus away from classical education and toward science.[5] At the college level, this led to a proliferation of science majors, each having its own set of particular course requirements in addition to the basic science requirements of mathematics (calculus), chemistry, and physics. For those choosing to major in one of the sciences, courses in the humanities such as theology, history, art, literature, philosophy, and language were sacrificed in order to meet the increased academic demands of the scientific disciplines.

At many schools, especially the large public universities, majoring in a natural science meant little or no exposure to the humanities or social sciences. In my own case, I was able to graduate with honors in biology, with my only nod to the humanities being a course on the history of motion pictures, followed up by a course on the history of television. That's it. No world history, no politics or cultural studies, no religious studies, no literature, no philosophy, not even a foreign language. And my case is not unusual by any means; in fact, it was the norm for science majors at the time. Despite this, most university graduates, like myself, would likely say that as far as science goes, we got a good education, albeit, an education in the knowledge and methods of science without any regard to other realms of human experience or learning.

---

5. John L. Rudolph, *Scientists in the Classroom: The Cold War Reconstruction of American Science Education* (New York: Palgrave Macmillan, 2002), 1–8.

For college graduates in the sciences, the scientific method became the lens through which we viewed everything. Doctoral training only crystallizes that lens further, so that by the time a student becomes a professional scientist, any other way of thinking or relating to the natural world or to other people is viewed with suspicion or confusion. The childhood wonder that may have led you into the sciences in the first place is lost in vast disciplinary knowledge of natural mechanisms, quantitative relationships, and empirically derived data. In my own discipline, biochemistry, there are over two hundred scientific journals, each publishing hundreds if not thousands of pages per year on the latest research. Keeping abreast of the latest research, while advancing one's own research and career, is an all-consuming task. Those childish thoughts of wonder and awe are left behind as romantic notions or mere illusions. Anyone attaching religious significance to them is mistrusted or even dismissed altogether.

To be sure, the advances in knowledge about the natural world that scientists have provided over the past fifty years is a magnificent achievement. The journey to the moon and the Human Genome Project are bookends to an era of scientific achievement the likes of which humankind has never before witnessed. But as great as this period of discovery was, it is just the beginning. New scientific knowledge answers old questions and poses new ones every day. Every year brings new breakthroughs. Yet despite all the victories of modern science, I can't help but feel that something important has been lost from the scientific community. Modern science was founded, after all, within the Catholic universities and institutions of medieval Europe. For the majority of early scientists, such as Albertus Magnus and Roger Bacon, the study of nature and the worship of God were inseparable.[6] Where has the sense of studying creation for the "greater glory of God" gone? Is it not possible to think both scientifically *and* religiously? A verse from Matthew comes to mind:

> At that time Jesus exclaimed: "I give praise to you, Father, Lord of heaven and earth, for although you have hidden these things

---

6. Benjamin Wiker, *The Catholic Church and Science* (Charlotte, NC: TAN Books, 2011), 31–33.

from the wise and the learned, you have revealed them to the childlike." (Matt 11:25)

In a comprehensive study, sociologist Elaine Ecklund surveyed the religious beliefs of scientists at elite American universities. In this study, 64 percent of scientists reported being either atheist or agnostic relative to belief in God, compared to only 6 percent of the US population.[7] Only 23 percent of scientists reported some belief in God, compared to 80 percent of the US population. Over half of the scientists surveyed reported that they do not ever attend religious ceremonies or services of any kind, while less than a quarter of the general population never participates.[8] The survey focused only on the top twenty-five research universities in the United States. So while the level of unbelief among scientists in this survey might be high relative to the proportion at all colleges and universities, based on my own experience with college faculty at a wide range of institutions, I would not expect to see a lot of difference in religious attitude at other schools either. This includes schools affiliated with religious institutions like mine.

Why would the level of unbelief among academic scientists be so high? Ecklund offered three reasons, based on her conversations with respondents reporting to be atheist or agnostic:

1. The belief that scientific reasoning is superior and has replaced religious thinking in its explanatory power. This would be consistent with the scientific materialism of Richard Dawkins and others. Scientists who think in this way are sometimes openly hostile to religious believers.[9]
2. Negative personal experiences with religion, either directly through interaction with overly restrictive fundamentalist religious communities, or indirectly through the negative effects that religious fanaticism can have on society. In addition, the ridicule of scientific colleagues who condemned them for religious prac-

7. Elaine Howard Ecklund, *Science vs. Religion: What Scientists Really Think* (New York: Oxford University Press, 2010), 16.

8. Ibid., 37.

9. Ibid., 17–20.

tice was also cited as a reason some scientists abandon religious belief.[10]

3. Religion was just never important in their lives. A large number of the scientists surveyed stated that they grew up in homes with either no religious practice or, if a religious affiliation was claimed by the parents, it was only weakly practiced. Thus, these scientists had very little exposure to religion or religious belief in their lives, so it is viewed as insignificant.[11]

Underlying all these reasons, it seems to me, is a profound lack of exposure to broad religious experience and/or language for talking about religion that leaves scientists intellectually impoverished on religious topics. This can then result in the development of atheistic or agnostic views toward religion. Ecklund makes special note of the naïve and stereotypical ways in which the atheist or agonistic scientists interviewed for her study spoke about religion, such as "All religion is fundamentalism," or that religious people are mainly uneducated.[12] Hence, while the early life experiences of young scientists are certainly influential in their career choices, an educational system that is focused on narrowly defined majors and highly specialized intradisciplinary training exacerbates differences that will lead to future misunderstandings. The Ecklund study also found that even though as many as one-third of the surveyed "elite" scientists do acknowledge having a religious faith, they are most commonly "closeted." They do not discuss their beliefs with colleagues for fear of condemnation or being somehow considered to be "less" of a scientist.[13] The science professions are thus dominated by a materialist worldview in which the miracle of existence, the glory of God's creation, and a genuine spirit of thanksgiving are totally disregarded, at least in public.

Beyond the Sciences

Disciplinary focus is not exclusive to the sciences but is a feature of academia in general. In fact, it has been my experience that faculty

10. Ibid., 20–24.
11. Ibid., 24–27.
12. Ibid., 152–56.
13. Ibid., 43–45.

and scholars in the humanities (except for religious studies or theology) are perhaps even less inclined to entertain religious or theological discussion than my natural science colleagues. Most academics, regardless of specialty, would say that interdisciplinary discussion and debate is a vital function of the university. However, faculty at colleges and universities are rewarded primarily through tenure and promotion systems based on their accomplishments (publications, grants, performances, exhibitions, critique, etc.) within their discipline of specialty. As long as this type of reward structure remains in place, disciplinary focus will be the norm and cross-disciplinary exploration the exception. If faculty members conduct virtually all their scholarly work within a single discipline, it only stands to reason that they will expect the same from any students enrolled in their classes. Students are graded based on how well they master the discipline-focused subject matter of a course, not how well they integrate new material with what they have learned in other courses.

Even at liberal arts institutions, the rise of professional schools in business, teaching, engineering, law, and nursing or other medical fields has meant less emphasis on breadth of education in favor of meeting accreditation standards for these vocational specialties. Despite calls from university presidents, provosts, deans, and other administrators to maintain "interdisciplinary connections" in the work of the faculty, the very actions of these same academic leaders in creating new and trendy programs that they can trumpet as their own professional tickets to advancement and promotion run counter to the goal of a holistic education. Student success in attaining professional employment and sufficient postgraduation salaries, rather than quality of education, has become the new standard by which colleges and universities are measured.[14]

The result of these long-term changes to the university curriculum is that students move through a fragmented array of "distribu-

14. Jerry Z. Muller, "The Tyranny of Metrics," *The Chronicle of Higher Education*, January 21, 2018; Kelly Field, "How Much Will I Make after Graduating? College Scorecard Offers Only Clues," *The Chronicle of Higher Education*, September 15, 2015; Andy Thomason, "5 College Rankings Based on the White House's New College Scorecard Data," *The Chronicle of Higher Education*, January 14, 2015.

tion requirements" in which there is often no attempt to integrate alternative forms of inquiry and thinking into the knowledge or skill sets attained in their major of choice. Students go out into the professional world as doctors, nurses, lawyers, accountants, engineers, and scientists empowered only to think within their discipline. The competitive nature of the job market functions to lock these mindsets into place permanently, and the result is that we live in a world full of specialists. Our college graduates are highly trained in their fields but are often disconnected from one another and from God.

It is certainly not our educational system alone that has led to the loss of religious influences in our lives. In his monumental work *A Secular Age*, Charles Taylor explores a variety of historic trends that have contributed to the significant decline in public and private practice of religion in our postmodern society. Taylor asks the question, "Why was it virtually impossible not to believe in God in, say, 1500 in our Western society, while in 2000 many of us find this not only easy, but even inescapable?"[15] There are many reasons that Taylor puts forward in this work to explain this phenomenon, including the "disenchantment" of the natural world by the progress of science, the reform movement in Christianity and the splintering of the Christian church, growing disillusionment with organized churches due to various scandals, the hyperspecialization of disciplinary work, and the hard-driving forces of our global consumer economy.

But Taylor rejects the common "enlightenment argument," loudly proclaimed by atheists such as Richard Dawkins and Daniel Dennett, as being naïve and overly simplistic. Over time, argue the "brights"—as some of the new atheist writers call themselves—religion will continue to decline in the face of the relentless advance of science until only a few lingering pockets of irrationality remain. On the contrary, Taylor argues that "death of God" atheism such as this is reliant on a closed framework of thought in which alternatives to simple mechanical materialism need never be considered.[16] Atheistic arguments thus remain captive to a rigid, and oversimpli-

15. Charles Taylor, *A Secular Age* (Cambridge, MA: Harvard University Press, 2007), 25.

16. Ibid., 567.

fied, worldview. This way of thinking is exactly the opposite of the open-mindedness that any good scientist would say is essential to the practice of his or her profession. In our postmodern times, we seem to have an abundance of influential and outspoken public "experts" who, however brilliant and talented they may well be within their scientific disciplines, are simply incapable of considering any viewpoints other than their own.

The gradual loss of religious influence in society is hardly something to be celebrated by our atheist friends, however. Taylor maintains that in our current secular world there is a general feeling of malaise:

> The secular age is schizophrenic, or better, deeply cross-polarized. People seem at a safe distance from religion; and yet they are very moved to know that there are dedicated believers, like Mother Teresa.[17]

Journalist Paul Griffiths found in a small survey of atheists who are not antagonistic toward religion that there was "a sense that something has been lost, something without which a rich and meaningful life cannot be lived."[18] A recent Gallup Poll has reported a twenty-year decline in institutional religious participation, yet many of those no longer attending church services still identify as religious or spiritual.[19] Charles Taylor describes several "conversions" that indicate that the human search for a transcendent spirit and for God's presence is still alive within our world.[20] And finally, David Tacey notes that the recent declines in Western church participation coincide with a strong "religious impulse" within the human community and a new longing for other forms of spiritual expression.[21] Interestingly, a quarter of the atheists and agnostic scientists from Ecklund's sur-

17. Ibid., 727.

18. Paul Griffiths, "Fellow Travelers? Four Atheists Who Don't Hate Religion," *Commonweal* (October 26, 2012): 24.

19. Jeffrey M. Jones, *U.S. Church Membership Down Sharply in Past Two Decades* (Washington, DC: Gallup, April 1, 2019), https://news.gallup.com/poll/248837.

20. Taylor, *A Secular Age*, 728–72.

21. David Tacey, *The Spirituality Revolution: The Emergence of Contemporary Spirituality* (London: Routledge, 2004), 11–29.

vey reported themselves to be "spiritual" though not in any religious tradition.[22] Something seems to be going on here. Perhaps there is hope for religion after all. We might get a glimmer of that hope from the life and work of Teilhard de Chardin.

Teilhard de Chardin's Life of Science and Faith

Early Sparks of Interest

Pierre Teilhard de Chardin was born in 1881 into an aristocratic family of the Auvergne region of central France, where he was educated at a Jesuit-run boarding school. His desire to study science as well as a vocational calling to the priesthood led him to the Jesuit order in 1899. He received his formal education at the University of Caen, where he studied literature, followed by studies at a Jesuit college on the English Channel island of Jersey, which specialized in the natural sciences (geology, chemistry, and physics). He completed his training with an advanced degree in theology at the French Jesuit scholasticate located in Hastings, England.[23] Teilhard thus received a breadth of learning and academic exposure quite unlike that experienced by the vast majority of academic specialists today. Throughout his life he drew on these intellectual resources in his scientific studies on geology and human evolution as well as in his later theological writings.

Teilhard was drawn to a life of science as a small boy when he became fascinated by metal objects and later by mineral crystals such as quartz and amethyst. His draw to these inanimate objects proved to be a gateway leading him to an insatiable curiosity about the planet Earth and all of nature.[24] Ultimately, he found that his earliest interest in the materials of the world was also a spiritual awakening for him, which he wrote about years later in the *Hymn to Matter*.[25] Coincident with his entry into the Society of Jesus, his early

---

22. Ecklund, *Science vs. Religion*, 58.

23. Ursula King, *Spirit of Fire: The Life and Vision of Teilhard de Chardin* (Maryknoll, NY: Orbis Books, 1996).

24. Ibid., 7.

25. Ibid., 85.

fascination with matter and nature developed into a cosmic sense that he would carry with him the rest of his life. In his spiritual autobiography, *The Heart of Matter*, which was written a few years before his death, Teilhard describes how his scientific work led him to discover the heart of God burning within all of nature:

> The Diaphany of the Divine at the heart of a glowing Universe, as I have experienced it through contact with the Earth—the Divine radiating from the depths of blazing Matter.[26]

A very important part of Teilhard's professional life was the science of evolutionary biology, which he embraced during the time he was doing theological studies. As a young scientist in England, Teilhard was well aware of the ongoing discussions of Darwin's theory of natural selection that were taking place in scientific circles. But he had trouble reconciling the science of evolution with the static traditional theology of the time.[27] According to Teilhard's biographer, Ursula King, the book *Creative Evolution* by French philosopher Henri Bergson brought about a profound transformation in Teilhard's theological thinking. For Teilhard, the discovery of evolution freed him from the dualistic theological pairings of body and soul, or matter and spirit, so that he came to regard these two aspects, or "substances," of nature as one and the same.[28]

Mining the Secrets of Fossils

Teilhard's specialty within geology was vertebrate paleontology, and he spent many hours collecting and categorizing fossils from the French and English countrysides. In 1911, he completed his theological studies in Hastings and was ordained as a Jesuit priest. His first assignment was to Paris, where he began working with the paleontologist Marcellin Boule, of the Museum of Natural History, who was well known for his characterization and description of the first complete Neanderthal skeleton. While working at sites in France and

26. Teilhard de Chardin, *The Heart of Matter*, 16.
27. King, *Spirit of Fire*, 36.
28. Ibid., 37.

Spain with Boule, Teilhard became especially interested in human evolution.[29]

Teilhard's academic work was interrupted by the outbreak of World War I in 1914. From the start of the war until he was discharged from military service in early 1919, Teilhard served as a chaplain and stretcher bearer on the front lines in France, seeing action in nearly every major battle. During the war, Teilhard wrote many essays and reflections that would later serve as the starting points for his theological works. Scholars of his work have noted that these war essays contain some of his most beautiful reflections on nature, even though he was surrounded every day by the battlefield horrors of that brutal war.[30] Even in the midst of vast human carnage, Teilhard was able to sense and draw inspiration from the presence of God. If ever there was a model for the Jesuit spirit of "finding God in all things," Teilhard surely provided that through his war experiences.

After the war, Teilhard returned to his research in Paris and was assigned to a teaching position at the Institute Catholique. During this time, he became widely regarded as a top-notch paleontologist, conducting research at many sites around the world. Teilhard's most important scientific work was conducted between the years of 1929 and 1931 after moving to China to work as an official advisor to the Chinese Geological Survey.[31] During these years, the fossil remains of "Peking Man," (*Homo erectus)* were uncovered in excavations of the Zhoukoudian caves near present-day Beijing. The bones at the Zhoukoudian site have been dated as 750,000 years old and are important because they are the first site at which the use of fire by a human ancestor had been conclusively demonstrated. Teilhard was involved in the classification of the ash, cinders, and charred animal bones that provided the evidence for this conclusion, and he authored several papers on the geological strata of the area in which the remnants were found. Biographer Ursula King notes how thrilled Teilhard must have been to be involved in this landmark discovery in human cultural

29. Ibid., 41.
30. Ibid., 53.
31. Ibid., 126–32.

evolution, "for the image of fire meant so much to him, the spark and blaze of a roaring fire!"[32]

Teilhard the Theologian

As important as Teilhard de Chardin's scientific work was to the field of human paleontology, it is his many theological works, most notably *The Divine Milieu* (completed in 1927) and *The Phenomenon of Man* (completed in 1940) for which he is best-known today. Teilhard published his scientific work in many research papers for geology and paleontology journals throughout his lifetime—yet, despite his best efforts, his books in theology were blocked from publication by Catholic Church officials.[33] In the years prior to the Vatican II reforms of the 1960s, the Catholic Church was struggling to come to grips with emerging theories in physics and biology, which some scholars in the church saw as oppositional to the philosophy of Thomas Aquinas (1220–1274), on which much Catholic doctrine was based.[34]

Teilhard's revolutionary ideas integrated his scientific and theological training. He saw the emergence of human consciousness through biological evolution as a vital part of a still-unfolding cosmic history. These thoughts were made public during his lectures or through private distribution of his letters to colleagues and caught the attention of Vatican officials. In 1950, Pope Pius XII issued the encyclical *Humani Generis* in which he sought to correct "some false opinions threatening to undermine the foundations of Catholic Doctrine."[35] One of these false ideas identified by Pius XII was "evolutionism," which many interpreted to be targeted directly toward Teilhard, though he was not singled out by name.[36] Teilhard died in New York on Easter Sunday in 1955. He suffered a heart attack while visiting a friend after attending Mass at St. Patrick's Cathedral in Manhattan.[37]

32. Ibid., 130.

33. Ibid., 212.

34. Peter M. J. Hess and Paul L. Allen, *Catholicism and Science* (Westport, CT: Greenwood Press, 2008), 92.

35. Pope Pius XII, *Humani Generis* (Vatican City, 1950).

36. Hess and Allen, *Catholicism and Science*, 100.

37. King, *Spirit of Fire*, 230.

At the time of Teilhard's death, his religious writings, most of which had not yet been published, were highly controversial. Critics within the church condemned him for being an incompetent theologian, while experts from the scientific community started to trivialize his scientific achievements despite that fact that he had received many accolades from that same community throughout his lifetime. Professional animosity was focused not only on Teilhard but also toward those who supported him or admired his work. For example, Teilhard's friend, the well-known evolutionary biologist Sir Julian Huxley, was severely criticized by scientific colleagues for writing the foreword to *The Phenomenon of Man* when the English translation was finally published in 1959.[38] Even after allowing for the publication of his works, the Catholic Church issued a *monitum* in 1962 that warned Catholics to be cautious about reading too much into Teilhard's theories.[39]

It seems to me that much of the controversy surrounding Teilhard de Chardin and his work stems from the fact that he had the audacity to cross between fields of academic endeavor in a truly interdisciplinary way. He allowed his scientific understanding of the natural world to inform his religious thinking, and this was not acceptable to many theologians of his time. Scientists, on the other hand, viewed Teilhard's scientific work as being derived from his Christian religious beliefs, which was similarly unacceptable.

Decades after Teilhard's death, the popular evolutionary biologist and writer Stephen J. Gould attempted to discredit him by resurrecting a historically debunked claim that Teilhard had been responsible for the infamous "Piltdown Man Hoax" of 1912.[40] Gould, the

38. Ursula King, *Christ in All Things: Exploring Spirituality with Teilhard de Chardin* (Maryknoll, NY: Orbis Books, 1997), 138–41.

39. Hess and Allen, *Catholicism and Science*, 109.

40. Stephen J. Gould, *The Panda's Thumb: More Reflections in Natural History* (New York: W. W. Norton, 1980), 108–24. In 1911, Charles Dawson claimed to have found the "missing link" between ape and man after unearthing fossilized remains at a site near Piltdown, East Sussex, England. The find was later found to be a forgery in which the bones of an ape and human were combined. Teilhard de Chardin participated in the initial excavation, but a 2016 study exonerated him from being involved in the hoax itself. See Isabelle De Groote, Linus Girdland Flink, Rizwaan Abbas, Silvia M. Bello et al., "New Genetic and

architect of NOMA, as discussed in chapter 1, seemed to be distressed that anyone could cross the disciplinary boundaries of science and religion and maintain credibility. He therefore sought to undermine that credibility. Gould's "Piltdown reprise" was quickly dismissed by scholars of science history and definitively refuted in 2016.[41] But this fallacious charge would continue to be bandied about by atheistic writers such as Daniel Dennett and Christopher Hitchens for many years after Gould's claim.

Clearly, Teilhard's reputation suffered due to his willingness to cross disciplinary boundaries. His work was consequently overlooked by both scientists and theologians for many years. But by being open to the cross-fertilization of ideas that comes about when thinking from multiple perspectives and by allowing God's spirit to work within him, Pierre Teilhard de Chardin developed a groundbreaking new theology that has inspired many modern-day Catholic theologians such as Christopher Mooney, John Haught, Elizabeth Johnson, and Ilia Delio, to name but a few. Teilhard's theological influences are also starting to be seen in the work of popular spiritual writers such as Richard Rohr.[42]

A New Theology

Two major theological paradigm shifts, derived from Teilhard's scientific understanding of evolution, are most relevant here. The first is the realization that evolution is an *ongoing* process. Species continually come into existence, thrive for a certain amount of time, and go extinct, only to be replaced by newly emergent species. The process of natural selection, which is the main driver of evolutionary change, has resulted in gradually increasing levels of complexity in the ever-changing diversity of life forms inhabiting Earth over the 4.5 billion years of its history. To Teilhard, this implied that the traditional theology of his time, which was based on the idea of an initial "perfect" creation that had been degraded to an imperfect state through the

Morphological Evidence Suggests that a Single Hoaxer Created 'Piltdown Man,'" *Royal Society Open Science* 3 (August 10, 2016).

41. Thomas King, SJ, "Teilhard and Piltdown," in *Teilhard and the Unity of Knowledge*, ed. Thomas King, SJ, and James Salmon, SJ (New York: Paulist Press, 1983), 159–69.

42. Richard Rohr, *The Universal Christ* (New York: Convergent Books, 2019).

consequences of human sinfulness, was simply not consistent with modern scientific understanding and was in need of revision.[43] It is not surprising that church officials of his time, fully invested in the Thomistic theology of centuries past, were not interested in such a project. It is only now, sixty years after Teilhard's death, that his ideas are beginning to enter the mainstream of theological discussion.

The second major theological shift has to do with Teilhard's ideas regarding the unique *place of humankind* in cosmological history. Teilhard was fond of Julian Huxley's expression that humankind is "nothing else than evolution become conscious of itself."[44] Our human species, *Homo sapiens,* is one of the more recent major species to emerge in the evolutionary history of Earth. We are also the first species on our planet that is able to contemplate its origins, its sense of purpose, and its future. The search for human origins is a story that thousands of scientists have dedicated their lives to over the past century. Teilhard himself was involved in the discovery and characterization of *Homo erectus* fossils in China in the early 1930s, which at the time was our earliest known ancestor. Since Teilhard's time, the remains of several other archaic human descendants of *Homo erectus* have been identified, such as the diminutive *Homo floresiensis*, or "hobbit," discovered in 2004 in a remote part of Indonesia. *Homo floresiensis* appears to have gone extinct as recently as 18,000 years ago.[45] The evolutionary history of modern humans is an endlessly fascinating and complex story that will continue to unfold as more and more of the paleontological, genetic, and cultural pieces of the puzzle are fit into place.

Cosmic Significance of Human Evolution

Teilhard de Chardin was just as fascinated by the study of human origins as any of his contemporary scientific colleagues and anthropologists since his time. But to Teilhard, our evolutionary history

---

43. John Haught, *Deeper than Darwin: The Prospect for Religion in the Age of Evolution* (Cambridge, MA: Westview Press, 2003), 161–75.

44. Pierre Teilhard de Chardin, *The Phenomenon of Man* (London: William Collins Sons, 1959), 221.

45. Bernard Wood, *Human Evolution: A Very Short Introduction* (New York: Oxford University Press, 2005).

had *cosmic* significance and was only just the beginning of a still-unfolding story. He was one of the first paleontologists to speculate about what the future might hold for our species. Teilhard saw the emergence of human consciousness, a consciousness that was not only self-aware but one that could begin to sense the presence of a relational God, as a critically important event in the history of the universe. He went so far as to predict that:

> After having been regarded for many years as a scientific subsidiary or element of the universe, humankind will in the end be recognized as a fundamental phenomenon—*the* supreme phenomenon of nature; that in which, in a unique complexity of material and moral factors, one of the principal acts of universal evolution is not only experienced by, but lived by us.[46]

The most significant aspect of human consciousness, according to Teilhard, is its self-reflectiveness.[47] Our reflective nature has provided the foundation from which the many and various human endeavors such as art, philosophy, mathematics, logic, and even science could emerge. The "hominization" of the evolutionary process on Earth has resulted in the emergence of a species that is now participatory in creation.[48]

Looking forward, Teilhard conceived of an Omega Point toward which all of evolution, both biological and psychic, will ultimately converge. As a Christian, Teilhard expresses his faith that the Omega and Christ are one and the same and that the coming convergence will center upon divine love:

> Then as St. Paul tells us, *God shall be all in all. . . .* The universe fulfilling itself in a synthesis of centres in perfect conformity

46. Pierre Teilhard de Chardin, *Science and Christ* (London: William Collins and Sons, 1968), 97.

47. Ilia Delio, *Making All Things New: Catholicity, Cosmology, Consciousness* (Maryknoll, NY: Orbis Books, 2015), 48.

48. Patrick H. Byrne, "The Integral Visions of Teilhard and Lonergan: Science, the Universe, Humanity, and God," in *From Teilhard to Omega: Co-Creating an Unfinished Universe*, ed. Ilia Delio (Maryknoll, NY: Orbis Books, 2014), 83–110.

with the laws of union. God, the Centre of centres. In that final vision the Christian dogma culminates.[49]

Teilhard's view of evolution has an implied directionality to it. One way to interpret this is that humankind was predestined to emerge in our present state from the very moment of first creation. While this is entirely consistent with traditional religious interpretations, in which humankind is the high point of God's creation, most biologists would surely argue that the evolutionary process shows no specific directionality. Although one might, from our point in history, look back at the past and see the arrow of evolution pointing directly at us through endless eons of time, modern evolutionary biology would say that this perspective is, in fact, an illusion. One could do the same thing for any species currently alive. All of Earth's history has been leading up to humans, or to emperor penguins, or to carpenter ants, as the case may be, depending on the species you are talking about. But from a scientific perspective, the evolution of any species is never a purely linear path. And for every species that we are aware of, either historically or presently, that path will ultimately lead to the dead end of extinction.

So, at the very least we should be highly suspect of anthropocentric interpretations of evolutionary history. As we will discuss in chapter 7, *Homo sapiens* was subject to the same random twists and turns of evolutionary fate as any species that ever inhabited the Earth. According to one theory, our species faced an extinction event only 70,000 years ago. Evidence suggests that a volcanic eruption of Mount Toba in Sumatra triggered global climatic change that reduced the African population of *Homo sapiens* to a few thousand.[50] Since it is thought that the emergence of *Homo sapiens* from Africa occurred sometime between 50,000 and 70,000 years ago, it is interesting to speculate that the near extinction experience perhaps had something to do with the African emigration as our species recov-

49. Teilhard de Chardin, *The Phenomenon of Man*, 294.

50. Stanley H. Ambrose, "Late Pleistocene Human Population Bottlenecks, Volcanic Winter, and Differentiation of Modern Humans," *Journal of Human Paleontology* 34 (1998): 623–51.

ered. Perhaps the experience was even connected to the emergence of our modern human consciousness.

Teilhard himself understood that the majority of scientists would disagree with his interpretation of evolutionary history. To him the gradual "complexification" of animal nervous systems over time, culminating in the emergence of human consciousness, was something that "could not be the result of chance" and was evidence that evolution has a direction.[51] But if we conclude, from the perspective of many modern-day scientists, that the emergence of consciousness in the *Homo* lineage was due to chance and blind natural selection, must we also conclude that consciousness, any consciousness, is simply an accident of nature?

A number of years ago, the *West of Eden* science fiction series by Harry Harrison was built on the premise that if the comet impact that caused the extinction of dinosaurs had not happened, a sentient species of dinosaur might have emerged. In the *West of Eden* saga, the sentient dinosaur descendants, the Yilane, come into eventual contact with a more primitive hominid species, the Tanu, triggering a long series of interspecies conflicts and adventures. Of course, this is all quite far-fetched. Such is the great fun of science fiction for its many fans. But it raises the question, could consciousness possibly have occurred in a species other than modern humans? While our *Homo* evolutionary lineage may not have survived to our present time, is there something inherent in the composition of the universe and in biological processes that "predestines" the emergence of consciousness in some species in some place, or even many places, at some time? Is a "Star Trek" universe, with a wide diversity of sentient species scattered across the galaxy, a possibility, however remote?

Teilhard de Chardin's theology starts with the very nature of matter, proceeds through the history of biological evolution, and leads to the emergence of consciousness and the development of human spirituality, culture, and technology. To Teilhard, the cosmic story concludes with the far-off union of a cosmic consciousness with the Christ-Omega. Many of Teilhard's ideas have become the seeds from

51. Byrne, *From Teilhard to Omega*, 86.

which a new theology, sometimes called a "theology of evolution" or "theistic evolution," has sprung.[52] Theistic evolution takes the findings of modern cosmology, biological evolution, and molecular biology as the grounds from which we might re-examine traditional Catholic doctrine such as original sin, the meaning of suffering, redemption, and hope.[53] An exciting aspect of this theology is that the story of life is open-ended and human destiny has not been predetermined. There is a future that is filled with opportunity, perhaps even including the possibility of human participation *with* God in the ongoing process of creation. Theistic evolution states that creation is happening every day, every minute, and every second; and humans, for better or worse, are a part of the creative process.

The Inevitability of Consciousness?

From a philosophical standpoint, Teilhard's theology may be too anthropocentric for most modern scientists to agree with. But we might also look at Teilhard's trajectory of evolution in a different way. If we take humans out of the picture for a moment, Teilhard's theology is really based on the evolutionary emergence of consciousness, a consciousness that can relate to a creator God in a personal way. Evolutionary biologist Simon Conway Morris has looked at the question of the "inevitability" of consciousness emerging through the evolutionary process.[54] Morris focuses his analysis not on the differences between humans and other species but on the way in which the evolutionary process operates on preexistent organizational structures to produce remarkably similar biological outcomes in widely disparate organisms. Some examples include: the complicated eyes of squids and fish; nerve sheaths that speed impulses in vertebrates, crustaceans, and annelid worms; or the use of the neurotransmitter acetylcholine as a signaling molecule in plants as well as animals.

52. John F. Haught, *God after Darwin: A Theology of Evolution* (Boulder, CO: Westview Press, 2000).

53. John F. Haught, *Resting on the Future: Catholic Theology for an Unfinished Universe* (New York: Bloomsbury Academic, 2015).

54. Simon Conway Morris, *Life's Solution: Inevitable Humans in a Lonely Universe* (Cambridge: Cambridge University Press, 2003).

The more we understand about the biological world, the more evolutionary convergences such as these become apparent to us.

Morris also notes that we see forms of "primitive" intelligence in the animal world that are identical in many ways to aspects of our own highly developed intellect.[55] Animal models are widely used by psychologists and neuroscientists to gain insights into human behavior. Increasingly, it seems more reasonable to think that our human consciousness and even our capacity for religious thought could be a natural consequence of the evolutionary process, rather than just a freak accident. Elephants, crows, and many species of monkeys and apes fashion tools from sticks and stones to assist them in the tasks of daily life. Both elephants and dolphins exhibit complex behavior patterns in response to the dead remains of relatives. Our species may not even be the only one to have ever developed some form of religious expression.

In 1908, the paleontologist brothers Jean and Amédée Bouyssonie, along with their father, Louis Bardon, uncovered a complete Neanderthal skeleton at a cave site near the village of La Chapelle-aux-Saints in central France. The disposition of the skeleton led the team to conclude that the burial had been intentional and suggested that Neanderthals practiced primitive religious rituals.[56] The fossil was given the nickname "the Old Man" and became the most famous Neanderthal finding in Europe. Other Neanderthal burial sites have been found in Europe and the Middle East since the discovery of the Old Man, including one in Iraq that included flowers at the grave site.[57] Whether or not these sites represent actual deliberate burials that had any religious significance has been hotly disputed in the archaeological literature.

Recent work on the La Chapelle-aux-Saints site tends to support the Bouyssonie's original conclusions.[58] Although the issue

---

55. Ibid., 243–61.

56. Juan Luis Arsuaga, *The Neanderthal's Necklace: In Search of the First Thinkers*, trans. Andy Klatt (New York: Four Walls Eight Windows, 2002).

57. Ralph S. Solecki, "Shanidar IV, a Neanderthal Flower Burial in Northern Iraq," *Science* 190 (1975): 880–81.

58. William Rendu et al., "Evidence Supporting an Intentional Neandertal Burial at La Chapelle-aux Saints," *PNAS USA* 111 (2014): 81–86.

remains far from settled scientifically, what if a consciousness like ours, capable of symbolic behavior and culture, had developed in another species? If Neanderthals had not gone extinct, would they have developed complex forms of religious expression as their evolutionary cousins *Homo sapiens* eventually did? I cannot help but think that Pierre Teilhard de Chardin would have enjoyed entertaining such considerations.

Listening to the Voice of God

Teilhard de Chardin's theology of an unfinished universe in which humankind participates with God in the ongoing creative process may have been too revolutionary for widespread acceptance during his lifetime, but it has proven to be an inspiration for many modern-day theologians.[59] Teilhard's ideas, as complicated as they might sometimes seem, are rooted in his childhood fascination with metal objects and mineral crystals. It is within these natural objects that he discovered the "heart of matter," which for him was the presence of God calling him to a life of science and theological reflection. Although Teilhard is certainly unique in the theology that emerged from his scientific investigations, his earliest inspirations are not unusual. An early encounter with the natural world is frequently the inspiration that draws one to a scientific career.

Autobiographical sketches made by many scientists corroborate this claim. For insect sociobiologist E. O. Wilson it was an early fascination with ant colonies.[60] For animal behaviorist Konrad Lorenz it was the experience of raising orphaned ducklings with his sister.[61] In my own case it was summer vacations at the Jersey shore and one delightful afternoon spent watching a spider weave her web outside my bedroom window. I have heard similar stories from many of my

---

59. Ilia Delio, ed., *From Teilhard to Omega: Co-Creating an Unfinished Universe* (Maryknoll, NY: Orbis Books, 2014).

60. Edward O. Wilson, "In the Queendom of Ants: A Brief Autobiography," in *Studying Animal Behavior: Autobiographies of the Founders*, ed. Donald A. Dewsbury (Chicago: University of Chicago Press), 465–86.

61. Konrad K. Lorenz, "My Family and Other Animals," in *Studying Animal Behavior: Autobiographies of the Founders*, ed. Donald A. Dewsbury (Chicago: University of Chicago Press), 259–88.

scientific colleagues over the years. Something in these experiences resonates deeply within the heart and soul of a child, stirring an imagination yet unconstrained by artificial disciplinary boundaries. We hear the voice of God calling us forth to learn about and understand the created universe in all its mystery. Not everyone identifies this "call" as the voice of God; it might be referred to as the Mystery that permeates the universe,[62] or as a relentless force that draws us irresistibly out of ourselves, but the call comes, nonetheless.

Some readers might say that it is only an individual's own interests, talents, or a unique set of circumstances that leads one to a life in science. There is nothing relational about it. But to deny that there is a Presence that calls to us, something or Someone beyond that which can be reliably measured by our scientific instruments, seems to me an irrational turning away from what could be so much more. It is as if to say, "If I cannot explain it, I will ignore it." This, to me, is the antithesis of the scientific method, which always should be open to new explanations. Catholic sacramentality, most conspicuous in celebration of the Holy Eucharist, though richly embedded throughout the religious tradition, recognizes and rejoices in the Divine Presence that resides within all aspects of nature and human life. In spiritual direction, religious seekers look beneath and through the experiences of everyday life to discover how a relational God is present for them. If scientists look beyond the disciplinary boundaries that define our fields to sense the wonders of the greater Reality that exists beyond what we can measure physically, our sense of awe and gratitude for our natural world will only be increased. New paths of investigation might even be opened.

I am certainly not suggesting that everyone should believe as I do. I have friends who are religious believers and those who are not; those who are agnostic to faith but are spiritual; and those who dispute religion and spirituality in any form. Diversity of expression adds to the richness of life. I am only asking that those with differing belief systems be open to the thoughts and, yes, beliefs of others. We all have a set of core beliefs, whether we acknowledge them or not.

---

62. Ursula Goodenough, *The Sacred Depths of Nature* (New York: Oxford University Press, 1998).

To the extent that we can share our wonder with those who are called to other disciplines, professions, and lifestyles, then we might better appreciate the goodness of nature and our responsibilities to care for our world. If we endeavor to bring some coherence between scientific understanding and other ways of human knowing, as Teilhard de Chardin attempted with his theology, then we truly might become co-creators. Perhaps we may even usher in a new era of more refined, more mature, and less restrictive religious sensibility in which scientific knowledge, human consciousness, and heartfelt gratitude can propel us forward to a better future with God, with one another, and with our Earth.

There is a reason why religious retreat centers are almost always located in places of great natural beauty. One of the first exercises often suggested for a new retreatant is to go out somewhere on the property and simply notice nature. This might be by taking a slow walk on the grounds, sitting still and watching a brook trickle by or the leaves of a tree rustling in the breeze, or even just lying on the grass in the sun and gazing up at the sky. The purpose of the exercise is to calm the spirit, remove oneself from the frantic activity and concerns of daily life, and listen quietly for the voice of the transcendent God who calls to us from beneath and beyond the wonders of the natural world. This first-day experience of nature is one of the things I most look forward to when I go on retreat. This is true whether I am returning to a retreat center I know well or one that I have never visited before. As I enter into one of these retreats, I know that visiting prayerfully with nature will return me to my earliest childhood memories. I inevitably return to that time when I was one with the natural world, close to God and in touch with my truest self. As I sit quietly, overcome with gratitude for all creation, I begin to get answers to the questions I am bringing with me to the retreat. Many of these questions are about my personal life and relationships. They are the questions that I am trying to discern and decisions I am trying to come to through my intellectual efforts and the whispers I hear from God.

New questions will always emerge. These are not only about my own life but include the big philosophical questions that have captured the imagination of the human mind for at least as long as we have written records. As a scientist and as a Christian believer, the big questions that most frequently come to my mind have both a scientific and a religious component. Although I might seek partial answers through either scientific inquiry or religious reflection, a satisfactory answer will only come, for me, if I try to integrate these thoughts and feelings. I want not only to understand the science; I want to encounter the depth and meaning that lies beyond the physical explanations. I know my answers will only be provisional; when I revisit the same questions in a year or in a decade, things will have changed. I will be forced to come to grips with new scientific breakthroughs and new religious insights. Through all of these cycles, I know that as I am coming to a more complete understanding of nature as it really is, I am also coming to know God more fully. To me, this is the greatest reward that a human person, whether scientist, believer, or both, could ever hope for in this life.

The four big scientific and religious questions that come up for me most frequently as I sit contemplatively on retreat will be the subjects for the rest of this book. I will focus on both the historical and current scientific knowledge of each topic as well as what the religious and theological responses to the science have been. In our postmodern era, scientific progress is very fast, and theology thus must react and change in response. This has not always been the case, and I think a time will emerge in the future when theological questions might again drive scientific inquiry. Religion and theology are often portrayed as static, resistant to change, or obsolete. But a healthy religion, just like a robust science, is always open to skepticism and new exploration, a spirit of inquiry that recognizes and honors tradition but is open to new inspiration and new encounters with the Spirit of God. Father Massad, the pastor of St. John Neumann Catholic Church in Columbia, South Carolina, during the 1990s, once told a discussion group I was participating in that "if you do not ever question your faith, you will eventually lose it." It is in the spirit of scientific and religious inquiry that we will examine my big questions.

As a biologist, my questions have a decided orientation toward the living world. Other scientists would likely have other, perhaps more significant questions, but these are mine:

1. Where did our universe come from? What is the meaning of creation? Why is there anything at all, rather than nothing? What is our cosmological future?
2. How did living things emerge from the nonliving? Can the underlying chemistry of life give us any insights into religious questions? Are there any lessons that can be learned from life's earliest history that can impact us today? Is life on Earth all that there is in the universe?
3. What do we know about the evolutionary process that binds all life on Earth together as a family? Why is there such an antagonism between science and religion, centered around the topic of evolution? Can we find a way past this unhelpful dynamic?
4. What twists and turns of life's journey on Earth led to the emergence of creatures who would seek a creator God? How did humankind come to know God, and is there still more to know? Is God calling us to be co-creators in our world rather than simply consumers of nature's richness? What is the future of life?

As I initially reflect on these questions, it strikes me that, in some ways, they ask for the answers that are provided in a religious sense by the familiar first chapter of the book of Genesis. However, Genesis gives us no scientific answers. Humankind's understanding of the natural world in ancient times was very different than ours is today, and science, as we know it, did not exist. In the spirit of thanksgiving, recalling the goodness of creation we are told of in Genesis, I will use one of our earliest stories to begin each of my reflections on these questions. It is my hope that with the knowledge of the universe and our natural world afforded us by modern science, we might find a deeper and more meaningful appreciation of our Earth and its life than was ever possible in ancient times. In that way perhaps we will be more inclined to join with Pope Francis in his encyclical on the environment, when he recalls the words from a famous prayer of St. Francis of Assisi: "*Laudato si', mi' Signore*" ("Praise be to you, my Lord").[63]

63. Pope Francis, *Laudato si'*, 1.

PART II
Big Questions

4

Creation

> In the beginning, when God created the heavens and the earth—and the earth was without form or shape, with darkness over the abyss and a mighty wind sweeping over the waters—Then God said: Let there be light, and there was light. God saw that the light was good. God then separated the light from the darkness. God called the light "day" and the darkness "night." Evening came and morning followed—the first day. (Gen 1:1–5)

Biblical scholars have determined that Genesis was first written down sometime around the eighth century BCE and finally collected with the other four books of the Torah or Pentateuch, namely, Exodus, Leviticus, Numbers, and Deuteronomy, during the fifth century BCE.[1] The purpose of the Genesis story was to set a mythological context and grounding for the unfolding of the early history of the Hebrew people and the law established for them by God as described in the Torah.[2] Thus, Genesis is not historical; it is mythological. It is meant to convey in an allegorical way the religious belief that Earth was established *by* God and *for* the Jewish people. Since the focus of the Torah was the Jewish people and their God, it made good literary sense to place the Earth on which they lived in the center of everything. In 332 BCE Alexander the Great and his armies swept out of

1. Karen Armstrong, *A History of God: From Abraham to the Present: The 4000-Year Quest for God* (London: William Heinemann, 1993), 20.
2. Lawrence Boadt, *Reading the Old Testament: An Introduction* (New York: Paulist Press, 1984).

Greece and soon conquered all the Persian areas of the Middle East, including the Jewish homelands in Palestine. With the coming of the Greeks came many aspects of Hellenist culture, including commerce, art, and philosophy. By 200 BCE, Greek was the dominant language of the Middle East, and the Torah was translated from Hebrew into a Greek version, the Septuagint, which spread through the Greek civilized world and was widely circulated at the time of Jesus.[3] The Septuagint brought the faith of the Jewish people into contact with Greek philosophy and eventually to the emerging Roman Empire. The synergism between Hebrew mythology and the philosophy of Aristotle would lead to the establishment of a model of the cosmos that would dominate Western thought for over a thousand years.

Models of the Cosmos

Aristotle

Aristotle (384–322 BCE) was the student of Plato, the founder of Western philosophy, and a teacher of Alexander the Great. Like the Jews and much of the rest of the civilized world of the time, Aristotle believed that Earth was the center of the universe. However, he did not think that Earth was flat, as it was in Hebrew cosmology, but spherical.[4] Aristotle's belief that the world was round was based not on an ancient mythology such as Genesis but on his own empirical observations. For example, the shadow Earth casts on the moon during lunar eclipses is always curved, and the height of stars above the horizon changes when traveling from north to south. The only way to explain these observations is if the surface of the Earth is curved rather than flat. Aristotle shifted Greek philosophy away from Plato's considerations of the abstract "perfect forms," which comprise an unknowable reality, toward a reliance on observation and logic to deduce the true nature of physical reality.[5] Aristotle observed the sun, the moon, and the closer planets such as Mars, rising and set-

3. Armstrong, *A History of God*, 77.

4. Richard DeWitt, *Worldviews: An Introduction to the History and Philosophy of Science*, 3rd ed. (Oxford: Wiley-Blackwell, 2018), 82.

5. Ibid., 121.

ting each day and explained this by picturing a static, unmoving Earth around which the heavenly objects rotated in perfect circles once each day.

Aristotle's conception of the universe became the dominant cosmology of the regions conquered by Alexander the Great. This cosmology was assimilated by the Romans as they rose to become the controlling power of Mediterranean civilization and culture two centuries after Alexander. The idea that the Earth was spherical, rather than flat as imagined by the authors of Genesis, was never a concern for religious believers or for anyone else for that matter, either in Roman antiquity or at any time since. The notion that Christopher Columbus and other European explorers of the fifteenth century had to overcome their fear of sailing off the edge of the flat Earth is, in fact, a historical misconception that emerged in the late 1800s. It was promoted by Cornell University president Andrew Dickson White and other writers who wished to portray Christianity as antagonistic to science.[6] Aristotle's concept that both sun and moon orbited around the Earth was confirmed by the life experiences of the ancient peoples of his time and accepted as "common sense."[7]

In the days before artificial lighting, the nighttime sky was a dominant feature of everyone's life, and the ever-changing positions of the various heavenly objects were a subject of great importance. The positions of the sun, moon, and planets could be used to predict seasonal changes and were thought to convey information about the fates and fortunes of humankind. Calendars that could accurately predict the future positions of the celestial bodies were used to discern the will of the gods in many civilizations of the ancient world. The Greeks used their knowledge of mathematics and geometry to explain their astronomical observations and give them robust predictive powers. The most refined and powerful of these predictive models was published as the *Almagest* around 150 CE by Claudius Ptolemy, a Greco-Roman citizen of Alexandria, Egypt.[8]

---

6. David C. Lindberg and Ronald L. Numbers, "Beyond War and Peace: A Reappraisal of the Encounter between Christianity and Science," *Church History* 55 (1986): 338–54.

7. DeWitt, *Worldviews*, 84.

8. Ibid., 81.

Ptolemy described a system of eight concentric spheres of heavenly motion with a stationary Earth at the center. Traveling around the Earth in perfect circles were the moon, Mercury, Venus, the sun, Mars, Jupiter, and Saturn. The outermost sphere contained the fixed stars, which moved about the Earth every twenty-four hours at a constant distance and position relative to one another.

Because of its predictive power, the Ptolemaic model was widely adopted throughout the Middle East and was used for centuries to produce astronomical charts and tables. It could predict the best dates for agricultural plantings and harvests as well as the timing of important cultural and religious festivals throughout the Roman and newly emergent Islamic empires of the Mediterranean. The *geocentric* (Earth-centered) cosmology of Aristotle and Ptolemy was kept alive in the Arab world through the first millennium CE after Rome fell and Christian Europe descended into the Dark Ages of the early medieval period. The *Almagest* was finally translated into Latin from Arabic during the twelfth century CE, and Ptolemaic cosmology became central to Christian theology until the time of the Renaissance.[9]

In the early 1500s, Nicolaus Copernicus, a young Dominican priest, astronomer, mathematician, and physician from Poland, began to question the Ptolemaic system of rotating spheres.[10] It has been suggested by some historians that Copernicus may have also been inspired by his own Christian religious beliefs.[11] Another possibility is that Copernicus simply did not agree with some of the mathematical complexity of the Ptolemaic system.[12] Whatever the motivations for his *heliocentric* (sun-centered) cosmology, Copernicus relied primarily on the same empirical observations of planetary position and motions, with minor corrections, that Ptolemy had fourteen hundred years before. Copernicus, like Ptolemy, based his cosmology on

9. Charles Homer Haskins, *Studies in the History of Mediaeval Science* (New York: Frederick Ungar, 1967).

10. Stephen Hawking, *On the Shoulders of Giants: The Great Works of Physics and Astronomy* (Philadelphia: Running Press Book Publishers, 2002), 3.

11. Thomas Kuhn, *The Copernican Revolution* (Boston: Harvard University Press, 1957), 128–33.

12. DeWitt, *Worldviews*, 123.

perfect circular motions, but his new system had the moon orbiting around the Earth, which he described as the third of six planets orbiting the sun. Copernican theory provided better explanations for some astronomical observations, but it was no more accurate in predicting planetary positions than the Ptolemaic model had been.[13] Copernicus's life work was published as a book entitled *On the Revolutions of the Heavenly Spheres* on the day of his death in 1543.

The new Copernican system was viewed by some astronomers of the time as a significant achievement. Others regarded it less highly, preferring the Ptolemaic system, which remained a useful predictor of the seasons. Unlike astronomers, philosophers were opposed to anything other than the geocentric view of Ptolemy, and they had a far greater political influence than astronomers did in the sixteenth century.[14] Thus, Copernicanism was slow to catch on. However, the prominent Jesuit mathematician Christopher Clavius, who had led Pope Gregory XIII's major calendar revision of 1582, expressed admiration for Copernicus despite his general disagreement with the heliocentric model for theological reasons.[15] For fifty years after the introduction of the Copernican model, both the old and the new systems had their advocates and were debated in European intellectual circles. The geocentric Ptolemaic system was eventually discarded but not until a brand-new technology provided new evidence in support of the heliocentric Copernican model. This did not happen easily. The scientific discoveries of a well-known Italian physicist confirmed Copernicus's system, but they also triggered the most famous story of "conflict" in the history of science and religion.[16]

Galileo

Galileo Galilei was born in Pisa, Italy, in 1564, two decades after Copernicus published his life's work. His father, Vincenzo Galilei,

---

13. Ibid., 118.

14. David Wootton, *Galileo: Watcher of the Skies* (New Haven, CT: Yale University Press, 2010), 51.

15. Ibid., 55.

16. Thomas Dixon, *Science and Religion: A Very Short Introduction* (London: Oxford University Press, 2008), 22–31.

was an accomplished musician and musical theorist who experimented in the production of pitch and harmony with stringed instruments. His mother, Giulia, was the daughter of a successful textile merchant. Galileo entered the University of Pisa in 1581 to study medicine but soon switched his studies to mathematics and music.[17] By embracing his father's love of experimentation in his own work, Galileo forever changed the way in which science is done and is widely regarded as the father of modern physics and astronomy.[18]

During his early career, Galileo engaged in a variety of physics and engineering problems, including the design of a hydraulic balance for measuring weights, investigations on the motion of pendulums, the behavior of falling objects, the development of an early form of thermometer, and the buoyancy of ships.[19] He made his living by lecturing at the universities of Pisa and Padua and by giving private lessons in mathematics to wealthy clients.[20] In 1608, two Dutch spectacle-makers created a magnification device by placing a lens in a hollow tube behind another lens. The telescope had been born. Galileo learned of the invention during a stay in Venice and by 1609 was selling an improved version, in competition with the Dutch version that was being sold throughout Europe. Within a few years, Galileo's advanced version of the device, which could magnify up to thirty times, was being referred to as "Galileo's' telescope," giving the false impression that he was the original inventor. With the commercial success of his telescopes, Galileo secured a lifetime appointment to his university position.[21]

The most famous of Galileo's scientific studies began in 1609 when he pointed his telescope at the nighttime sky over Venice, setting him on a collision course with the Inquisition of the Roman Catholic Church. Galileo's telescope provided him views of the heavens that no person had ever seen before and yielded new discover-

17. J. L. Heilbron, *Galileo* (Oxford: Oxford University Press, 2012), 1–27.
18. Wootton, *Galileo*, 9–13.
19. Heilbron, *Galileo*, 28–134.
20. Wootton, *Galileo*, 67–73.
21. Ibid., 87–92.

ies night after night. Galileo saw that the Milky Way was not a pale white cloud in the sky but a vast array of distant stars, that the moon's surface had mountains and valleys like the Earth, and, most surprising of all, that the planet Jupiter had four moons. Most importantly, the positions of these moons changed each day, and over time each would disappear behind Venus only to reappear later, on the opposite side of the planet.[22] The discovery that a distant planet could have its own orbiting moons and that not everything revolved around the Earth convinced Galileo that the Copernican model was correct.[23] Galileo quickly published his telescopic observations along with his Copernican interpretation of them in *The Starry Messenger*, a book that was distributed throughout Europe. This brought Galileo the widespread fame he had long been seeking.[24]

Galileo used his discoveries to his political advantage by naming the moons of Jupiter the "Medicean Stars" after corresponding about them with Cosimo Medici, the grand duke of Florence, who was a former student of Galileo.[25] A short time afterward, he was named as the chief mathematician of the Medicean court, resigned his permanent university post, and moved to Florence. In just a few years, Galileo had achieved financial success, curried the favor of Italy's most powerful political family, and become the most famous scientist in all of Europe. But Galileo's shooting star would soon run into trouble.

Throughout history, change and the anxieties it triggers have often been met with a reversion to literal interpretations of foundational documents. This seems to be the case whether the change in question is a new scientific understanding, a new political movement, or sometimes perhaps both. In the early-seventeenth century there were those who disagreed with Copernicanism because it seemed to contradict literal interpretations of the Bible.[26] Galileo answered these

---

22. Ibid., 96–106.
23. DeWitt, *Worldviews*, 143.
24. Wootton, *Galileo*, 96–106.
25. Ibid., 100.
26. Dava Sobel, *Galileo's Daughter: A Historical Memoir of Science, Faith, and Love* (New York: Bloomsbury, 2011), 64.

objections by referring to St. Augustine of Hippo, a father of the early Christian church, who had argued that the Old Testament should not be read literally, especially if newly acquired knowledge contradicts the limited understanding and language of past generations.[27]

Following Augustine's example, Galileo suggested that the stories of the Bible, which mainly have to do with humankind's salvation and not science, should be reinterpreted in the light of his new discoveries.[28] However, the Catholic Church was still feeling the sting of the great schism that was the Protestant Reformation of the sixteenth century. One of the central claims of Protestantism was that all people should be able to read and interpret the Bible for themselves. The church's response to the Reformation had been the Council of Trent (1545–1563), which condemned many of the Protestant practices, including the practice of individual scriptural interpretation, declaring that only "Holy Mother Church" could interpret their true meanings.[29] Thus, by advocating for new interpretations of sacred scripture, Galileo was in effect committing heresy in the eyes of the very church officials and members of the Italian aristocracy he was trying to convince to accept the Copernican system.[30]

Galileo's success and his outspoken embrace of Copernicanism had earned him the enmity of some influential people in the Italian royal courts and in the church. So, he set out to bolster the strength of his scientific evidence and gather allies to his side of the argument. Soon after *The Starry Messenger* was published, Galileo discovered that Venus goes through phases that vary between crescents and a full circle as it orbits around the sun, much like our own moon does as it orbits around the Earth. His observations of the phases of Venus was Galileo's greatest argument in favor of the Copernican model. He communicated this finding to Johannes Kepler, the imperial mathematician and astrological advisor to Emperor Rudolf II of Germany.[31] Galileo's discoveries, with the backing of Kepler, were

27. Peter M. J. Hess and Paul L. Allen, *Catholicism and Science* (Westport, CT: Greenwood Press, 2008), 8–11.

28. Heilbron, *Galileo*, 200–212.

29. Dixon, *Science and Religion*, 27.

30. Sobel, *Galileo's Daughter*, 76.

31. Wootton, *Galileo*, 120–24.

gradually confirmed and accepted by others, including Jesuit astronomers at the Vatican in Rome. One of the Jesuits who was impressed by Galileo's findings was Cardinal Robert Bellarmine, the leading authority on church doctrine. Bellarmine was knowledgeable about astronomy and had himself confirmed Galileo's observations of Jupiter's moons.[32] But Bellarmine was no fan of Galileo's claims of proof for the Copernican system.

In Galileo's time, Protestantism was spreading rapidly throughout Europe. Parts of the remaining Holy Roman Empire that were loyal to the church, such as Galileo's home municipality of Venice, were seen to be coming more and more under Protestantism's negative influences. Even though Copernicus himself was a loyal Catholic, he had spent most of his life in Prussia, an area of strong Protestant confession. Copernicanism itself was therefore suspect for reasons that had nothing to do with science. In 1616, a committee of the Roman Inquisition issued an edict declaring that Copernicanism was in fact heretical and contrary to church teaching.[33] At the behest of Pope Paul V, Galileo was summoned to meet with Cardinal Bellarmine, who warned him, in private, to abandon his writing and teaching about Copernicanism. Although Galileo was not formally charged with any wrongdoing, he did acquiesce to Bellarmine's request and stopped his public discussion of Copernicanism. However, he did not take kindly to the treatment he received in Rome or the rumors of his punishment by the Inquisition, which spread across the countryside even after he received a letter from Bellarmine exonerating him.[34] When he finally received permission to write about Copernicanism from a new pope, Galileo's simmering antagonism toward church officials resurfaced with disastrous consequences.

In 1623, an old friend of Galileo from Florence, Cardinal Maffeo Barberini, was elected as Pope Urban VIII. In the years immediately prior to the election of Pope Urban VIII, Galileo's main antagonist, Cardinal Bellarmine, had died, and Galileo completed a treatise on the scientific method titled *The Assayer*. In this work, Galileo argued

32. Sobel, *Galileo's Daughter*, 76.

33. Heilbron, *Galileo*, 218.

34. Sobel, *Galileo's Daughter*, 80.

that the workings of the universe are better described using the language of mathematics rather than the language of philosophers.[35] The new pope was taken by Galileo's new book, which the politically expedient scientist dedicated to his old friend.[36] Everything seemed to be working in Galileo's favor. While in Rome to celebrate his friend's election to the papacy, Galileo received permission from Pope Urban to publicly discuss Copernicanism but only if it was presented as one of several possible theories. In Pope Urban's view, God could, in fact, do anything God wanted with heavenly objects, so it was impossible to claim that any one scientific theory could be absolutely correct while others were absolutely wrong.[37] With the new pope's blessings, or so he thought, Galileo spent the next six years writing his most passionate defense of Copernicanism. In 1632, Galileo published his *Dialogue concerning the Two Chief World Systems: Ptolemaic and Copernican*, which he dedicated to the grand duke of Tuscany, Ferdinando II, the son of his longtime patron, Cosimo II.[38]

In *Dialogue*, Galileo presented his arguments as a four-day debate between two philosophers, an Aristotelian loyal to the old Ptolemaic system, and a Copernican, moderated by a "neutral" third party. But the philosopher's debate was in no way neutral, as the Copernican continually gained the upper hand in the conversation. Even the Aristotelian philosopher's name, "Simplicio," revealed Galileo's true feelings toward the church officials and their Aristotelian philosophers. Adding insult to injury, Simplicio makes the same "God can do anything God wants" argument that Pope Urban had given personally to Galileo during their meeting in 1624. Galileo's thinly veiled portrayal of the Ptolemaic system as one for simpletons, while arguing the unquestionable superiority of Copernican theory, was not lost on anyone in Renaissance Europe of the seventeenth century.[39] Unfortunately, the times were

---

35. Heilbron, *Galileo*, 247.

36. Sobel, *Galileo's Daughter*, 109.

37. Dixon. *Science and Religion*, 28.

38. Galileo Galilei, *Dialogue concerning Two Chief World Systems* (London: Folio Society, 2013), republished from the translation of Stillman Drake (1953, University of California Press).

39. Hawking, *On the Shoulders of Giants*, 396.

not right for anything that could possibly be perceived as public mockery of the church and its officials.

As it turned out, Pope Urban VIII and the Holy See were directly embroiled in the political acrimony of the Thirty Years War between France and Spain. Any tolerance that Urban showed toward his old friend Galileo could have had negative political consequences.[40] The pope ordered Galileo back to Rome to stand trial before the Inquisition for the heretical promotion of Copernicanism in direct violation of the 1616 edict, which had prohibited him from doing so. Galileo was imprisoned in Rome by the Inquisition for eighteen days in April of 1633. Initially he denied that he was defending Copernicanism in his book. He also denied having ever seen the "official" edict of 1616 that banned him from discussing the topic publicly.[41] With the pope and high church officials promising torture and eventual conviction unless he recanted, it was a good thing for Galileo that he still had some powerful friends in the courts of Florence and Venice. In retrospect it was probably a shrewd political move on his part to dedicate *Dialogue* to the grand duke.

Eventually a way out for Galileo was negotiated. Galileo admitted to overstating his arguments out of intellectual pride, thereby appearing to defend Copernicanism.[42] Galileo was placed under house arrest but was permitted to return to his home near Florence, where he lived out the last eight years of his life in relative peace and luxury. His last major work, *Discourses and Mathematical Demonstrations Relating to Two New Sciences*, published five years after his trial, was a summary of his thirty years of work as a physicist. But by then Galileo had lost much of the widespread public attention and influence he had enjoyed before his trial.[43]

Galileo's famous struggles with the church were never really about his science. Although Copernicanism ran counter to official church doctrine, many astronomers, even some in the Vatican, had quietly confirmed Galileo's observations. In hindsight, it seems likely that

---

40. Dixon, *Science and Religion*, 28.
41. Wootton, *Galileo*, 220
42. Ibid.
43. Ibid., 229.

the famous "Galileo Affair" was mainly a political crisis that erupted because Galileo's writing style and argument seemed to belittle and undermine church authority. This caused Pope Urban VIII and the church acute public embarrassment at an inopportune moment in history.[44] Powerful church and state officials sought to protect themselves and their authority at Galileo's expense. It also did not help that both Urban VIII and Galileo were proud and arrogant men who did not like to be upstaged by those they deemed "below" themselves.[45] Galileo felt slighted by his treatment at the hands of Cardinal Bellarmine and other church officials years before, while Urban was outraged at Galileo's seeming portrayal of him as a simpleton. Had Galileo taken a humbler stance in his portrayal of the church-favored Ptolemaic argument that he presented in the *Dialogue*, and had Urban been willing to publicly admit his prior admiration for his old friend, this embarrassing sequence of events might have been avoided.

Isaac Newton

Galileo's public censorship by the church did not deter the discoveries that were coming through new and ever-improving telescopes, and it did not stop the eventual widespread acceptance of Copernican cosmology. One of the chief innovators of telescope technology after Galileo was the English physicist Isaac Newton. Early in Newton's career, he developed a new kind of telescope that relied on curved mirrors rather than lenses, as did the popular Galileo telescopes. Newton's reflector telescopes eliminated some of the optical aberrations caused by lenses and produced larger images.[46] During his work with lenses and mirrors, Newton further discovered that light could be broken up into the colors of a rainbow by passing it through a prism and then "reassembled" into its original state by focusing the colored rays through a lens. He further proposed that the color of an object was the result of the interaction of that object with light, rather than something that was produced by the object

44. Dixon, *Science and Religion*, 30–31.
45. Heilbron, *Galileo*, 253–63.
46. James Gleick, *Isaac Newton* (New York: Vintage Books, 2004), 71.

itself.[47] These were the first insights on the quantum nature of light that would lead eventually to Einstein's theory of relativity.

Newton's work with light and optics was just a precursor to the ways in which he would permanently revolutionize the field of physics. The "new science" that Newton described in his landmark treatise *Philosophiæ Naturalis Principia Mathematica*, published in 1687, was the intellectual culmination of the physical study of moving objects. This had also been the focus of Galileo's last major publication. In the *Principia*, Newton mathematically describes what are usually called his three "laws of motion," as well as the concept of universal gravitation, which is the physical force of attraction that any two bodies have for each other.[48] Newton showed that his laws of motion and universal gravitation could be used to derive Kepler's laws of planetary motion.[49] Using his own laws, Newton could also explain the cycles of the ocean tides, the trajectories of comets, and indeed, the movements of any object, whether on Earth or out in space. Newton was also central to the development of the field of mathematics known as calculus. He was knighted in 1705 by Queen Anne for his contributions to the English monetary system. When Sir Isaac Newton died in 1727, he was afforded the highest of royal honors and was buried in Westminster Abbey.[50]

Newtonian mechanics dominated the field of physics for many years after his death. But Newton's discoveries influenced much more than physics. His work ended the Aristotelian worldview that an object's (or person's) behavior was due to its inherent essential nature.[51] In the Newtonian worldview, the behavior of an object was the result of the external forces acting upon it. Physical objects behaved with mechanical precision according to the fixed laws of nature. Isaac Newton was a deeply religious man with a keen side interest in theology. To him, God was hidden from sight, but God's work could be revealed using mathematics, which he thought of as

47. Ibid., 79–89.
48. DeWitt, *Worldviews*, 164–70.
49. Gleick, *Isaac Newton*, 122–25
50. Ibid., 5.
51. DeWitt, *Worldviews*, 167.

the language of God.[52] The laws of motion that Newton had discovered had therefore been written by a divine author. Although Newton argued against looking at the universe as a mere machine, the mathematical precision with which the Earth and planets behaved led many others to support mechanistic interpretations. Before long, this mechanical view of nature would spread to the other fields of science such as chemistry, biology, and even psychology.[53]

The view of the universe that emerged in the centuries after Newton's death was one in which our sun was one star among many in a vast galaxy, the Milky Way, containing billions of stars, each perhaps with its own solar system. Further, the Milky Way is just one of many galaxies in a vast eternal universe of fixed size and shape. Within each galaxy and within each solar system, objects were assumed to behave according to the same fixed laws that Newton had described for Earth. But each galaxy, star, and solar system occupies its own fixed position in space, too far away from its distant neighbors to have any physical effects on them. For some people, the notion of God, who once was credited with moving the sun and stars through the heavens, seemed to become irrelevant. God was no longer needed to explain planetary motions or, for that matter, any physical process. The endless static universe was all that there is and all that there ever was. For over two centuries, the static model of the universe governed by mechanical Newtonian laws dominated the field of physics—that is, until the work of an American astronomer and an obscure Belgian priest placed creation at a distinct moment in time and revealed a new expanding universe for scientists to explore and for theologians to ponder.

The Big Bang

Our modern cosmology centers on a white hot singularity possessing infinite heat and gravitational force, occurring approximately 14 billion years ago.[54] From the instant of the singularity forward, the

52. Gleick, *Isaac Newton*, 99–113.

53. DeWitt, *Worldviews*, 179–90.

54. Peter Coles, *Cosmology: A Very Short Introduction* (Oxford: Oxford University Press, 2001), 54–56.

universe has been expanding, and while it has been increasing in size, the infinite heat of the initial explosion has been dissipating. According to particle physics, the energy contained by the early elementary particles would have been so high that when these particles interacted, they would have simply annihilated each other and been converted back into energy. But as the universe cooled, during its first few minutes, the particles began to stick together, giving rise to the protons, neutrons, and electrons that make up the atoms of physical matter. As cooling continued over the next million or so years, the small nuclei and electrons began to combine to form atoms, the "stuff" that all the physical matter we presently know about and understand is made of.[55]

Albert Einstein

Now Newton's force of gravity becomes important to the story. With the formation of matter, gravitational attractions would pull the atoms together and slow the rate of the universe's expansion. In regions of the universe with high concentrations of matter, the inward collapse eventually gave rise to large localized clouds of matter, the precursors of galaxies. Within the swirling clouds of the early galaxies, eddies emerged out of the chaos, and the hydrogen and helium gas in localized regions collapsed further under their own gravitational attraction. As the particles came closer together, collisions between the atoms resulted in a heating of the gas to temperatures high enough to start nuclear fusion reactions, thereby giving birth to the first stars.[56]

Within stars, hydrogen is converted into the more stable element helium, and the heat generated increases the pressure so that further gravitational collapse is resisted.[57] As the hydrogen fuel of stars burns away, the stars contract and heat further so that helium begins to be converted into heavier elements. It is thought that repeated cycles of

---

55. Stephen W. Hawking, *A Brief History of Time* (New York: Bantam Books, 1988), 117–18.

56. Ibid., 119–21.

57. Andrew King, *Stars: A Very Short Introduction* (Oxford: Oxford University Press, 2012), 14–28.

stellar expansion and contraction occasionally trigger catastrophic explosions called supernovae, in which the outermost regions of a star are blown off into space. The remaining material may then collapse completely into a black hole or begin a new cycle of gravitational accretion and eventually form a new star. Our own sun could be a second- or even third-generation star. Heavier elements and dust particles thrown off from stellar explosions can begin to accrete in regions of space slightly removed from the newly forming star and eventually, again through gradual gravitational accretion, give rise to planets that remain in orbit around the star that brought them forth.[58] One such planet, in a solar system of an unremarkable sun, in an obscure corner of one of the billions of galaxies that make up the universe, became our Earth—the only home we have ever known, and perhaps ever will know.

This modern scientific story of the creation of our universe is in some ways just as fantastical as the biblical story of Genesis, except that it is supported by empirical scientific evidence. Prior to the development of the *theory of special relativity* (1905) and the *theory of general relativity* (1907) by German physicist Albert Einstein, the prevailing cosmology of the time was the static and unchanging Newtonian universe. Einstein's theories simplify Newtonian mechanics so that the same physical laws could be applied to objects in motion, regardless of their movement relative to each other.[59] Einstein also developed the concepts of spacetime, gravitational time dilation, and the interconversion of mass and energy ($E = mc^2$). Physicists and mathematicians working with Einstein's equations quickly realized that the theory of relativity predicted an expanding universe with an origin in the distant past. The theories further predicted that due to gravity, the rate of expansion would slow over time, eventually reverse, and lead to a period in which the universe would shrink and eventually collapse in on itself. Einstein disagreed philosophically with these conclusions and introduced a "cosmological constant" into his equations to counteract the dynamic effects of gravity.[60]

58. Ibid., 49–71.
59. DeWitt, *Worldviews*, 193–218.
60. Coles, *Cosmology*, 30–31.

Edwin Hubble

In the 1920s, Edwin Hubble, using powerful new telescopes at the Mount Wilson Observatory in California, identified the nine galaxies closest to our own.[61] He also calculated the distances to these galaxies by measuring their relative brightness compared to the starlight of our own galaxy. The brighter the galaxy, the closer it must be to our own Milky Way. The light from stars in these distant galaxies, as well as the light from stars in our own galaxy, can be analyzed to determine the elemental composition of the stars. When Hubble and his colleagues at Mount Wilson compared the electromagnetic spectrum of light from distant galaxies to the spectra of stars in our own galaxies, they noticed that the light from all of the distant galaxies was shifted to longer, "redder" wavelengths.[62] In the visible part of the electromagnetic spectrum, which is the light we see as the color of the rainbow, shorter wavelengths of light appear as blue and longer wavelengths of light as red. When something emitting light is traveling away from an observer, the speed of the object is added to the speed of the light source, making it appear longer. This is called the *Doppler effect*. Hubble's observation that the light from distant galaxies was "red-shifted" indicates that our neighboring galaxies are all moving away from us. This provided the first hard evidence that the universe is expanding.

Georges Lemaître

As Hubble was conducting his studies at Mount Wilson, a quiet Jesuit priest, Georges-Henri Lemaître, who was teaching physics at the Catholic University of Leuven in Belgium, proposed a new cosmological model. A mathematician by training, Lemaître had become interested in astronomy while studying with Arthur Eddington, one of the world's leading astrophysicists, at Cambridge University.[63] Following his master's degree studies at Cambridge, Lemaître

61. Hawking, *A Brief History of Time*, 36–37.

62. Coles, *Cosmology*, 39–56.

63. Dominique Lambert, *The Atom of the Universe: The Life and Work of Georges Lemaître* (Krakow: Copernicus Center Press, 2011), 87–93.

traveled to the United States in 1924 to attend astronomy conferences and begin his doctoral studies in physics at the Massachusetts Institute of Technology in Boston. Lemaître applied Einstein's theory of relativity to cosmology in relation to the newly emerging data of Hubble and other astronomers. His calculations showed that relativity theory predicted an expanding universe, and drew support for this model from the astronomical data.[64]

Lemaître published his ideas on the expanding universe in 1927 in the *Annals of the Scientific Society of Brussels,* two years prior to the publication of Hubble's work. In his paper, he derived what would later become known as Hubble's Law, relating the speed of the universe's expansion to the measured distances to the known galaxies. This pioneering work, published in an obscure French journal, might have received little attention were it not for the interest expressed by Lemaître's mentor, Arthur Eddington. But with Eddington's encouragement, Lemaître published a more fully developed cosmological model in 1931 in the leading British science journal *Nature.*[65] This time, Lemaître solved Einstein's equations for a starting point in the distant past that he called the "primeval atom" or the "Cosmic Egg." Scholars have noted that Lemaître's "hypothesis of the primeval atom," supported as it was by Hubble's red-shift data, was also consistent with his religious views as a Catholic priest about creation.[66] In fact, however, Lemaître did not actually view the solution to Einstein's equations as the moment of creation. He fully allowed that something could have been in place before his zero (starting) point that had no observable effect on our present universe.[67]

Within a short time of the *Nature* publication, Lemaître and Hubble were widely recognized as the founders of a new physics of cosmology, although not all physicists were eager to accept the new theory. Lemaître's self-described theory of a "Cosmic Egg exploding at the moment of the creation" finally became known as the "Big

---

64. Ibid., 121–32.

65. Georges Lemaître, "The Beginning of the World from the Point of View of Quantum Theory," *Nature* 12 (1931): 706.

66. Lambert, *The Atom of the Universe*, 149.

67. Ibid., 335.

Bang theory" in 1949, through what was meant to be a sarcastic comment by British astronomer Fred Hoyle during a BBC radio interview.[68] Hoyle and some other physicists preferred a "steady state" model of the universe in which there was no beginning and no ending. By 1949, however, proponents of Lemaître's Big Bang theory were in the majority within the scientific community. But the debate was heated. Hoyle and some of his colleagues saw the Big Bang as religiously inspired pseudoscience.[69] The science-vs.-religion coin had been flipped. Galileo's scientific ideas were resisted by theologians because they challenged religious doctrine; now, Lemaître's opponents resisted the new scientific theory simply because of his commitment to his Catholic faith. These scientists preferred the materialistic (i.e., godless) implications of an eternal, steady-state universe to the idea of a suddenly appearing universe that even the pope could celebrate.

In 1936, Pope Pius XI established the Pontifical Academy of Sciences at the Vatican, which has the purpose of advising the Holy See on matters of science, technology, and associated ethical considerations.[70] The Pontifical Academy is nondenominational, inviting scientific experts regardless of religious belief, and it has included many Nobel laureates over its eighty-year history. Georges Lemaître, his reputation in physics and astronomy firmly established at the time of the academy's founding, was immediately elected to the body. Pius XI's successor, Pope Pius XII, had a keen interest in science, especially astronomy. In 1951, Pius XII delivered an address to a working group of the Pontifical Academy, praising the new cosmology as essentially a proof for the existence of God.[71] This only provided ammunition to those who claimed that the Big Bang theory was religiously, not scientifically, motivated. Lemaître strongly disagreed with the pontiff's use of science to validate a theological claim. Lemaître believed that science could not and should not be used for this purpose. He

68. Coles, *Cosmology*, 57.

69. Lambert, *The Atom of the Universe*, 336.

70. Hess and Allen, *Catholicism and Science*, 103.

71. Michael Heller, *Creative Tension: Essays on Science and Religion* (West Conshohocken, PA: Templeton Foundation Press, 2003), 70–74.

held the view that God was "hidden" from humanity as is told in the scripture passage: "Truly, you are a God who hides himself, O God of Israel, the savior" (Isa 45:15). In the year that he was elected to the Pontifical Academy, Lemaître had expressed this very Jesuit notion of nature and science at a Catholic congress in Brussels:

> The Christian seeker knows that everything has been done by God, but he knows also that God does not supplant his creation. The omnipresent divine activity is essentially hidden everywhere. It can never be a question of reducing the Supreme Being to the rank of a scientific hypothesis.[72]

As a scientist, Lemaître knew that like any scientific theory, the Big Bang was a provisional hypothesis that could never be absolutely proven.[73] In 1951, both the Big Bang and steady-state hypotheses offered different explanations for Hubble's red-shift data, and no conclusive evidence in favor of the Big Bang had yet been discovered. Making the doctrinal claim that the existence of God had been confirmed by physics would, Lemaître knew, become highly problematic for the church should the Big Bang theory ever be disproven by future scientific findings. Lemaître expressed his concerns to the pope, and when Pius XII addressed a conference of the International Astronomical Union in Rome a year later, he had greatly softened his use of science to assert religious claims.[74] In recognition of his contributions to science and the church, Lemaître was appointed to be the president of the Pontifical Academy of Sciences in 1960 by Pope John XXIII, the successor to Pius XII. This was a position he would hold until his death in June 1966.

Confirmation of the Big Bang

Just a few days before he died, Georges Lemaître received the joyous news from a friend that two research groups in New Jersey had discovered what they were describing as Cosmic Microwave

72. Lambert, *The Atom of the Universe*, 331.

73. Ibid., 342–43.

74. Heller, *Creative Tension*, 73.

Background (CMB) radiation.[75] Arno Penzias and Robert Wilson, physicists working at Bell Laboratories, discovered the CMB quite accidently while calibrating a brand-new radio telescope they were helping to build.[76] What they had first thought was a "noise" signal in the microwave part of the spectrum turned out to be of consistent strength no matter what direction or time of day they pointed the telescope to the sky. This suggested that what they were detecting with their Dicke Radiometer must be originating outside Earth's atmosphere and from the deepest regions of space. At the same time, Princeton University physicist Robert Dicke, the original inventor of the device that Bell Labs was building, and his colleague James Peebles were predicting that any remaining radiation from the Big Bang would be red-shifted all the way into the microwave region of the electromagnetic spectrum.[77] When the Bell Labs and Princeton groups compared notes, they realized that they had found the cosmic signature of Georges Lemaître's still-controversial Big Bang singularity. A very strongly red-shifted remnant of the Big Bang explosion, like the CMB, had been predicted by Lemaître in his 1931 *Nature* paper.[78] Lemaître had suggested that this was the final evidence needed to confirm the validity of the Big Bang theory. And so it was.

The CMB discovered by Penzias and Wilson would earn them the Nobel Prize in 1978 and by that time was widely regarded as the decisive confirmation of the Big Bang theory. Using the value that had initially been determined for the rate of the universe's expansion, the Hubble constant, Dicke and Peebles calculated the age of the universe to be approximately 10 billion years.[79] Refinements to the Hubble constant and the CMB frequency measurements have now placed the age of the universe at 13.8 billion years.[80] In addition to determining the age of the universe, the Big Bang theory has given cosmologists many new puzzles to consider, such as the shape

75. Lambert, *The Atom of the Universe*, 416.

76. Hawking, *A Brief History of Time*, 41.

77. Ibid., 42.

78. Lambert, *The Atom of the Universe, 416.*

79. R. H. Dicke, P. J. E. Peebles, P. G. Roll, and D. T. Wilkinson, "Cosmic Black-Body Radiation," *Astrophysical Journal* 142 (1965): 414–19.

80. P. Ade et al., "Planck 2015 Results," *Astronomy and Astrophysics* 594 (2015): A13.

of the universe, the earliest conditions at the moment of the Big Bang explosion, and the eventual fate of the universe. These questions have scientific, philosophical, and, to a believer, religious implications.

When we look out into space with our eyes or with our telescopes, we are looking back in time. Alpha Centauri, a three-star system that is the closest neighbor to our sun, is 4.37 light years away. That means the light from Alpha Centauri that we see today in the nighttime sky was emitted from the surface of those stars over four years ago. By contrast, it takes sunlight eight minutes and seventeen seconds to reach Earth's surface. The closest galaxy to our Milky Way, a mere 250 million light years away, is the Andromeda galaxy, one of the galaxies first studied by Edwin Hubble. The light from Andromeda that we see shining today left home long before the first dinosaurs appeared on Earth. The most distant galaxy so far discovered is the faint light of GN-z11, located within the constellation Ursa Major.[81] GN-z11 is 13.4 billion light years distant from Earth so it appears to us at present as it was approximately 400,000 years after the Big Bang. All stars have a finite life span. It is likely that the stars that show us GN-z11, along with many of the stars we see in the Milky Way and the other 200 billion galaxies that make up the universe, are no longer in existence, having already collapsed into black holes or exploded as the supernovae which then seed the universe with the cosmic debris from which new stars are born.

Our sun is approximately 4.6 billion years old, about middle-aged for a star of its size. Much of what we see in the nighttime sky either no longer exists or will someday, thousands, millions, or billions of years from now, be gone. What does the transience of the stars in the sky and even our own sun say to us about our place in the universe? What role, if any, do we have to play, across the vast expanse of time started by the Big Bang? Before the Big Bang there was no time nor space; there was nothing at all. If there was once nothing, why is there now something, that is, the universe, for us to contemplate? And why does the universe have the characteristics that we attribute to it and that make our lives possible?

---

81. P. A. Oesch et al., "A Remarkably Luminous Galaxy at Z-11.1 Measured with Hubble Space Telescope Grism Spectroscopy," *Astrophysical Journal* 819 (2016): 129–40.

Could it have been different? Can science or religion possibly provide answers to any of these questions?

The Anthropic Principle

Since the Big Bang theory emerged through the work of Lemaître, Hubble, and others, scientists have been trying to gain an understanding of the conditions present at the time of our universe's beginning that allowed matter to come into existence.[82] It is out of these conditions that the elementary particles that make up all matter, and the forces that govern how they interact, originated. In our time, 13.8 billion years later, these particles and forces continue to determine the physical nature of our universe and how it operates. Physicists have determined that there are four fundamental forces that govern the way in which our universe works.[83] These forces are:

1. the *strong nuclear force*, which is responsible for holding subatomic particles together;
2. the *weak nuclear force*, which produces radioactive decay;
3. *gravitational force*, as described originally by Newton;
4. *electromagnetic force*, which combines the phenomena of electricity and magnetism.

These four forces are what determine the *laws of physics*, which are mathematical expressions of how we see these forces working in our world.[84] In addition to these fundamental forces there are a number of *constants* that determine how these forces interact within each physical law. These constants include things like the speed of light, the mass of an electron, and Planck's constant, which determines the amount of energy in a photon of light.[85]

Physicists have also determined that, theoretically, these forces do not have to be what we observe them to be; any or all of these could

---

82. Ralph A. Alpher, Hans Bethe, and George Gamow, "The Origin of Chemical Elements," *Physical Review* 73 (1948): 803–4.

83. Hawking, *A Brief History of Time*, 63–79.

84. Paul Davies, *The Goldilocks Enigma: Why Is the Universe Just Right for Life?* (New York: Houghton Mifflin, 2006), 5–17.

85. Ibid., 154–55.

have been larger or smaller. Further, if any of these forces or constants were just slightly larger or slightly smaller, then the universe as we know it could not exist. The universe might instantly collapse back in on itself or perhaps expand haphazardly in such a way that primordial particles could not stick together and form the atoms that make up all matter. The universe thus appears to be "fine-tuned" for life. This cosmological fine tuning has been referred to as the *Goldilocks enigma* by Templeton Award-winning physicist Paul Davies.[86] We find that each of these physical parameters is "not too large" and "not too small" but "just right," as Goldilocks found in her visit to the house of the three bears in the popular English fairy tale. The universe we live in thus seems to be an unlikely universe, uniquely conditioned so that on at least one planet, life could emerge in such a way that an organism, such as us, could evolve to the point in history that we can now contemplate our own existence.

In 1973, the physicist Brandon Carter used the term *anthropic principle* to suggest that humankind is very fortunate to occupy a universe with these specific conditions at this particular moment in history, where such a realization is possible.[87] A decade or so later, physicists John Barrow and Frank Tipler distinguished between weaker forms of the anthropic principle (WAP) such as Carter's and stronger forms (SAP), which imply either inevitability or maybe even a deliberateness behind our finely tuned universe.[88] According to the anthropic principle, a universe like ours is necessary so that it could give rise to creatures like us, who are able to contemplate its meaning, its beginning, and its ending. In the strongest versions of this line of reasoning, the anthropic principle could even be viewed as proof for the existence of God! Most scientists, even religious ones, would not agree with this conclusion, however. We need only recall Georges Lemaître's caution to Pope Pius XII against using any scientific theory as a proof for God's existence. But if it was not God behind the apparent fine-tuning of our universe, what else could it have been?

86. Ibid., 2–3.

87. Ibid., x.

88. John Barrow and Frank Tipler, *The Anthropic Cosmological Principle* (Oxford: Oxford University Press, 1988).

The Multiverse

One way to solve the Goldilocks enigma is to throw the statistics of repetition at it. Our universe may be one of many universes, each of which contains a randomly generated combination of possible physical constants. Almost all of these other universes would not be conducive to the eventual emergence of life, but a very small number—maybe even only one—would have the physics that is "just right" for life. In the United States, many parts of the country sell lottery tickets that award periodically massive "Powerball" jackpots. In many weeks there are no winners, but the jackpot continues to grow, luring other customers to the lottery ticket windows. The odds against any one of these tickets winning are enormously high, on the order of one in a billion. Yet eventually, after many, many millions of tickets are sold, a lucky winner or two or three are announced. Someone eventually wins! Similarly, it seems, sooner or later a universe that is conducive to life pops into existence, and we just so happen to find ourselves in one of these. Paul Davies muses that "like winners in a gigantic cosmic lottery, we find ourselves in a rare bio-friendly patch."[89] Our universe is then just one in a vast multiplicity of alternative universes that is usually referred to as the *multiverse.*

A variety of different ideas have been proposed as to what the multiverse might look like. Columbia University physicist Brian Greene suggests that there are as many as nine different types of possible multiverses, ranging from a single but infinitely recycling single universe to a simulated multiverse hidden within a vast computer array.[90] Since there are so many different universes possible within each multiverse, the anthropic principle then becomes a nonissue; it is just a philosophical artifact of our self-indulgent perspective from one of the rare life-giving universes. Any thoughts of meaning or purpose for our existence are therefore mere speculations. But the prospect of a meaningless creation generated through some random mechanism operating within a mysterious multiverse still does not provide an

89. Paul Davies, "Reality in the Melting Pot," *The Guardian* 21 (2003): 26–28.

90. Brian Greene, *The Hidden Reality: Parallel Universes and the Deep Laws of the Cosmos* (New York: Alfred A. Knopf, 2011), 309l.

adequate answer to the question, "Why is there anything at all?" One can just go to the next step and ask, "Why is there a multiverse?" So, while a multiverse might provide an answer for the Goldilocks enigma, it does not provide an *ultimate* explanation for reality, either philosophically or scientifically. For an ultimate explanation of reality, we would need to have a *theory of everything.*

The Theory of Everything

Stephen Hawking (1942–2018) of Cambridge University was the best-known physicist of our time. A pioneer in the study of black holes, Hawking was largely responsible for making the science of modern cosmology accessible to the general public through his bestselling book *A Brief History of Time*. Hawking was a tireless advocate of science and science education throughout the world. He was a member of the Pontifical Academy of Sciences and received numerous awards for his work, including the United States' highest civilian recognition, the Presidential Medal of Freedom. In the final decades of his life, due to a degenerative illness (ALS), Hawking was able to communicate only through use of an electronic voice generator that he controlled with his facial muscles. His easily recognizable synthetic voice was featured in the music of the rock group Pink Floyd as well as on popular television shows such as *Star Trek: The Next Generation* and the appropriately named *Big Bang Theory.* It is extraordinarily rare for a scientist to achieve such widespread celebrity during his or her lifetime. Hawking's relationship with his first wife, Jane Wilde, was the subject of the 2014 feature film *The Theory of Everything.* The film's title refers to Hawking's long-time advocacy for finding a unified theory of physics.

Modern physics is based on two separate but well-established predictive models. The first of these is Einstein's *General Relativity,* which includes Newton's force of gravitation and the observed phenomenon of universal expansion. The second is the *Standard Model* of particle physics, which is derived from quantum mechanics and includes electromagnetism as well as the strong and weak nuclear forces. In the simplest terms, relativity theory reliably predicts the behavior of very large things such as planets, stars, and galaxies, while the Standard Model focuses on the behavior of the very smallest things, namely, atoms with their protons, neutrons, and electrons, and the even smaller subatomic particles of which they are composed. Each of these two main theories is exceptionally good at explaining what scientists can measure within the limits of cosmology *or* particle physics, but they do not work well together. For example, relativity theory predicts a smoothly curved, steady shape and flow to space and time, while quantum mechanics suggests that space and time are highly chaotic and essentially unpredictable. Our two best theories of physics appear to contradict each other.[91] For over forty years, Stephen Hawking and other theoretical physicists around the world have been trying to do something about this impasse. The most promising attempts to unify general relativity and quantum mechanics reside within an area of theoretical conjecture known as *string theory*, which emerged as separate field of quantum physics during the mid-1980s.[92]

String theory proposes that the smallest of all subatomic particles, those that come together to form the neutrons and protons of atoms, are composed of one-dimensional loops of energy called "strings."[93] The characteristic frequency or speed of the string vibration reflects the energy contained by the string. Since Einstein showed that mass and energy are interconvertible ($E = mc^2$), it is the different energies of the vibrating strings that produce the different observed masses of the subatomic particles. This is analogous to the different musical notes that are produced by vibrating guitar strings. The piercing high notes of an electric guitar solo would correspond to the larger, more massive particles. But it is not only the masses of the subatomic particles that arise from the vibrating strings. The four fundamental forces of physics also arise from string vibrations and can be thought of as the "force particles" that dictate the ways in which the particulate matter interacts. Even the mysterious force of gravity, which does not otherwise fit into the Standard Model, can, in string theory,

91. Davies, *The Goldilocks Enigma*, 103–15.

92. Hawking, *A Brief History of Time*, 159–69.

93. Brian Greene, *The Elegant Universe: Superstrings, Hidden Dimensions, and the Quest for the Ultimate Theory* (New York: W. W. Norton, 2003), 3–20.

be assigned a vibrational mode that gives rise to a "graviton" particle. String theorists think that through their work, relativity theory and quantum mechanics will no longer be contradictory but will actually become harmonious with each other. String theorist Brian Greene describes how the comings and goings of our physical universe can be thought of as a giant cosmic string symphony.[94] Could these invisible vibrating strings be the secret of creation?

There are several versions of string theory and they all require the existence of additional spatial dimensions in order to accommodate the different vibrational modalities needed for the strings. In 1995, Edward Witten of Princeton University proposed that the various string theories could be resolved within a single unifying framework that has been named *M-theory*.[95] M-theory proposes that there are eleven distinct dimensions to reality. We live our lives in three-dimensional space and are all too well aware of the passage of time, which is considered to be the fourth dimension of our familiar universe. Since Einstein, cosmologists have combined our three spatial dimensions (length, height, and depth or, graphically, x, y, and z) with the dimension of time to describe our four-dimensional reality as *spacetime*. Spacetime was brought into existence by the Big Bang 13.8 billion years ago. M-theory proposes that there are seven additional "unseen" spatial dimensions. These added dimensions can be modeled mathematically, but they are far too small to be detected by any scientific instruments we have available to us.[96]

Stephen Hawking has suggested that the eleven different dimensions of M-theory could be arranged in 10^{500} different possible multidimensional configurations, each of which could potentially give rise to a different universe, within a single grand multiverse.[97] Many of these universes would likely pop into and out of existence instantaneously; some would last longer; and in a very small number of these, perhaps only one, the multidimensional arrangement

94. Ibid., 135–65.

95. Ibid., 204.

96. Ibid., 184–210.

97. Stephen Hawking and Leonard Mlodinow, *The Grand Design* (New York: Bantam Books, 2010).

of spacetime would be such that existentially inquisitive life forms could emerge. Experts think it will take at least several decades to work out the details of M-theory—perhaps even longer if M-theory is also to explain the existence of *dark matter* and *dark energy*, which cosmologists now think make up as much as 73 percent of our total universe![98] The most optimistic string theorists, like Hawking, believe that everything imaginable, from the tiniest bits of matter to the possible existence of parallel and "pocket" universes, will eventually be explained by M-theory or one of its successors. Everything seems to have been brought together. Or has it?

How Can We Be Sure?

Coming to grips with all that there is in our vast, four-dimensional universe is difficult enough. How does one even begin to incorporate seven additional spatial dimensions into a working model of reality? Just where might those extra dimensions be found anyway? One reason we can't find them might be because these other dimensions are very, very small and therefore invisible to us. Brian Greene, author of the bestselling book *The Elegant Universe*, uses the example of a garden hose, which looks like a one-dimensional line when viewed from far away.[99] It is only when we get close to the hose that the additional spatial dimensions, as well as an ant crawling along the surface of the hose, can be seen. The seven additional dimensions, by analogy, are so tiny and curled up on each other that for all intent and proposes they are too "far away" for us to see, even though they are right under our noses. That does not mean they do not exist, only that we cannot measure them. String theorists hope that some of the experiments being done at high-energy physics labs might provide indirect evidence for these hidden dimensions. For example, an observed loss of energy following a high-energy particle collision might suggest that the energy disappeared into one of the other dimensions, but such a result has not yet been observed.[100]

---

98. Greene, *The Hidden Reality*, 25.
99. Greene, *The Elegant Universe*, 186.
100. Greene, *The Hidden Reality*, 95.

Another verification problem appears at the other end of the theoretical physics spectrum: the existence of other universes in the large multiverse. Because of the technological limits of our most sophisticated instruments, we can only see back to a time 400,000 years after the Big Bang. We cannot see back to the beginning of our own universe, much less any others. And any other universes, even if they do share multidimensional configurations similar to our own, would likely be receding away from us at least as fast as we move away from the Big Bang nexus. Because light from those universes could therefore never reach us, we will never be able see them, short of some currently unimaginable future technology. Because empirical verification of the hypotheses generated by string theory is extremely difficult if not impossible, at least at present, not all physicists have been eager to embrace these ideas. String theory relies primarily on mathematical speculation rather than traditional scientific methodology, so it has been criticized by some as a science based on faith and fantasy.[101]

Particle physicists think that a better approach for advancing our understanding of physical reality is to build a unified theory up from the bottom, step by step, as new particles are discovered one by one over time.[102] At a handful of high-energy physics laboratories located around the world, scientists use very expensive and technologically sophisticated equipment to accelerate atomic nuclei, protons, and other particles to very high velocities and slam them together, producing a shower of collision fragments that can be tracked and studied using specialized electronic detectors. As smaller and smaller particles are discovered, larger and larger facilities are needed like the Large Hadron Collider built by the Conseil Européen pour la Recherche Nucléaire (CERN) near Geneva, Switzerland. Particle-accelerator experiments have shown that protons and neutrons are composed of smaller particles called *quarks* and *gluons*. The familiar

---

101. Roger Penrose, *Fashion, Faith, and Fantasy in the New Physics of the Universe* (Princeton, NJ: Princeton University Press, 2016).

102. Lisa Randall, *Knocking on Heaven's Door: How Physics and Scientific Thinking Illuminate the Universe and the Modern World* (New York: HarperCollins, 2012).

electron is one member of a group of tiny particles called *leptons*.[103] The masses of each of these particle types can be measured with great precision, and the values that have been determined make up some of the "fine-tuning" constants of our universe that underlie the anthropic principle.[104]

As particle physicists explore the finest details of these smallest bits of matter, they are also doing cosmology at the largest scale possible since, as far as we know, most of these tiny bits of matter generated by the most powerful colliders have not existed naturally in isolation from each other since the first seconds after the Big Bang.[105] Eventually, it is thought, a unifying theory that explains everything we can observe will emerge through this more traditional scientific methodology. Particle physicists, it seems, would rather place their faith in technological empiricism than in sophisticated mathematical calculations. But this slow and steady approach, at least in theory, could also produce a grand unified theory, albeit at much greater cost and over a longer period of time. Brian Greene, for example, estimates that to approach the resolution required to see the tiny hypothetical strings of M-theory would require a particle collider the size of our galaxy.[106] So, no doubt, new technology would have to be invented along the way. That's not to say this can't happen! Technological advance is likely to be a hallmark of our species, at least until we pass the torch on to whomever, or whatever, succeeds us. Perhaps, someday, concrete evidence for a *theory of everything* will be found. What then? Will any Mystery for creation remain?

Ultimate Explanations

My brother Gregg was an electrical engineer. When faced with an inexplicable problem, Gregg would often just sigh and say, "It is what it is," and then go about the business of dealing with the new situation. There was clearly a certain practical wisdom to Gregg's approach. Stephen Hawking believed that with the development of

103. Ibid., 241–58.

104. Davies, *The Goldilocks Enigma*, 90–92.

105. Randall, *Knocking on Heaven's Door*, 3–25.

106. Greene, *The Elegant Universe*, 215.

M-theory, physicists at last have their long sought-after *theory of everything*, and the Goldilocks enigma has been solved. He declared:

> For these reasons, M-theory is the *only* candidate for a complete theory of the universe. If it is finite—and this has yet to be proved—it will be a model of a universe that creates itself. We must be part of the universe, because there is no other consistent model.[107]

In other words, the universe (now a multiverse) is self-explanatory and self-creating. Things are the way they are because they have to be that way. Ultimately there is no reason for it. No greater explanation of reality is necessary. M-theory will eventually push our knowledge of both the very large and the very small to their ultimate limits, and we will find nothing more. The equations will all be solved. The universe "is what it is." For those who believe in God, this is "game over." Or is it?

The explosive progress in physics of the last century, while bringing us so far scientifically, has really only brought us in a full circle philosophically. Instead of the eternal static universe of Newton, we find we may be part of an eternal though dynamic multiverse. And just as Newton believed the universe that he studied was created by God, there is no reason not to think that God might also have a hand in the creation of a multiverse. It seems odd to me that some scientists are eager to talk for hours on end about spatial dimensions that cannot be detected and alternative universes that cannot possibly be seen, yet any talk of a creator God leaves them impatient or even hostile. There is no rational reason for this. Both scientists and religious believers accept the possibility that there are things we cannot know directly. Brian Greene discusses the "Hidden Reality" of the multiverse and Georges Lemaître spoke about a God who is "hidden everywhere." Might this not all be one and the same?

In the introduction to her book on dark matter, particle physicist Lisa Randall of Harvard University examines the philosophical implications of the possible existence of a multiverse:

107. Hawking and Mlodinow, *The Grand Design*, 181.

> Existing physical theories suggest that multiverses are rather likely, especially given the many possible solutions in quantum gravity theories as currently formulated. Whether or not those calculations stand up to scrutiny, I would wager that other inaccessible universes should be present. Why shouldn't they. Given what we know about the limitations of physical laws and current technology, it is both formatively and literally shortsighted to decide they aren't. Nothing about our world is inconsistent with the existence of a multiverse.[108]

Most scientists, including myself, would likely agree with this thought. Experts in cosmology think that a multiverse is a fascinating possibility that ought to be considered further. But I would paraphrase Randall's thought and confidently say that nothing about our world is inconsistent with the existence of God either! One can easily envision a creator God who brings forth a multiverse in which all possible universes can potentially be realized. Biochemist and theologian Arthur Peacocke also did not find any reason why God cannot be included in our ultimate cosmic story:

> Why cannot one similarly conceive of God also operating through random exploration of all possible kinds of universe within whatever meta-law governs the range of possibilities. God would then be allowing chance to bring into existence a universe capable of generating and sustaining life. In which case, the existence of multiple universes would still be consonant with them being given existence by a Creator God who has the intention—some time, some place, some galaxy, some universe—of bringing into existence living organisms capable of evolving into persons.[109]

Peacocke was careful to point out that he is not talking about some form of "intelligent designer," but simply a greater reality that

---

108. Lisa Randall, *Dark Matter and the Dinosaurs: The Astounding Interconnectedness of the Universe* (New York: HarperCollins, 2015), 31.

109. Arthur Peacocke, *Paths from Science towards God: The End of All Our Exploring* (Oxford: One World Publications, 2001), 71.

includes a God who is the "ground of all being"—in other words, a God who is the ultimate reason for all of existence. In the Bible the name for God is given as "I am" (Exod 3:14).

I think some scientists erroneously think that the main reason anyone would believe in God is to provide a concrete, well-defined starting point for the beginning of the universe. Some of these same scientists then might become frustrated when people continue believing in God despite ongoing advances in cosmology or other fields that continuously change our story of the universe. We know the story of Genesis did not happen as it was written three thousand years ago! But an ultimate source or cause for creation is only one reason people believe in God. I think that what is more important is the relational aspects of religious belief. This includes the personal relationships among the historical and present-day community of believers, from which many people derive their sense of life's meaning and purpose. It also includes the lived experiences of religious believers in which they personally encounter the presence of God in a one-on-one relationship. There is a reason why so many people seek out spiritual directors to help them discern God's unique call to them, and that reason is certainly NOT an ignorance of science. Anyone who suggests that it is, is simply reflecting a personal philosophical commitment that deliberately excludes a portion of the greater reality that others are willing to accept.

Since the dawn of human history, we have been drawn forward by the desire to know more. We are drawn forth not only by what we will soon know but maybe even more so by that which we will never or can never fully know. As a Catholic, I believe that it is God who calls us forth into the unknown, scientist and nonscientist, believer and nonbeliever alike. But you do not need to share my religious beliefs in order to share my enthusiasm over new findings in cosmology or in any other scientific field. Discovery is part of being human. My very good friend and colleague Father James Bowler, SJ, often remarks on the many similarities in the language used by today's physicists and the language used by many of the great religious mystics! Lisa Randall's book, *Dark Matter and the Dinosaurs,* examines "the astounding interconnectedness of the universe," in which a substance we cannot see but nevertheless "know" is there may have brought about cosmic events that resulted in the extinction of the dinosaurs. The interconnectedness of the universe created by a God whom we cannot see but nevertheless know is there is certainly a dominant theme of the Christian mystics of the past two thousand years. At least in some ways, science and religion are not so different after all.

5

Life

> Then God said: Let the earth bring forth vegetation: every kind of plant that bears seed and every kind of fruit tree on earth that bears fruit with seeds in it. And so it happened: every kind of plant that bears seed and every kind of fruit tree that bears fruit with its seed in it. God saw that it was good. Evening came and morning followed—the third day. (Gen 1:11–13)

It is difficult to define life. The *Oxford English Dictionary* describes life as "the condition which distinguishes animals and plants from inorganic matter." For human beings, life is a "condition" that is synonymous with existence. Biologists can identify a number of characteristics that are shared by all living things, but a simple, single definition of life remains elusive. In fact, there are states of being that are somewhere between life and nonliving inorganic matter. We know that life did not begin with land plants, but likely somewhere else and in a more inhospitable environment. The best scientific evidence we have today is that life emerged from nonliving matter around four billion years ago, when the Earth was still quite young.[1] We know this not from a discovery of ancient fossils but from chemical traces that have been found in Greenland rocks of this age. It is through the science of chemistry that we can learn about the earliest days of Earth's history and how nonliving matter

1. Yoko Ohtomo et al., "Evidence for Biogenic Graphite in Early Archaean Isua Metasedimentary Rocks," *Nature Geoscience* 7 (2014): 25–28.

somehow became living. Chemistry can thus tell us how a gravitational accretion of inorganic matter orbiting a medium-sized star near the edge of the Milky Way galaxy became the lush blue living planet we call home. Chemistry can also give us ideas about how our living planet has changed over the last four billion years, many of those changes triggered largely by the ever-evolving life forms that have shared our home. And chemistry gives biologists a way of describing the physical characteristics that distinguish the living from the nonliving. Biochemistry is the chemistry of life. It transforms the existential question "Why is there anything at all?" from the cosmic to the molecular scale.

Stardust

At the most basic level, the matter that makes up our physical existence is all composed of atoms. Each different type of atom is called an element. Virtually every high school and college chemistry classroom across the globe has the Periodic Table of the Elements prominently displayed on one of the walls. This chart lists the chemical symbol of the 118 known chemical elements in sequential arrangement of rows by size, and in columns by shared physical properties. The position of each element in the table is defined by its atomic number, which is equal to the number of protons found in the nucleus. The smallest atom is hydrogen, which has a single, positively charged proton in its nucleus. Beyond hydrogen, all other atoms contain both protons and neutrons, which together make up the bulk of the atomic mass of that element. The first 94 elements of the periodic table are naturally occurring, but other elements have been "discovered" or, in other words, created in chemistry and physics laboratories since the mid-1900s. It is remarkable to consider that while there are so many elements that make up our world, at the dawn of time, in the earliest moments of the Big Bang, there were only two: the gases hydrogen and helium. The other 92 natural elements exist because of what happens inside stars.[2]

2. Andrew King, *Stars: A Very Short Introduction* (Oxford: Oxford University Press, 2012).

During the period of very rapid universe expansion, within a few seconds of the Big Bang singularity, the white-hot energy cooled to the point where protons, neutrons, and electrons could form from their constituent subatomic parts. As the expansion rate of the early universe began to slow, the cloud of matter in each region of space was drawn inward by gravitational attraction toward the nearest galactic center. This resulted in a rotational motion that collapsed the clouds of matter into spinning disks. Within each new galaxy, the rotational collapse of the hydrogen and helium clouds brought the dispersed matter closer together, and billions of localized accumulations resulted. As massive numbers of hydrogen atoms coalesced in various parts of the nascent galaxies, temperatures and pressures gradually increased until the giant fusion reactors we know as stars exploded into brilliant life.[3] In stars, hydrogen atoms fuse together to form helium atoms with the release of enormous amounts of energy as light and heat. The hydrogen bombs of our world's nuclear arsenals are but a tiny example of the vast energetics of these reactions. As hydrogen was converted into helium in the early stars, helium atoms began to fuse together to form larger atoms.

Of special importance for all things now living, carbon atoms were formed in the stars by the fusion of three helium atoms.[4] Stellar nucleosynthesis reactions like this are thought to be the main source of the first twenty-six elements of the periodic table. These are the most abundant, or *primary*, elements of the universe. By the time iron (element 26) has formed in the deepest interior of stars, the energy released by the atomic fusion reactions that have led to its formation has been exhausted and is no longer sufficient to support the external layers of the star. The burning outer layers of the star collapse onto the iron core and then rebound in a titanic shockwave called a supernova, which spews atomic debris out into space. The tremendous energy of the supernova also sets off a new set of nucleosynthesis reactions that produce the heavier, and rarer, elements such

3. John Gribbin, *Galaxies: A Very Short Introduction* (Oxford: Oxford University Press, 2008), 86–101.

4. Jim Baggot, *Origins: The Scientific Story of Creation* (Oxford: Oxford University Press, 2015), 123–45.

as copper, gold, mercury, and uranium, which are scattered out into the cosmos along the with primary elements.[5]

As the elemental stardust from the first supernova explosions traveled through space, these atoms encountered other atoms, and chemical reactions began to occur. Molecules began to form. In the early universe the first simple molecules to form were likely to be hydrogen gas (H_2), carbon dioxide (CO_2), ammonia (NH_3), and water (H_2O).[6] These simplest of molecules are central to the biochemistry of the complex biological macromolecules that make up all living organisms. Heavier elements, those that would become the crust of the Earth, began to combine with oxygen and with each other to form the first tiny mineral grains. But before stardust could become life, it needed a place for molecular complexity to happen.

There's No Place like Home

The atomic and molecular debris ejected from the supernovae of the first stars brought a diversity of matter to the primeval clouds of hydrogen and helium that made up the early Milky Way galaxy. As these new elements and molecules interacted with the existing matter, new centers of gravity formed. By the same process as before, new stars were formed by gravitational attraction. The hydrogen that fuels stars is the most abundant element in the universe, and even the second generation of stars did not exhaust the supply of hydrogen in our part of the galaxy. It is thought that our sun may be a third-generation star that burst forth from yet another gravitationally concentrated mixture of elements and gases 4.6 billion years ago.[7] The gas cloud out of which our sun formed was a much more diverse mixture than the simple hydrogen and helium clouds that formed the first stars. The growing solar nucleus drew in the vast majority of all the hydrogen and other elements within our region of space. Our sun burst into existence once the growing mass of hydrogen gas at the center of the cloud reached a critical temperature and pressure.

5. King, *Stars*, 59–71.
6. Baggott, *Origins*, 132.
7. Ibid., 146–70.

The sudden flash of heat energy from the solar ignition vaporized or melted everything that remained in the molecular cloud. Much of the lighter gases were blown toward the outer parts of the solar system. Heavier elements and molecular debris more resistant to the solar wind settled into orbit closer to the sun's surface. This material formed the molten beginnings of the sun's inner planets.[8]

The Earth was one of those planets that formed from this molten debris, approximately 4.56 billion years ago. One hundred million years after the birth of the sun, five small accreting inner planets enriched in the elements oxygen, iron, silicon, magnesium, aluminum, and calcium orbited the young star.[9] As the planets of the solar system were coming together, these elements reacted with one another forming the minerals that would make up the bulk of the rocky mass of the planets. Slow cooling of the planet surfaces began a gradual partitioning of the minerals, forming a fragile, early outer crust. Iron, the heaviest of the primary elements, settled toward the center to become a molten liquid core that persists on Earth today, providing the heat that turns over and continually reworks the surface of our planet. Sometime within the first 100 million years of Earth's formation, a spectacular collision occurred between our young planet and a smaller fifth planetoid that was destroyed in the cataclysm.[10] The Earth completely absorbed the molten mass of its smaller sibling and was knocked off its axis of rotation by the collision. The legacy of that cataclysmic event is deeply embedded in Earth's unique history and physical make-up, indeed in its very essence; it is evidenced by the moon, which later formed from the ejected planetary debris, and by our four seasons, which result from Earth's peculiar angle of rotation.

Even after the Earth began to recover from the interplanetary collision, the solar system was still a very unsettled place. For tens of millions of years, a constant bombardment of asteroids, meteors, and other cosmic debris kept the Earth's surface molten and unformed. As the rain of cosmic debris came to an end, the surface of the Earth

8. Robert M. Hazen, *The Story of Earth* (New York: Penguin Books, 2012), 7–30.
9. Ibid., 24–25.
10. Ibid., 31–52.

cooled, and the first rocks began to solidify out of the magma brought up from the interior. The oldest rock formations on Earth, located in the Canadian Shield of northwestern Canada, are approximately four billion years old. The first ocean formed from water vapor released by eruptions from the Earth's hot interior.[11] Water vapor (H_2O) collected as part of the early atmosphere, along with other volatile molecular gases including carbon dioxide (CO_2), nitrogen (N_2), and hydrogen sulfide (H_2S). As the atmosphere cooled, water precipitated out and rained down on the hot Earth, furthering the surface cooling and accumulating in low points as puddles, ponds, lakes, and eventually oceans. The planet we call home is just far enough from the sun that the surface temperatures are cool enough for liquid water to exist, but not so far away that all the water freezes. In contrast, on our nearest neighbors, Venus and Mars, all the water is either a gaseous vapor or locked up in subsurface permafrost. But on our Earth, we have all three phases of this precious substance; most important of all is the liquid phase without which life, at least as we know it, could not exist.

The Water of Life

Water is one the most common molecules in the universe.[12] Water's unique V-shaped structure, two hydrogen atoms bound to a single oxygen, results in a slightly charged molecule that attracts other charged or slightly charged molecules. Water molecules stick to each other and to other molecules. The surface tension of water allows tiny insects to literally "walk on water," and causes water to be drawn upward from the soil into a plant to replace the water evaporating from leaf surfaces. The cohesion among water molecules also gives water its high heat of vaporization, which makes water an efficient cooling agent as perspiration evaporates from our skin's surface. Water's *polar* nature—the uneven distribution of electron density within the molecule, resulting in one pole with a partial negative charge and the other pole with a partial positive charge—makes it an exceptional solvent, allowing other polar substances to be dis-

11. Ibid., 94–99.
12. Ibid., 84–91.

persed within it. These include the fundamental biochemical building blocks such as amino acids, sugars, and nucleic acids, from which the major biological macromolecules are composed.

The chemistry of life relies entirely on the chemistry of water. Water is the essence of biochemistry, not only as the solvent in which life's chemistry occurs but as a critical player in many biochemical reactions. Removal of water (condensation) in a reaction joins two molecules together, and adding water (hydration) across a chemical bond breaks a larger molecule into two smaller ones. The utter dependence of life on water is deeply ingrained within all living things, plants and animals alike. The living world is rife with adaptations for both obtaining water and conserving water. The biological drive for water is instinctual. Our earliest human ancestors, living on the arid savannahs of eastern Africa, would have been tied to open water sources for their existence, just like all other animals of their time. Humans can go without food for several weeks or even a month, but without water and in a dry environment, we would be lucky to survive for a day.

Water is so central to human existence that it came to symbolize the spirit of God, that which gives spiritual life, for the great Abrahamic religions that arose in the eastern Mediterranean four thousand years ago, beginning with Judaism. In Exodus 17:6 Moses strikes a rock in the wilderness at God's command, and water begins to flow out so the thirsty Israelites can drink. The prophet Jeremiah (17:7–8) compares a person who believes in God to a tree that grows by a stream and continues to bear fruit even in times of drought. In the Gospel of John, Jesus takes this symbolism still further in his famous conversation with a Samaritan woman, comparing the water from Jacob's well to the "living water" or spirit that comes from God:

> Jesus answered and said to her, "Everyone who drinks this water will be thirsty again; but whoever drinks the water I shall give will never thirst; the water I shall give shall become in him a spring of water welling up to eternal life. (John 14:13–14)

The linkage between the natural water on which all biochemistry depends and the "living water" that is central to spiritual life has been a central theme for Christian writers ever since. With water, the simple molecule H_2O, we not only have the universal solvent on which all organic life depends, we also have a powerful symbol of God's spirit, upon which all spiritual and religious life depends. These are the waters of life!

The Vital Element

Organic chemistry, a subject required for all college biology, chemistry, and premedical students, is the chemistry of carbon. Carbon atoms, formed in stellar nucleosynthesis reactions, have six protons, six neutrons, and six electrons. Every carbon atom forms four chemical bonds with neighboring atoms. Organic chemistry is, on the one hand, deceptively simple, focusing exclusively on carbon and a handful of other elements such as hydrogen, oxygen, nitrogen, phosphorous, and sulfur, with which carbon most frequently interacts. But, on the other hand, and as sophomore undergraduates soon learn, the complexity of organic chemistry comes not from the number of elements but from the dizzying array of chemical structures that can emerge using only a small number of reaction types. Organic chemistry has a wide variety of practical, industrial, and medical applications, from the creation of soaps, to the "cracking" of crude petroleum to produce gasoline, to the synthesis of new polymers, dyes, and pharmaceutical compounds. Organic chemistry is central, in modern times, to the global economy.

Biochemistry is a subdiscipline of organic chemistry. Biochemistry focuses primarily on four classes of organic compounds that make up all living things. These are *carbohydrates, nucleic acids, proteins,* and *lipids.* In simplest terms, these biological molecules can be thought of as chains of carbon and a few other chemical groups, strung together in class-specific ways, each providing unique functional characteristics to a living cell. The major classes of biological molecules are all composed of smaller subunits or monomers called *sugars* (carbohydrates), *nucleotides* (nucleic acids), *amino acids* (proteins), and *fatty acids* or *isoprenes* (lipids). These subunits are linked together in particular ways to give the four types of macromolecule the great functional diversity we see in living cells.

When biochemists wish to study any of the four classes of biological macromolecules, we usually start with a living organism. Any protein, fatty acid, or sugar one might wish to study or incorporate into a natural product can likely be more easily obtained from a living source than synthesized from scratch; but in the earliest days of Earth's history, there were no living sources of carbon. Thus there were no readily available sources of proteins, DNA or RNA, carbohydrates, or cell membranes. Life somehow arose from the nonliving material on the Earth's surface. We might reasonably venture that many of these ancient building blocks of life are still around today, found among the various biomolecules of cellular metabolism. But what do we know about the building blocks of life that were available on Earth almost four billion years ago?

The Secret of Slime

From the time of the ancient Greeks it was commonly thought that living organisms could emerge from nonliving material through a process of *spontaneous generation*. For example, puddles that formed in the ruts of a dirt road after a summer rainstorm could be teeming with tiny plants and swimming animals a few days later. In the mid-nineteenth century, the French microbiologist Louis Pasteur disproved the theory of spontaneous generation. Pasteur showed that a flask of boiled nutrient broth that was exposed to air but shielded from airborne spores could remain pure and unchanged for many weeks, while in a similar but unshielded flask, many organisms would appear in just a few hours.[13] Pasteur's conclusion from this study was "*omne vivum ex vivo*," that is, that all life must come from other life. His work became central to the germ theory of modern medicine, and his *pasteurization* process is still used today by our dairy industry.

Origins of Life

While Pasteur was revolutionizing microbiology in France, the British naturalist Charles Darwin had just published his seminal work *On*

13. Garland Allen and Jeffrey Baker, *Biology: Scientific Process and Social Issues* (New York: John Wiley & Sons, 2001), 59–66.

the Origin of Species, which gave *omne vivum ex vivo* a much broader context. We will give Darwin's work a closer examination in the next chapter, but one of his major conclusions was that all modern life forms are descended from a single ancestral form. In the second edition of *On the Origin of Species,* Darwin suggested that life may have been "breathed by the Creator" into one or a few ancestral forms.[14] But he also speculated in private about an *abiotic* or nonliving origin for life. In a letter to his longtime friend and mentor Joseph Hooker, Darwin acknowledged Pasteur's important work but wrote:

> It is often said that all the conditions for the first production of a living organism are now present, which could ever have been present.—But if (and oh what a big if) we could conceive in some warm little pond with all sorts of ammonia & phosphoric salts,—light, heat, electricity etc. present, that a protein compound was chemically formed, ready to undergo still more complex changes, at the present day such matter would be instantly devoured, or absorbed, which would not have been the case before living creatures were formed.[15]

Here Darwin is implying that there could have been a time in Earth's history when conditions were such that life could have emerged from nonliving materials, however impossible that might be today. Darwin's suggestion of an abiotic origin of life was not lost on the generation of scientists who came after him. In the 1920s, Russian biochemist Alexander Oparin and the British biologist J. B. S. Haldane suggested that Earth's early atmosphere would have been a reducing atmosphere that was free of oxygen.[16] In such an atmosphere, energy sources such as ultraviolet radiation and lightning could trigger the formation of organic molecules from volcanic gases. Amino acids and other biological building blocks would accumulate

---

14. Charles Darwin, *On the Origin of Species by Means of Natural Selection, or the Preservation of Favoured Races in the Struggle for Life*, 2nd ed. (London: John Murray, 1860), 490.

15. Darwin Correspondence Project, Letter no. 7471, February 1, 1871 (Cambridge: University of Cambridge), http://www.darwinproject.ac.uk/DCP-LETT-7471.

16. Michael J. Benton, *The History of Life: A Very Short Introduction* (Oxford: Oxford University Press, 2003), 23–25.

over millions of years in the warm oceans of ancient Earth, and this "prebiotic soup" would eventually give rise to macromolecules that could become organized into living cells.

In 1953, Stanley Miller, a graduate student in chemistry at the University of Chicago who was working in the laboratory of Nobel Prize–winner Harold Urey, tested the Oparin–Haldane hypothesis. Miller mixed the reduced gases methane (CH_4), ammonia (NH_3), and hydrogen (H_2) in a sealed flask to simulate Earth's early atmosphere. The flask was connected to a container of gently boiling water to simulate a hot early ocean. Electrical sparks discharged into the gas mixture were used to simulate lightening. After a few days, Miller found that a dark organic slime accumulated at the base of the apparatus. Chemical analysis of the slime yielded the simple molecules hydrogen cyanide and formaldehyde, along with the amino acids alanine, glycine, and aspartic acid.[17] The Miller-Urey experiment spawned a host of similar studies in other laboratories. In those studies, a number of other amino acids, sugars, and many nitrogen-containing compounds could all be produced.[18] Thus it seemed possible that the earliest building blocks of life were the result of Earth's atmospheric chemistry.

Some geochemists were critical of these experiments because volcanic gases consist mainly of carbon dioxide (CO_2) and dinitrogen (N_2), not ammonia and methane, and have very little hydrogen.[19] The discovery of deep sea hydrothermal vents in the 1980s, however, provided a new type of prebiotic soup to investigate.[20] In numerous places along the mid-ocean ridges where new crust is formed, cold seawater is pulled down into cracks in the crust where it mixes with red hot magma. The superheated acidic water, along with dissolved minerals and gases, jets from vents in the crust in dramatic "black

17. Stanley Miller, "A Production of Amino Acids under Possible Primitive Earth Conditions," *Science* 117 (1953): 528–29.

18. Stanley Miller and Harold Urey, "Organic Compound Synthesis on the Primitive Earth," *Science* 120 (1959): 245–51.

19. David C. Catling, *Astrobiology: A Very Short Introduction* (Oxford: Oxford University Press, 2013), 32–33.

20. Ken C. MacDonald and Bruce P. Luyendyk, "The Crest of the East Pacific Rise," *Scientific American* 244 (1981): 100–16.

smokers" named for the various dark sulfide precipitates that fall out in a cloud around them. The black smokers also emit hydrogen sulfide (H_2S), a source of chemical energy that can drive chemical synthesis. At greater distances, cooler and alkaline "white smokers" bring a different host of minerals and organic compounds to the surface. Work by the mineralogist Robert Hazen and colleagues at the Carnegie Institution of Washington has shown that the high pressure and temperature conditions of black smokers can also produce mixtures of sugars, lipids, and amino acids.[21]

Another possible cauldron for prebiotic cooking was warm pools on barren ancient landscapes associated with volcanic hot springs. Simulations of these conditions by John Sutherland of Cambridge University has shown that all the precursors for lipids, amino acids, and RNA can be derived from water and hydrogen cyanide (HCN) dissolved from rock, with the sun's ultraviolet radiation as an energy source.[22] Finally, millions of tons of organic carbon, formed somewhere in space, rains down on the Earth's surface every year with meteorites and micrometeorites. Many of these burn up due to friction as they fall through the atmosphere, but meteoric dust that floats down without burning or very large meteorites that only partly decompose can survive the fall to the surface. A single large meteor that fell in Australia in 1969 was found to contain thousands of different molecules, including fifteen amino acids as well as nucleic acid bases.[23]

So, it is now evident that there are in fact many ways in which the building blocks of biological molecules either formed on Earth or arrived by "take-out" delivery from space. Scientists might argue about what the "most important" carbon source was for ancient Earth, but it is likely that all of these mechanisms and more played some role in the formation of the organic slime that dispersed

21. Hazen, *The Story of Earth*, 135–39.

22. P. H. Parel, C. Percivalle, D. J Ritson, C. D. Duffy, and J. D. Sutherland, "Common Origins of RNA, Protein and Lipid Precursors in a Cyanosulfidic Protometabolism," *Nature Chemistry* 7 (2015): 301–7.

23. Keith A. Kvenvolden, James Lawless, Katherine Pering, Etta Peterson, Jose Flores, Cyril Ponnamperuma, Isaac R. Kaplan, and Carleton Moore, "Evidence for Extraterrestrial Amino-Acids and Hydrocarbons in the Murchison Meteorite," *Nature* 228 (1970): 923–26.

through the depths of a turbulent ocean, accumulated on rocks and mineral grain surfaces, or floated on the surface of shallow lakes and ponds. Once significant accumulations of organic monomers were brought close together, the next step is to begin linking them together chemically into larger polymers. That takes energy.

Thermodynamics

The science of thermodynamics, or energy flow in chemical transformations, is based on two fundamental physical laws. The first law of thermodynamics, also called the conservation of energy, states that energy can be neither created nor destroyed. The second law of thermodynamics states that in an isolated system, molecules will always tend to a more disordered or higher *entropy* state. One implication from the second law is that for any system, the degree of disorder will always tend to increase. Hence large molecules, such as the ink and paper of this book and the biological macromolecules of this book's author will, over time, disintegrate into smaller, simpler, more disorganized subunits. Fortunately, living systems do not exist in isolation but are always in contact with a universe containing many other systems. Systems may therefore exchange matter and energy with the universe and the multitude of other systems that comprise it. Because of this feature, entropy can be overcome in any system by the input of energy coming from somewhere else. So for example, the books strewn about my office as I write this volume can be returned to their proper places on the shelves, provided I spend the time and energy to organize my office one Saturday afternoon. The integrity of my body and the physiological systems that make it work are maintained by the input of energy derived from the food that I eat each day. The only way for entropy to be overcome—for biological homeostasis, growth, and even reproduction, to be achieved—is to invest energy into the reactions necessary for these processes.

In a prebiotic world filled with organic slime, even if the subunits of a potential macromolecule were close together on the surface of a clay particle, they would be unlikely to react unless energy were put into the system. In living cells, the energy used to drive synthesis reactions, as well as most other cellular processes, is present in the high-energy bonds of adenosine triphosphate, or ATP. ATP is derived from adenosine, one of the same nitrogen sugars found in RNA and DNA. In ATP-driven reactions, one or two of the high-energy phosphate groups are transferred to one of the reactants, boosting it to a higher energy level and therefore making it more likely to react with its neighbor. The breaking of the high-energy bonds in ATP represents the energy that is invested into making the new compound. In living cells, protein enzymes catalyze these reactions, acting to bring the reactants close together in a three-dimensional orientation that favors the reaction. In the prebiotic world, clay particles or other mineral grains could have served this purpose.

The reactions that join two monomers together in a macromolecule are condensation reactions, in which a water molecule is lost in the process of binding the monomers together. The phosphate group released from ATP is a negatively charged ion with very high attraction for water molecules. Phosphate can therefore act as a dehydrating agent, soaking up the water lost from the reactants as a new chemical bond is formed. It is thought that ATP, or a phosphate-containing molecule like ATP, could have functioned in this way in the prebiotic soup of ancient Earth.[24] So the ancient prebiotic world likely had the organic compounds necessary for building macromolecules, solid surfaces on which these compounds could aggregate, and high-energy agents that could link them together. But this is still not life. Even the simplest of modern-day cells are highly organized. Where did that organization come from?

Forms of Life?

We do not know what the first living things were or when they first appeared. One issue confounding this question is that there is no single definition of life that every scientist engaged in these questions would agree to. Can a molecule that is able to replicate itself be regarded as "living"? Some say that self-replication is the defining characteristic of life, while others say that a compartment enclosing

24. Nick Lane, *The Vital Question: Energy, Evolution, and the Origins of Complex Life* (New York: W. W. Norton, 2015), 98.

a biochemical metabolism is the defining characteristic. Many biologists would say that both are requirements for life. Regardless of how one defines life, most researchers interested in the origins of life would like to ultimately understand how the first cell or cells came into existence. It is a very large step to move from a collection of organic ingredients collected on a mineral surface to an organized, self-replicating, and metabolizing cell. As any amateur chef knows, just having all the ingredients for a recipe does not guarantee the successful preparation of a gourmet meal!

At the most basic level, a cell consists of a cell membrane that encloses an internal compartment where chemical conditions differ from the external environment, and in which is housed an informational molecule, such as DNA, which not only directs cellular activity but allows the cell to replicate. Cells like this exist in abundance today, making up the vast majority of all the biomass on the planet. We call them bacteria and think of them as the simplest of all life forms. As "simple" as we might picture them being, however, we must bear in mind that the bacteria living today are themselves the product of billions of years of evolution and likely very different from the first living cells. Nevertheless, we can still use them as a place to begin thinking about life's origins.

The easiest step to imagine in the formation of the first bacteria-like cells is the construction of the cell membrane. Lipids are *hydrophobic*, or water hating, and will spontaneously organize into closed lipid bilayers when they are placed in contact with water. Such structures, called *liposomes*, are routinely made in biochemistry laboratories around the world for any number of reasons. In the lab I worked in for many years, we made liposomes to simulate the mineralizing matrix vesicles found in cartilage and bone.[25] Liposomes of different sizes and permeability can be made by altering the types and ratios of the various lipids placed in the original mixture, the temperature and composition of the solution, and the force of mixing. The lipids in such a mixture are a self-organizing system that does not need an

25. Nicholas R. Blandford, Glenn R. Sauer, Brian R. Genge, Licia N. Y. Wu, and Roy. E. Wuthier, "Modeling of Matrix Vesicle Biomineralization Using Large Unilamellar Vesicles," *Journal of Inorganic Biochemistry* 94 (2003):14–27.

external template or mold. One can easily imagine liposomes forming on the shores of an ancient sea as waves crash down on rocks that had become coated with an abiotic film of lipids over several tidal cycles. Once the liposomes form, the interior compartment could provide a place where sugars or amino acids could concentrate and eventually polymerize into proteins, carbohydrates, and nucleic acids.

Origins-of-life research received a big boost in 1982 when Thomas Cech, a biochemist at the University of Colorado who was interested in the DNA transcription process, discovered that RNA molecules were autocatalytic, that is, they could act as enzymes and facilitate their own replication.[26] Prior to this discovery it was thought that only proteins could act as biological catalysts. Proteins are needed as catalysts for DNA and RNA synthesis, but the information needed for making such proteins is contained only within DNA. So which came first, DNA or protein? This was a classic "the chicken or the egg" kind of dilemma. Cech's discovery of RNA *ribozymes*—an RNA molecule able to act like an enzyme—provided a possible solution by suggesting that RNA provides both a template for the replication of new RNA models as well as the chemical means for facilitating this process.

The discovery of ribozymes led to the development of the *RNA world hypothesis*, first expressed by Harvard biochemist Walter Gilbert in 1986.[27] According to this idea, RNA molecules initially formed randomly from nucleotide bases in the prebiotic organic soup. Some of these first polymers were able to act as ribozymes and therefore enhance the copies of themselves in the mixture. Accidental changes or mutations in the RNA sequence would produce some molecules that were better or more efficient ribozymes, which would then come to dominate the population of the RNA world. The RNA molecule itself was thus evolving in the prebiotic soup. Over time, the replicating RNA molecules could have become associated with

26. Kelly Kruger, Paula J. Grabowski, Arthur J. Zaug, Julie Sands, Daniel E. Gottschling, and Thomas R. Cech, "Self-splicing RNA: Autoexcision and Autocyclization of the Ribosomal RNA Intervening Sequence of Tetrahymena," *Cell* 31 (1982): 147–57.

27. Walter Gilbert, "The RNA World," *Nature* 319 (1986): 618.

liposomes to form *protocells*, where ribozyme activity could catalyze not only the replication of the RNA but the first few steps of an early metabolism. Within these earliest cells, and with RNA serving as the original template, the more stable double-stranded DNA molecule would become the primary genetic material, and protein would become the main catalyst. Today, RNA continues to serve as the mediator between the genetic information in DNA and the expression of proteins.

Although the RNA world scenario remains very hypothetical, many aspects of it have been tested in the laboratory. For example, RNA ribozymes have been shown to undergo molecular evolution in the laboratory, becoming more efficient at synthesizing longer RNA strands over relatively short periods of time.[28] Laboratory-based RNA world scenarios have been devised to show how RNA might serve simultaneously as both a ribozyme and an informational molecule,[29] functioning within model protocells formed from liposomes.[30] But most laboratory tests of the RNA world have always supplied the chemical energy needed to drive the synthesis of the RNA polymers. Recent work has drawn attention to the thermodynamics needed to drive polymerization in the absence of cellular energy sources. This has, in turn, shed new light on where and when the first cells may have formed.

In a tantalizing new idea, biochemist Nick Lane, of University College London, has proposed that the surfaces of mineral crystals in hydrothermal vent areas in the deep oceans might actually have functioned as the first cell membranes of early protocells.[31] In white smokers, warm, mineral-rich alkaline water is vented into the cooler, more acidic seawater. As the minerals precipitate out of the solution, they form a massive network of tiny crystalline chambers and a pH gradient that favors the movement of protons into the chambers

28. James Attwater, Aniela Wochner, and Phillip Holliger, "In-ice Evolution of RNA Polymerase Ribozyme Activity," *Nature Chemistry* 5 (2013): 1011–18.

29. Tracey A. Lincoln and Gerald F. Joyce, "Self-sustained Replication of an RNA Enzyme," *Science* 323 (2009): 1229–32.

30. Katarzyna Adamala and Jack W. Szostak, "Nonenzymatic Template-directed RNA Synthesis inside Model Protocells," *Science* 342 (2013): 1098–1100.

31. Lane, *The Vital Question*, 122–53.

across the mineral surfaces. Lane argues that these abiotic proton gradients could be the precursors of the membrane-based gradients that living cells today use to drive ATP synthesis. In another scenario, favored by English chemist John Sutherland, and mirroring Darwin's "warm little pond," the drying of surface ponds in desert-like conditions could have resulted in the simultaneous emergence of all the ingredients for making an RNA protocell and its metabolism.[32]

Either of these scenarios would be favored if the prebiotic conditions included high temperatures. This would increase the reactivity of the original chemical precursors. No undergraduate chemistry laboratory is ever without a full set of Bunsen burners for heating test tubes. In 2015, zircon crystals from the oldest sedimentary rocks on Earth, the Jack Hills formation of Western Australia, were found to contain carbon with an isotopic composition similar to cellular biomolecules.[33] The 4.1–billion-year age of the Jack Hills zircons suggests that some form of living cells were present all the way back in the hellish early days of Earth, when the planet was still very hot. Apparently, life on Earth has very ancient roots. The early Earth can be thought of as a bioreactor that produced all the materials necessary for life to emerge. The miracle of life did not require a cosmic "designer" to make the first cell some 4,000 million years ago. The miracle of life is embedded within the very fabric of creation. Life sprang from the *heart of matter* itself, as we recall in the insights of Teilhard de Chardin. But what was our earliest ancestor like?

The Search for the Last Universal Common Ancestor (LUCA)

When I was an undergraduate student, we were taught that there were two main categories or domains of life. The prokaryotes, or bacteria, are single-celled microorganisms that lack a central nucleus where

---

32. P. H. Parel, C. Percivalle, D. J Ritson, C. D. Duffy, and J. D. Sutherland, "Common Origins of RNA, Protein and Lipid Precursors in a Cyanosulfidic Protometabolism," *Nature Chemistry* 7 (2015): 301–7.

33. Elizabeth Bell, Patrick Boehnke, T. Mark Harrison, and Wendy L. Mao, "Potentially Biogenic Carbon Preserved in a 4.1 Billion-Year-Old Zircon," *PNAS USA* 112 (2015): 14518–21.

the DNA is housed. This is the primary distinction between them and the other domain, the nucleated eukaryotes, which includes the protozoans and all complex multicellular organisms including fungi, plants, and animals. So in my college days it was thought that some ancient form of bacteria cell was the last universal common ancestor (LUCA) of all other bacteria as well as of all of the more complicated eukaryotic life forms.

Bacteria are well known to us. These microorganisms thrive almost everywhere on Earth, where they mostly live in complete harmony with other life forms. For example, they live on the surface of our skin and throughout our gastrointestinal tract, where their activity assists in the digestive process. In the H. G. Wells novel *The War of the Worlds,* bacteria were the saviors of Earth after all human responses to the invading Martians failed. As in that novel, bacteria can also be the "germs" that cause illness and disease. For this reason, they have received intense study ever since the 1800s when this causal link was made by Louis Pasteur and the German physician Robert Koch.[34]

As microbiology progressed over the past two centuries, some peculiar species of prokaryotes were found in very harsh environments like volcanic hot springs or desert salt ponds. These "bacteria" were placed within prokaryote taxonomic groupings labeled as "extremophiles" after the types of habitat in which they were found. The extremophiles had significant differences from other prokaryotes in metabolism and membrane lipid composition. The proteins of this group of prokaryotes can withstand close-to-boiling temperatures that would be lethal to virtually anything else. They were commonly considered by microbiologists to be the likely ancestors of the more ubiquitous and well-known disease-causing bacteria.

In the late 1970s, using new genetic sequencing technology, Carl Woese of the University of Illinois, who was one of the earliest advocates of the RNA world hypothesis, found that the ribosomal RNA of some of the extremophiles differed very significantly from that of other bacteria. In fact, the bacteria were as different from the

34. Allen and Baker, *Biology*, 92.

extremophile group as they were from eukaryotes. Woese suggested that they be reclassified under the new name, *archaea*, to designate their ancient ancestral origins. The other two domains, according to Woese, were the *bacteria* and *eukarya*.[35] In Woese's branching, three-domain tree of life diagram, the archaea were closest to the ancestral, so extreme environments became the prime places for addressing early life-origin questions. Many species of archaea are found associated with volcanic springs such as those found in Yellowstone National Park. Archaea are also abundant in the black smokers and white smokers of hydrothermal vent areas of the deep oceans. The vent areas are an ancient geological feature, as old as Earth's crust and earliest oceans, and they contain chemical energy sources such as hydrogen sulfide, which could have been the driving force for early biosynthesis reactions.

The three-domain tree of life featured in biology textbooks of the past two decades was based upon Carl Woese's analysis of a single gene common to all known organisms. But more recent studies, using multiple gene sequences, have caused those texts to be revised again. It now appears that the nucleated eukaryotes, which include all multicellular complex life including humans, are in fact descended from the archaea.[36] So we are now back to a two-domain tree of life, with the root of that tree located somewhere between modern-day archaea and bacteria. The search for the LUCA continues and provides clues for which of the above environments it called home. An extensive analysis of all known archaean and bacteria gene sequences performed by microbiologist William Martin and his research group in Germany concluded that only 355 prokaryotic genes are held in common between the two groups.[37] The genes that are shared point

---

35. Carl R. Woese, Otto Kandler, and Mark L. Wheelis, "Towards a Natural System of Organisms: Proposal for the Domains Archaea, Bacteria, and Eukarya," *PNAS USA* 87 (1990): 4576–79.

36. Tom A. Williams, Peter G. Foster, Cymon L. Cox, and T. Martin Embly, "An Archaeal Origin of Eukaryotes Supports Only Two Primary Domains of Life," *Nature* 504 (2013): 231–36.

37. Madeline C. Weiss, Filipa L. Sousa, Natalia Mrnjavac, Sinie Neukirchen, May Roetiget, May, Shijulal Nelson-Sthi, and William F. Martin, "The Physiology and Habitat of the Last Universal Common Ancestor," *Nature Microbiology* 1 (2016): 1–8.

to an ancient metabolism in an oxygen-free environment chemically similar to that found in hydrothermal vent areas. So in the present moment, the deep sea seems to be the ancient home of LUCA, but that is subject to change. There are some who even support an extra-planetary home such as the surface of ancient Mars.[38] And although all life that we know of seems to be descended from LUCA, life may have originated more than once and possibly in different environments. Ancient life forms unrelated to LUCA may have gone extinct or might still be among us, lurking in the dark and unexplored parts of our world.[39] There are few fields of science today as fascinating, to me anyway, as origins-of-life research.

Life Energy

LUCA was the ancestor of all life. It is likely that LUCA and its first descendants relied on chemical energy sources such as hydrogen sulfide or hydrothermal proton gradients to fuel their metabolism. LUCA was also very ancient. There is now evidence for the existence of hydrothermal vent microbes living 3.77 billion year ago, and possibly even earlier.[40] The oldest, widely agreed-upon fossils on record are stromatolites of around 3.48 billion years of age, found in western Australia.[41] Stromatolites are dome-like structures that form layer by layer in shallow water environments, as thin films of photosynthetic bacteria trap and deposit water-borne sediment. These structures eventually get buried under accumulating sediment and become fossilized. The presence of fossilized stromatolites suggests that sometime in the first 500 million years of life's history a new energy source, light, was being used to drive cellular processes. In

38. Peter Ward and Joe Kirschvink, *A New History of Life* (New York: Bloomsbury Press, 2015), 57–60.

39. Paul Davies, *The Eerie Silence: Renewing Our Search for Alien Intelligence* (New York: Houghton Mifflin Harcourt, 2010), 42–63.

40. Matthew S. Dodd, Dominic Papineau, Tor Grenne, John F. Slack, Martin Rittner, Franco Pirjano, Jonathan O'Neil, and Crispin T. S. Little, " Evidence for Early Life in Earth's Oldest Hydrothermal Vent Precipitates," *Nature* 543 (2017): 60–64.

41. Abigail C. Allwood, Malcolm R. Walter, Balz S. Kamber, Craig P. Marshall, and Ian W. Burch, "Stromatolite Reef from the Early Archaean Era of Australia," *Nature* 441 (2006): 714–18.

photosynthesis, light is captured by colored pigments and used to energize electrons, which move along carriers in the cell membrane to set up proton gradients across the membrane. These proton gradients then drive the formation of ATP to meet the energetic needs of the cell.

Photosynthesis appears to have developed several times in different bacteria lineages, but it never emerged among the archaeans.[42] The earliest forms of photosynthesis are thought to resemble that which occurs in modern purple sulfur bacteria that live in hot springs and warm stagnant ponds.[43] These bacteria use hydrogen sulfide as the source of high-energy electrons. At some point over the next billion years of life's history, another lineage of photosynthetic bacteria discovered a new source of electrons, one that was more common and widely available than hydrogen sulfide.[44] The new electron source was the elixir of life itself: water. When water molecules are stripped of electrons by photosynthesis, they lose their protons, and oxygen is liberated in the form of O_2 gas. *Oxygenic photosynthesis* was a signature event in the history of Earth. On a planet bathed in the light of the sun and with surface water everywhere, populations of oxygenic microbes exploded, and Earth's atmosphere was forever changed. The gradual accumulation of oxygen in the atmosphere, a process that happened slowly at first, eventually transformed the face of the Earth and set the stage for the emergence of complex life forms. The Earth was changed from a rocky galactic outpost, where primitive life clung to existence in extreme habitats, to a living planet!

A Living Planet

One of my favorite film comedies is *My Cousin Vinny*, in which a New York lawyer, played by Joe Pesci, is summoned to rural Alabama

42. Robert E. Blankenship, "Early Evolution of Photosynthesis," *Plant Physiology* 154 (2010): 434–38.

43. Jin Xiong, William M Fischer, Kazuhito Inoue, Masaaki Nakahara, and Carl R. Bauer, "Molecular Evidence for the Early Evolution of Photosynthesis," *Science* 289 (2000): 1724–30.

44. Roger Buick, "The Antiquity of Oxygenic Photosynthesis: Evidence from Stromatolites in Sulfur-deficient Archaean Lakes," *Science* 255 (1992): 74–77.

to defend his cousin and a friend who have been mistakenly arrested for the murder of a shopkeeper. The clash of cultures that occurs when Vincent Gambini and his fiancé, Mona Lisa Vito, memorably played by Marisa Tomei, set foot in a tiny Southern town is quite hilarious. In one scene, the couple spend the night sleeping in their car during a thunderstorm. As Vinny steps out of the car the next morning, he takes a full header as he slips on the saturated ground. The car is hopelessly stuck, and Vinny's good suit gets ruined as the unfortunate pair try to free it from the mud. After arriving late to court dressed in a ridiculous outfit from a secondhand store, Vinny must explain himself to a hostile judge. But all present in the courtroom nod knowingly as Vinny describes his mishap with the red Alabama clay, and the judge allows the trial to proceed.

Red clay and other red mineral deposits are found all over the world. About 2.4 billion years ago rising atmospheric oxygen levels, the result of photosynthesis, caused the world to rust. Iron that was dissolved in ocean water reacted with oxygen to form insoluble iron oxides that gradually colored the sedimentary rocks of this period red.[45] Geologists refer to this time in Earth's history as the Great Oxygenation Event. Water chemistry changed; the atmosphere changed; the Earth changed; and life would soon change, too. The availability of oxygen provided the opportunity for new complex aerobic metabolic pathways to diverge from what had previously been simple anaerobic metabolisms.

Metabolism that makes use of oxygen is called *respiration* and is much more efficient in providing ATP to the cell than anaerobic pathways. Many of the same electron carriers and the same mechanism of ATP synthesis found in photosynthesis are used in respiration. The adaptiveness of life, even in its earliest stages, never ceases to amaze. A more efficient utilization of food molecules in newly aerobic environments would lead to diversification of microbial life forms. This diversification included the photosynthetic a*utotrophs,* which make their own food, and *heterotrophs,* which are adapted to consuming the food produced by the autotrophs and/or the autotrophs themselves.

45. Hazen, *The Story of Earth*, 154–80.

This was the beginning of ecological food chains. But this long-ago microbial diversification is nothing compared to what would soon follow when two microbes (or populations of microbes), one bacterial, the other archaean, by now far-distant relatives of LUCA, decided to join forces. After 1.5 billion years of simple cellular life, a change was in the wind. The eukaryotes were about to arrive.

Why Can't We Just Live Together?

The name eukaryote, literally "true nut," means that the cells have a distinct, membrane-bound nucleus that houses the DNA. The prokaryotes, or "before nut," archaea and bacteria, lack a distinct nucleus. All animals, plants, and fungi are composed of eukaryotic cells. Eukaryotic cells are, on average, one hundred times larger than prokaryotes and have a much more complex internal structure, with numerous membranous inclusions called *organelles*, literally "little organs," dispersed throughout the cell. These organelles are specialized to carry out specific metabolic functions of the cells. The eukaryotic cell can be compared to an industrial complex with each organelle having specific tasks. The *mitochondria* are the main source of energy production, like an electrical generator. The *endoplasmic reticulum* acts as a conveyer belt that receives the proteins assembled by machinery, the *ribosomes*, positioned along its length. The *Golgi complex* receives assembled proteins and packages them for shipping to other parts of the cell or to the outside. *Lysosomes* recycle waste and damaged cell components. The *cytoskeleton* provides scaffolding that supports the other organelles and anchors them in place. Plant cells, in addition to the above, have *chloroplasts*, which function as solar panels, collecting the light of the sun and converting it to chemical energy that can be used by the cell.

In the mid-1960s, Lynn Margulis (then Sagan), a young professor at Boston University, proposed that the various organelles of eukaryotic cells arose from gradual symbiotic associations between ancient prokaryotes.[46] *Symbiosis*, literally "living together," is the direct

46. Lynn Sagan, "On the Origin of Mitosing Cells," *Journal of Theoretical Biology* 14 (1967): 225–74.

physical contact and interdependence between two or more species. Symbiosis is widely known in the biological world. Common examples include the bacteria of the human digestive cavity, the nitrogen-fixing bacteria that live in root nodules of soybeans and peanuts, or Nemo the clownfish (in the Pixar/Disney film *Finding Nemo*), who lives within a protective circle of sea anemones while keeping his host free of invertebrate parasites and potential predators. Margulis observed that the size and structure of some eukaryotic organelles, especially the mitochondria and the chloroplast, resembled some free-living prokaryotes. From this, she proposed that these modern cell structures are derived from ancient prokaryotes that were taken up and assimilated in some way by larger host cells. She further predicted that these acquired organelles should be traceable through the inheritance of some "nonnuclear" genes. Initially, her ideas were rejected by many in the scientific community.[47] The conventional wisdom at the time was that DNA existed only in the nucleus and that the nucleus alone was the source of all inheritance.

Margulis was vindicated when gene-sequencing data became available in the 1970s and confirmed her *serial endosymbiosis theory* (SET). Both mitochondria and chloroplasts were found to have DNA that closely resembled the genes of exiting bacteria lineages.[48] Suddenly, Professor Margulis was hailed as a visionary scientist and role model for women scientists in what was, at the time, a male-dominated profession.

It appears now that the first eukaryote was the result of a symbiotic acquisition of anaerobic bacteria, which released H_2 as a waste product, by an anaerobic H_2–dependent archaean that released methane into the environment.[49] It is believed that the nuclear envelope and other internal membranous structures evolved from this first symbiotic cell.[50] Sometime later, a descendent of this cell acquired pho-

47. Lynn Margulis, *Symbiotic Planet: A New Look at Evolution* (Amherst, MA: Basic Books, 1998), 13–32.

48. R. Schwartz and M. Dayhoff, "Origins of Prokaryotes, Eukaryotes, Mitochondria, and Chloroplasts," *Science* 199 (1978): 395–403.

49. William Martin and Miklos Muller, "The Hydrogen Hypothesis for the First Eukaryote," *Nature* 392 (1998): 37–41.

50. Lane, *The Vital Question*, 208–10.

tosynthetic cyanobacteria through another endosymbiosis event, giving rise to the first chloroplasts. Fossil evidence for the earliest eukaryotes is disputed but ranges from 1.5 to 1.9 billion years ago.[51] The earliest eukaryotes were all single-celled organisms, but by 1.2 billion years ago, multicellular forms of eukaryotes appear in the fossil record.[52] These earliest multicellular forms would eventually give rise to fungi, plants, and animals in which different body cells specialize for specific life functions. And some of those cells were specialized for sex.

Sexual reproduction is, from an evolutionary standpoint, the distinguishing feature between prokaryotic and eukaryotic life.[53] In eukaryotes, the genes necessary for biological structure and activity are organized along sets of paired chromosomes. Humans have 23 pairs of chromosomes for a total of 46. We might think of this as a deck of 46 cards but with only 2 suits and numbered 1 to 23. One suit is from the mother, the other from the father. The chromosomes of the 23rd pair are the jokers, the sex chromosomes, designated X and Y. Different species have different numbers of chromosomes, from as few as 1 pair in ants to over 7,000 pairs in some protozoans. Cats have 19 pairs; dogs have 37 pairs. Our nearest genetic relative, the chimpanzee, has 24 pairs. During sexual reproduction, DNA is replicated, and the pairs of chromosomes are separated out in the formation of the sex cells or gametes; so in humans each egg or sperm has 23 chromosomes. In every person, half of those chromosomes came from the mother and half from the father. But in each generation, the cards of the deck are shuffled as the chromosomes are dealt out to the egg or sperm. So a single egg could receive any mix of chromosomal contributions from the paternal or maternal side of the individual. In addition, during the sorting of chromosomes, pieces of each pair can be exchanged during the process of *recombination*. So, there can also be a shuffling of pieces of the genetic deck of cards before the final

---

51. Benton, *The History of Life*, 41–42.

52. Nicholas Butterfield, "Bangiomorpha pubescens n. gen., n. sp.: Implications for the Evolution of Sex, Multicellularity, and the Mesoproterozoic/Neoproterozoic Radiation of Eukaryotes," *Paleobiology* 26 (2000): 386–404.

53. Benton, *The History of Life*, 43–50.

hand of 23 chromosomes is dealt to the egg or sperm. When an egg and sperm combine to form the *zygote*, or the first cell of the embryo, the chromosomal number of 46 (23 pairs) is restored.

In contrast to eukaryotes, bacteria generally have a single, unpaired circular chromosome. Bacteria primarily reproduce asexually; each cell divides into two cells, a process called *binary fission.* Prokaryotes can release or pick up bits of DNA from the environment so there is a level of sharing of DNA among prokaryotic cells, even cells from very different types of bacteria. But this sharing is chaotic and highly randomized. A prokaryotic cell might contain hundreds of copies of a gene for a single protein. It is thought that the evolution of sexual reproduction in an early eukaryotic ancestor brought stability to the genome while still maintaining a high degree of variability among members of a population.[54] The natural variability within a population is the raw material on which Darwinian natural selection operates to form new species over time. Sexual reproduction is what made the great diversity and complexity of life on Earth possible. It has allowed complex life forms to inhabit virtually every ecological niche on the planet. Sexual reproduction made life relational, and chemistry and biochemistry show us that those relationships extend beyond the living world.

Our Interconnected World

At the same time Margulis was proposing SET to explain the evolutionary origins of complex life, James Lovelock, an English scientist and inventor, was working with NASA (US National Aeronautics and Space Administration) to develop a means for determining whether or not there was life on Mars. Lovelock was interested in the atmospheric compositions of Earth and our neighboring planets.[55] Lovelock proposed that planetary atmospheres were the result of self-regulatory systems that maintained a chemical equilibrium through feedback mechanisms, as if the planet was, by analogy, a living

54. Lane, *The Vital Question*, 211–26.

55. James Lovelock, "Gaia as Seen through the Atmosphere," *Atmospheric Environment* 6 (1972): 579–80.

organism. He named his theory the *Gaia hypothesis*, after the Greek mother-goddess Gaia.[56] Working with Lynn Margulis, Lovelock extended his theory to include the entire biosphere.[57] Although many ecologists and environmentalists were open to Lovelock's main idea, most of the scientific community either thought his arguments were overstated or rejected them outright. Geologists viewed the Earth as operating on very long time scales that were immune to the perturbations of short-lived plants and animals. Evolutionary biologists saw biological diversity as the result of genetically driven responses to environmental conditions, not as something that could drive large-scale change itself.[58] Just as with Lynn Margulis's endosymbiotic theory, Lovelock faced the entrenched theoretical biases of his colleagues. In the fifty years since the Gaia hypothesis was originally proposed, Lovelock has remained a maverick in the scientific community. For years he has been an outspoken herald of global climate change and has embraced controversial positions such as favoring nuclear energy to reduce carbon emissions and advocating for a gradual withdrawal of populations from coastlines.[59]

The deep link between humans and their physical environment is embedded in our biological and cultural history. Advances in the Earth and biological sciences of the past fifty years have only emphasized how deep this link goes. Life emerged from the nonliving "stuff" of the Earth through reactions driven by simple energy sources. As life evolved and adapted to new resources, oxygen, a by-product of photosynthesis, changed the chemistry of the oceans and the atmosphere. New minerals, geological features, and even weather patterns emerged. Life itself multiplied and diversified and became more abundant, reshaping the ocean depths, shorelines, and eventually the land itself. Throughout almost four billion years of life's history, there existed a dynamic harmony between the Earth and the

56. James Lovelock, *Gaia: A New Look at Life on Earth* (Oxford: Oxford University Press, 1979).

57. James Lovelock and Lynn Margulis, "Atmospheric Homeostasis by and for the Biosphere: the Gaia Hypothesis," *Tellus* 26 (1974): 2–10.

58. Richard Dawkins, *The Extended Phenotype: The Long Reach of the Gene* (Oxford: Oxford University Press, 1982), 357–61.

59. Nicholas Kristoff, "Nukes Are Green," *New York Times*, April 9, 2005.

innumerable life forms that it supported. But now the activities of one species, *Homo sapiens,* is changing the surface of the Earth again and at an accelerating rate that threatens the existence of all the other species on which we depend.

Lynn Margulis, James Lovelock, and thousands more in the scientific community have clearly demonstrated the interconnectedness and interdependency of all life on Earth. From a theological perspective, Pope Francis argues that Christianity's central text, the Bible, articulates the sacredness, goodness, and mutual interdependence of nature.[60] Artistic depictions of life in the Garden of Eden show a harmonious existence between humankind and all living things:

> This is the basis of our conviction that, as part of the universe, called into being by one Father, all of us are linked by unseen bonds and together form a universal family, a sublime communion which fills us with a sacred, affectionate and humble respect.[61]

From this, according to Pope Francis, ought to come a religious imperative to care for nature. But through the centuries, any religious sense of stewardship for nature that we may have once had has been lost to the demands of a global consumer economy. We have misunderstood the true meaning of Genesis, and the world now suffers from our modern anthropocentric focus.

> An inadequate presentation of Christian anthropology gave rise to a wrong understanding between human beings and the world. Often, what was handed on was a Promethean vision of mastery over the world, which gave the impression that the protection of nature was something only the faint-hearted cared about. Instead, our "dominion" over the universe should be understood more properly in the sense of responsible stewardship.[62]

60. Pope Francis, *Laudato si' ("Praise Be to You")* (Vatican City: Libreria Editrice Vaticana, 2015), 65–88.

61. Ibid., 89.

62. Ibid., 116.

From Pope Francis's perspective, as well as the perspective of more than one hundred nations that signed the 2015 Paris Climate Agreement, it is time to end our selfish anthropocentric focus. Our species, and our species alone, is the source of the environmental disruptions that are sweeping the planet and threatening not only our lives, but *all* life. The chemical traces of these disruptions are found everywhere: in the toxic pollutants we find in the air and water, in the acidification of the oceans, in atmospheric carbon dioxide, and in the changing chemistries of forest soils.[63] Unfortunately, many still view our planet's many environmental problems as a political football. Candidate Donald Trump repeatedly referred to climate change as a "Chinese hoax" during his 2016 US presidential election campaign.[64] We should not need more scientific data to change people's minds. We have plenty of information about how and why this is happening. We need a change of heart. Otherwise we may, within a few generations, be looking for another place to call home.

Is There Anybody Out There?

Research into the origins of life on Earth is an integral part of a larger field of scientific investigation called *astrobiology*, which, in addition to studying the history of life on our planet, seeks to find evidence of life elsewhere in the universe.[65] Our knowledge of what life could be like somewhere else is constrained by our knowledge of life here on Earth; so astrobiologists assume that life on another planet would require the availability of liquid water, a stable environment, and carbon-based biological molecules, just as it apparently did here.[66] We know from spectroscopic measurements that water is abundant in the universe, and organic precursors of life have been found in meteors that have fallen to Earth from Mars or from other extraterrestrial sources. Of course, a stable planetary or other home for the development of life is required as well.

63. Ibid., 17–42.

64. John Schwartz, "Trump's Climate Views: Combative, Conflicting and Confusing," *New York Times*, March 10, 2017.

65. Catling, *Astrobiology*, 5.

66. Ibid., 9–12.

Astronomers had long assumed that planets existed that were orbiting stars other than our sun, but none were confirmed until 1992 when two planets were identified orbiting a dense star called a pulsar, located 2,300 light years from Earth.[67] The first planet of a sun-like star was found in 1995 by Didier Queloz and Michel Mayor of the University of Geneva, who noticed a rhythmic shifting of spectral lines in the star Pegasi 51, located 51 light years from Earth in the constellation Pegasus.[68] The shifting spectrum is the Doppler effect caused by a wobbling of the star from the gravitational influences of a nearby planet. In addition to using the Doppler effect, *exoplanets* (planets outside our solar system) can be detected by a variety of other astronomical techniques, such as a brief dimming as a planet moves across the face of a star viewed from Earth's perspective. The detection of exoplanets has accelerated with the emergence of newer observational technology such as the Kepler space telescope. As of July 2019, over four thousand exoplanets have been detected in over three thousand different star systems. The ever-increasing number of exoplanets are carefully catalogued in the online resource Extrasolar Planets Encyclopedia.[69] It is now estimated that as many as two-thirds of all sun-like, main-sequence stars are part of a star system with at least one planet. Exoplanets are not rare; they are actually a rather common feature of our galaxy. No doubt many more planets will be added to the official list when the Transiting Exoplanet Survey Satellite (TESS) begins to provide data.[70]

Most of the exoplanets detected so far have been called "hot Jupiters," massively sized planets orbiting close to their sun and consequently not good candidates for life as we understand it.[71] They are big and fairly easy to find with our current technology. Smaller,

---

67. Aleksander Wolszczan and Dale Frail, "A Planetary System around the Millisecond Pulsar PSR1257 + 12," *Nature* 355 (1992): 145–47.

68. Didier Queloz and Michel Mayor, "A Jupiter-mass Companion to a Solar-type Star," *Nature* 378 (1995): 355–59.

69. Jean Schneider, C. Dedieu, P. Le Sidaner, R. Savalle, and I. Zolotukhin, "Defining and Cataloging Exoplanets: The Exoplanet Database," *Astronomy and Astrophysics* 532 (2011): 79–90.

70. Jamie Shreeve, "Who's Out There?" *National Geographic* 235 (2019): 42–75.

71. Catling, *Astrobiology*, 110.

Earth-like rocky planets that have a chance of harboring life are more difficult. To be "Earth-like," a planet must have a rocky or oceanic surface that can provide a substrate for living organisms to live on or in, be large enough to provide sufficient gravitational pull to retain an atmosphere, and be a suitable distance from its sun so that water can exist on it in liquid form. The dependency of life on liquid water restricts the search for life to planets that are within the so-called *habitable zone* (HZ) of a star.[72] The width of the HZ varies from one star to the next, depending on the size and brightness of the star. In our solar system, Earth is on the inner edge of the HZ and Mars is at the outer edge. Mercury and Venus are too close to the sun's surface for liquid water to exist. While Mars is safely within the HZ of the sun and it has frozen water in its polar ice caps, it is very small compared to Earth, and it has only a very thin atmosphere. In short, for a planet to be Earth-like, conditions have to be "just right."

In 2014, the first Earth-like planet was found within the HZ of a cool dwarf star, 490 light years from Earth. This planet, designated as Kepler-186f, is the outermost of a five-planet star system. It is slightly larger than Earth and appears to meet all the conditions required to maintain liquid water on its surface.[73] A survey of the Kepler images of sun-like stars determined that ten of the 603 planets identified as of 2013 were approximately Earth-sized and likely within the HZ of their stars. This study predicted that as many as 22 percent of sun-like stars would have at least one Earth-like planet, and that the closest should be within twelve light years of Earth. This suggests that there could be over 10 billion Earth-like planets in the Milky Way galaxy alone! By 2019, forty-seven Earth-like planets had been identified, and the number is sure to grow as new detection systems are developed.[74] But how often does life emerge on an Earth-like planet?

Scientists have proposed looking to Mars or the icy moons of Jupiter as possible places life could have formed. From 2004 to 2011, three solar-powered, remotely controlled Mars Exploration Rover

72. Ibid., 115–18.

73. Elisa V. Quintana et al., "An Earth-Sized Planet in the Habitable Zone of a Cool Star," *Science* 344 (2014): 277–80.

74. Shreeve, "Who's Out There?" 42–75.

Vehicles were sent to study planetary features and mineralogy.[75] The data collected from these missions give conclusive evidence of a time in Mars's history when water flowed at least periodically across the surface, but as of now, they show no traces of organic life. Mineralogical studies suggest that this water may have pooled at times in craters or other low-lying terrain features, forming small pools and lakes—environments in which simple life could have formed. Some scientists believe that pockets of water trapped below the surface could still harbor microbial Martian life forms. Any traces of extraterrestrial life found on Mars or anywhere else in our solar system would surely be very simple, akin to the prokaryotes found on our planet. But what of more complex forms of life, perhaps even intelligent life? These are the kinds of extraterrestrial life that fuel the imaginations of science-fiction writers, summer movie audiences, and home-grown conspiracy theorists. What, if anything, can be said about higher life forms?

The Search for Extraterrestrial Intelligence (SETI) is an umbrella term for a wide variety of projects started in the 1950s to attempt to detect the technological signature of advanced civilizations elsewhere in the cosmos.[76] The opening scene of the popular 1997 film *Contact* was shot at the Very Large Array facility in New Mexico, part of a network of observatories supported by the National Science Foundation. The author of the book on which the film was based is Carl Sagan, who was an astronomer at Cornell University and host of the popular public television science series *Cosmos*. Sagan was one of the leading advocates of SETI efforts of the 1980s and 1990s. Before he achieved widespread fame, Sagan had been the first husband of Lynn Margulis. At Cornell, Carl Sagan worked with Frank Drake, often regarded as the founder of SETI research, in the design of visual and recorded messages that were included on the Pioneer and Voyager exploration satellites that were sent beyond the solar system. Sagan and Drake also sent radio messages, aimed toward extraterrestrials, into space using Cornell's large Arecibo radio telescope located in Puerto Rico. So far, none of the messages SETI par-

75. Catling, *Astrobiology*, 88–99.
76. Ibid., 120–24.

ticipants have sent into space have been answered. As astrophysicist Paul Davies says, there has been an "eerie silence," suggesting that we are indeed alone in the universe.[77]

In 1961, Carl Sagan's future Cornell colleague Frank Drake proposed the now famous "Drake equation" to estimate the number of advanced civilizations in the galaxy:

$$N = R^* \times f_p \times n_e \times f_l \times f_i \times f_c \times L$$

where

R^* = the formation rate of sun-like stars,
f_p = fraction of stars with planets,
n_e = average number of Earth-like planets in each solar system,
f_l = fraction of Earth-like planets where life emerges,
f_i = fraction of living planets where intelligent life evolves,
f_c = fraction of intelligent planets developing communication technology,
L = average lifetime of an advanced civilization.[78]

The Drake equation has helped to shape SETI efforts over the past fifty years, but it is very difficult to solve to anyone's satisfaction. Part of the problem is that for many of these parameters, all we have is a sample size of one (our Earth), although astronomical surveys are starting to provide estimates at least for the numbers of stars and planets. Given that life emerged very early in Earth's history, the fraction of Earth-like planets with simple life might be high, perhaps even close to one. Some biologists think that the endosymbiosis between a single bacterium and a single archean that started eukaryotes is exceedingly rare, perhaps an isolated freak event.[79] Intelligent life is another matter altogether. This would place the fraction of intelligent-living planets very close to zero. On the other hand, others have argued that once life emerged on Earth, the evolution of

77. Paul Davies, *The Eerie Silence: Renewing Our Search for Alien Intelligence* (New York: Houghton Mifflin Harcourt, 2010).

78. Ibid., 77.

79. Lane, *The Vital Question*, 10–11.

human-like intelligence was inevitable.[80] If intelligence is inevitable, is communication technology inevitable also? Western civilization has a history of approximately six thousand years. But how long have we had a technologically advanced civilization? Perhaps just one hundred years. And how long will this civilization survive? Who can say?

Drake equation solutions give wildly divergent answers. Astrobiologist David Catling of the University of Washington has calculated that there are perhaps four intelligent civilizations in our Milky Way galaxy.[81] In a recent article examining the Drake equation in the journal *Astrobiology*, the authors found that it is "very, very unlikely" that Earth has the *only* advanced civilization to ever emerge in the universe.[82] This suggests there could be, or could have been, thousands or even millions of advanced civilizations during the 13.8 billion-year history of the universe. So perhaps we live in a *Star Trek* type of universe after all. Only time will tell.

The verification of life on other planets, whether it turns out to be intelligent life or not, would have profound sociological, religious, and theological implications for humans on Earth. First, it would greatly diminish our anthropocentric focus and the exceptionalism of many of our religious beliefs. If life exists elsewhere, then Earth is not the center of the universe as people have historically thought. Theologians and ethicists would struggle with what our relationship to other worlds and other possible civilizations should be. Second, it would force us to expand our ideas about our relationship to nature and to other peoples. How should we interact with other worlds? Do religions exist on other worlds, and, if so, what are they like? Would the religious traditions of other worlds have a Moses, a Muhammad, or a Christ-like figure and comparable beliefs? If so, would this bring harmony to the universe or chaos? Finally, how will we look at our

80. Simon Conway Morris, *Life's Solution: Inevitable Humans in a Lonely Universe* (New York: Cambridge University Press, 2003).

81. Catling, *Astrobiology*, 121.

82. Adam Frank and Woodruff Sullivan, "A New Empirical Constraint on the Prevalence of Technological Species in the Universe," *Astrobiology* 16 (2016): 359–62.

home world? Will we consider Earth to be a place we can leave for greener pastures elsewhere, or will we instead look at Earth as a lush oasis to cherish all the more?

And what if Earth turns out to be the *only* planet on which complex intelligent life is ever found? How much more precious would that make our green-and-blue living world in the vast expanses of the cosmos? Perhaps Earth-life, and only Earth-life, *is* the point of creation after all. Would this realization prompt us to take better care of our living planet, as Pope Francis urges us to? We can only guess, for now.

6

Evolution

> Then God said: Let the water teem with an abundance of living creatures, and on the earth let the birds fly beneath the dome of the sky. God created the great sea monsters and all kinds of crawling living creatures with which the water teems, and all kinds of winged birds. God saw that it was good, and God blessed them saying: Be fertile, multiply and fill the water of the seas; and let the birds multiply on the earth. Evening came, and morning followed—the fifth day. (Gen 1:20–23)

Life began in the seas. For billions of years life was very simple. Prokaryotes, that is, the archaea and bacteria, eventually filled the seas but would have been invisible to human observers, save for accumulations in stromatolite formations or as a gooey slime along shallow seashores. Eukaryotic life, resulting from an ancient fusion of archaea and bacteria cells, brought sex into the world and with it a hereditary process that environmental conditions could influence through natural selection. The other great evolutionary change brought about by the eukaryotes was multicellularity. Prokaryotic cells such as bacteria and archaea exist as single tiny cells, far too small to be seen without a microscope. But eukaryotes can occur as single-celled microscopic protozoans such as the *Paramecium* or *Amoeba,* simple clusters of cells like the *Volvox*, a colonial algae just visible to the naked eye, and complex multicellular plants and animals ranging in size from a tiny flea to the great blue whale or the mighty redwood trees. The great diversity of life we know on Earth today is due to the evolutionary explosion of multicellular life forms that came sometime after the emergence of the first eukaryotes.

Multicellular existence offers many advantages over single-celled life, including greater efficiency in movement, feeding, and reproduction. This is because each cell in a multicellular organism can become specialized and adapted to provide one important life function to the whole organism, whereas a single-celled organism is constrained to handle all life activities on its own. In geological terms, the appearance of complex multicellular life forms on Earth was long thought to have taken place at the beginning of the Cambrian period, the first time segment of the Paleozoic era, which began 542 million years ago. *Paleozoic* means "ancient animals," and fossil beds from this era are characterized by diverse assemblages of animals that are no longer alive today. Trilobites, thought to be ancient relatives of modern-day crustaceans and insects, are the most commonly known fossils of this period and have been well represented in museum collections for several centuries. Over the geologically short time period of approximately 50 million years, almost all the major taxonomic animal phyla living today, including our own, *Chordata,* abruptly appear in rock strata of this age. This sudden evidence of life bursting forth across the Earth is often called the "Cambrian explosion."[1]

But from what we can tell from the fossils, the life in the Cambrian period, almost entirely in the oceans, was very different from life on Earth today. The study of how life transformed from these ancient ancestors to the modern day, and how it will continue to transform into the future for as long as life exists on Earth, is the science of evolutionary biology. And any discussion of evolutionary biology begins with the work of Charles Darwin.

Charles Darwin

Charles Darwin was born in Shrewsbury, England, on February 12, 1809.[2] His father, Robert, was a wealthy physician, as had been his grandfather Erasmus Darwin. Erasmus was a well-known public figure in his day as a philosopher, poet, and abolitionist. His many published

1. Michael J. Benton, *The History of Life: A Very Short Introduction* (Oxford: Oxford University Press, 2008), 56–61.

2. Janet Browne, *Charles Darwin: Voyaging* (Princeton, NJ: Princeton University Press, 1995), 6.

writings include references to the relatedness of all living things. During his childhood, Charles was an avid collector of coins and natural objects such as rock, seashells, and insects. But, it was decided that Charles should follow in the footsteps of his father and grandfather, and he was enrolled in medical school at the University of Edinburgh at the age of sixteen. Darwin disliked medical school intensely and found surgery especially distressing. He preferred to spend his time at Edinburgh riding horses, hunting birds, and exploring the Scottish countryside where he could continue his collections.[3]

Displeased over his son's neglect of his medical studies, Robert arranged for Charles to transfer to Christ's College, Cambridge, to pursue a bachelor of arts degree. Robert's hope was that this would be the first step for Charles to eventually become a quiet country parson.[4] In this way, Charles would be able to pursue his studies of nature while still earning a respectable living. At Christ's College, Darwin was an average student who still preferred his outdoor collecting adventures to sitting in lectures, but he did become a close acquaintance of his botany professor, John Stevens Henslow.[5] Darwin assisted in the collection and cataloging of plants for Henslow's herbarium project, and during this time was introduced to the writings of other prominent naturalists such as William Paley and John Herschel.[6] These *natural theologians*, as they are sometimes called, saw the designs they observed in nature as evidence of God's divine work. Although Darwin's later work would refute "the argument from design," at the time, these writers made a strong impression on Charles; and by the time he graduated in 1831, he was convinced that he wanted to devote his life to the study of nature.

The HMS Beagle

That opportunity arose later that year when Charles received a letter from Henslow proposing that he should serve as a collector and naturalist on the British surveying ship HMS *Beagle*, which was soon

3. Ibid., 63–64.
4. Ibid., 90–96.
5. Ibid., 116–27
6. Ibid., 128–29.

to embark on an expedition to chart the coastline of South America.[7] Charles overcame his father's initial objections to the expedition after his uncle, Josiah Wedgwood, agreed to fund Charles's participation in the voyage. The *Beagle* embarked from Plymouth harbor on December 27, 1831, on what was to become a five-year voyage around the globe. Darwin's role as a member of the crew was to serve as a gentleman companion to esteemed captain Robert FitzRoy and as a collector of geological and biological specimens from the locations surveyed during the expedition. Soon after departure, Darwin became seasick, a problem that bothered him throughout the voyage, so he spent as much time as possible on land pursuing his collections and touring the countryside of the many locations the ship visited.[8]

Almost three years of the voyage were spent along the South American coast while the *Beagle*'s surveying crew mapped the British colonial regions of the continent. While on board ship, Darwin spent his idle time reading books from Captain FitzRoy's shipboard library and his own copy of *Principles of Geology* by the Scottish geologist Charles Lyell, which FitzRoy had given him as a gift.[9] Lyell provided an updated formulation of James Hutton's *principle of uniformitarianism*, which states that existent landforms are the net result of accumulated small changes that occur over vast periods of time.[10] Lyell sought to explain the gradual development of observed geological features through the operation of natural processes that are constant over time and still ongoing. Lyell's ideas were in stark contrast to the popular notion that present-day landforms were the result of isolated ancient catastrophes such as Noah's flood, and that they were largely unchanged since biblical times. As Darwin traveled the coastline of South America, he saw evidence for uniformitarianism repeatedly and kept copious notes on the local geologies

7. Ibid., 145.

8. Ibid., 167–86.

9. Ibid., 186–90.

10. Keith Thompson, *Before Darwin: Reconciling God and Nature* (New Haven, CT: Yale University Press, 2005), 186.

that supported Lyell's arguments.[11] Darwin would later apply Lyell's concept of gradual change over time to biology.

In September 1835, the *Beagle* completed its detailed surveying work on the South American mainland and sailed west into the Pacific Ocean, stopping for a month on the Galapagos Islands, which, at the time, were uninhabited except for a small colony on one of the islands. The Galapagos Archipelago, located on the equator, is home to a unique assortment of flora and fauna, including large black marine iguanas and the giant Galapagos tortoises. While the *Beagle* charted these geologically young, volcanic islands, Darwin spent most of his time ashore collecting biological specimens that would later prove critical to the development of his theory. When Darwin visited Charles Island, the acting governor, Nicholas Lawson, told him that the shape of the tortoise shells varied distinctly from island to island and that he could "with certainty tell from which island any one was brought."[12] Soon afterward, Darwin noticed that a mockingbird he observed on Charles Island varied considerably from the one he had seen earlier on nearby Chatham Island.[13]

Indeed, as Darwin traveled from one island to the next, he found that each contained its own unique assemblage of inhabitants, with some species occurring on several islands but not others and many species occurring on only a single island.[14] He thus set out to collect, catalogue, and preserve as many of the species as possible from each of the islands that he visited so that he could make detailed comparisons at a later date. As Darwin proceeded with his collection, he was struck by how similar habitats on neighboring islands would frequently be occupied by seemingly related though quite different species or varieties of plants and animals.[15] Further, while most of these species appeared to be unique to the Galapagos, they did bear

---

11. Charles Darwin, *The Voyage of H.M.S. Beagle* (London: Folio Society, 2003), 46. Originally published in 1839 as *Journal of Researches into the Natural History and Geology of the Countries Visited during the Voyage of H.M.S Beagle Round the World under Captain Fitz Roy, R.N.* (London: J. M. Dent).

12. Darwin, *The Voyage of H.M.S. Beagle*, 393.

13. Ibid., 397–99.

14. Ibid., 393–97.

15. Browne, *Charles Darwin: Voyaging*, 299–305.

strong resemblances to species he had observed and collected previously along the coast of South America.

At the time of the *Beagle*'s voyage, the broad concept of evolution was not new in scientific circles, having been a topic of vigorous debate for several decades. The biological classification system that groups species of plants and animals according to shared characteristics was first introduced in 1735 by Carolus Linnaeus and is still used today. Linnaeus believed that each individual species was created perfectly by God as a part of the divine order of the universe.[16] Therefore, by studying and classifying the natural world, God's plan for creation could be discerned. Even though a new species might arise occasionally through hybridization, this view held that each species was "immutable" and unchanging over time. The alternative view, referred to as the *transmutation of species*, suggested that animals did change over time, progressing from some rudimentary original form along a steady gradient toward increasing complexity. Charles Darwin's grandfather, Erasmus, was one of the original proponents of the transmutation idea, but it was articulated most thoroughly in *Philosophie Zoologique*, published in 1809 by the French naturalist Jean Baptiste Lamarck.[17] According to Lamarck, all species arose in very simple form through the process of "spontaneous generation" and developed over time by gradually adapting to their environment and through an inherent drive toward increasing complexity. In Lamarckian evolution, organisms acquired and/or lost their own unique characteristics through the use or disuse of their biological structures as they tried to better adapt to environmental conditions. Each generation would then pass these acquired traits on to the next generation, where the developmental process would continue.[18]

For many years, archeologists had been collecting the fossilized remains of animal species for which no known living examples existed. According to Lamarckism, these observations could be explained by the transformation of the earlier form of a species into

16. Thompson, *Before Darwin*, 73.
17. Ibid., 210–17.
18. Ibid., 213–15.

a more modern form. Another Frenchman, Georges Cuvier, disagreed with Lamarck, arguing that the fossil record could be better explained by the occurrence of periodic extinctions.[19] According to Cuvier, species remained *immutable,* or unchanging, over time unless a natural catastrophe or other misfortune brought about their demise. Charles Lyell agreed with Cuvier on the immutability of species but suggested that rather than a periodic catastrophe, it was gradual, geological, physical change to a habitat that brought about extinction. Lyell argued that the many different habitats found around the world each housed the initial "created pair" of those species that occupied it.[20] Lyell thought humans especially were specific acts of God's creation. He was deeply critical of the evolutionary ideas of Lamarck or other formulations of the transmutation of species that preceded Darwin.[21]

The same cannot be said, however, for Darwin, who saw Lyell's methodology of geological explanation as extending naturally to biological evolution. Darwin was struck by the gradually changing morphologies he saw in birds and other animal species during his voyage. What's more, closely allied species seemed to replace one another as one traveled from place to place across the South American continent. To Darwin this meant that Lyell's principles of uniformitarianism might equally be applied to the biological world:

> After my return to England it appeared to me that by following the example of Lyell in geology, and by collecting all facts which bore in any way on the variation of animals and plants under domestication and nature, some light might be shed on the whole subject.[22]

---

19. Michael Ruse, The Evolution–Creation Struggle (Cambridge, MA: Harvard University Press, 2005), 36–40.

20. Alfredo Bueno-Hernandez and Jorge E. Lloorente-Bousquets, "The Other Face of Lyell: Historical Biogeography in His *Principles of Geology*," *Journal of Biogeography* 33 (2006): 549–59.

21. Stephen J. Gould, *The Structure of Evolutionary Theory* (Cambridge, MA: Harvard University Press, 2002), 195–96.

22. Charles Darwin, *Autobiography of Charles Darwin*, ed. Nora Barlow (London: Collins, 1958), 98.

By the time Darwin returned to England in October of 1836, he had become convinced that biological evolution was a better explanation for the great diversity of plants and animals on Earth than repeated acts of creation. Consistent with his Christian heritage, however, he still believed that "the one hand has surely worked throughout the universe."[23] In this way, the creator's influence on the world was more indirect, working through the natural processes that Darwin was trying to understand.

Natural Selection and Population

Darwin's next insight came from the world he knew best of all, rural England. The success of English farmers in producing the agricultural crops and livestock that supported the growing population of Great Britain was common knowledge. Darwin had an uncle who was a sheep breeder, and Darwin himself set up a domestic pigeon colony at his home in Downe, where he settled after marrying his cousin, Emma Wedgwood.[24] Through his conversations with various farmers and his own experimentation, Darwin learned how new varieties of plants or animals could be produced by deliberately selecting individuals that possessed the characteristic that one wanted to enhance to be the parents of the next generation. Frequently, the offspring of these deliberate crossings would inherit the desired traits from their parents. After several generations of such selective breeding, a new "Domestic Race" might result.[25] The idea that a new inheritable variation or trait could arise randomly within a population and then be *selectively* amplified over subsequent generations would figure prominently in Darwin's later master work. If variation of traits could emerge and spread within domestic plant and animal populations, why would the same thing not happen in wild populations, which, after all, were the predecessors of the domestic breeds? Darwin's

---

23. Richard Darwin Keynes, ed., *Charles Darwin's Beagle Diary* (Cambridge: Cambridge University Press, 2001), 402.

24. Browne, *Charles Darwin: Voyaging*, 521–26.

25. Charles Darwin, *On the Origin of Species by Means of Natural Selection* (London: Folio Society, 2006), 9–10. First edition originally published in 1859 by John Murray, London.

intuitive leap was to transfer the *agency* of population change from humans, in the case of domestic species, to the natural habitats in which the wild plant and animal species lived.

In 1838, Darwin read *An Essay on the Principle of Population*, which had been published forty years prior by the clergyman and economist Robert Malthus.[26] Malthus and other political economists of his time were concerned about why poverty persisted in English society despite the fact that other parts of the population were enjoying the fruits of the English industrial revolution.[27] Malthus had examined English church records of births and deaths over time and applied a mathematical analysis to these data. According to his analysis, human (or animal) populations follow a geometrical pattern of expansion, approximately doubling every generation (i.e., 2, 4, 8, 16, 32 . . .). On the other hand, food and other resources necessary to support the growing population only increased arithmetically at best (i.e., 1, 2, 3, 4, 5 . . .). Consequently, existence inevitably became a struggle in which population growth would be checked by a host of societal ills including disease, famine, war, unjust working conditions, and extreme poverty. In economic circles, extreme examples of exploding population growth became known as Malthusian catastrophes. Malthus suggested that a number of *positive* checks on population growth such as delaying marriage or the rationing of food supplies might help alleviate human suffering to some extent, but his main conclusion was that the "superior power of population" could not be overcome completely and that struggle was inevitable.[28]

Malthus's "struggle for existence" quickly became a central theme in Darwin's thinking about how new species could arise. Darwin's great contribution to the history of science, and to humankind for that matter, was that *natural selection*, not providence, or fate, or divine intervention, was the positive force that mediated this struggle. Individuals that possessed certain favorable characteristics, better adapted to a given habitat than other individuals, would, over

26. Browne, *Charles Darwin: Voyaging*, 385.

27. Garland Allen and Jeffrey Baker, *Biology: Scientific Process and Social Issues* (Hoboken, NJ: John Wiley and Sons, 2001), 152–54.

28. Browne, *Charles Darwin: Voyaging*, 388–90.

time, reproduce more successfully than their competitors, thus giving rise to new species. Darwin discovered natural selection at least as early as 1842, when he first sketched out his ideas on paper.[29] Many reasons have been offered as to why Darwin waited seventeen years to publish such an important discovery.[30] Whatever the actual reason or reasons were, we do know that what ultimately prompted Darwin to publish his new theory was a letter he received from fellow naturalist Alfred Russell Wallace in 1858.[31]

Wallace had, from his own scientific studies in Malaysia and Indonesia, conceived of a theory on how the process of evolution occurred that was virtually identical to Darwin's. Darwin shared this news with his friends, Charles Lyell and the botanist Joseph Hooker, who convinced him to quickly assemble his own paper on the subject.[32] It was agreed that Lyell and Hooker would then present both Wallace's and Darwin's papers simultaneously to the Linnaean Society, which they did on July 1, just three days after the death of Charles and Emma's youngest son from scarlet fever. Despite the loss of his son, Charles worked diligently over the next year in preparing his much more extensive masterwork for publication in book form. The first edition of *On the Origin of Species by Means of Natural Selection* was published in November 1859 and sold out immediately.[33] In all, six editions were published during Darwin's lifetime, and the book has never been out of print since its first year of publication. *On the Origin of Species* has been translated into every language spoken on Earth, and I have heard it said that, after the Christian Bible, Darwin's book is the mostly widely read written work in human history.

On the Origin of Species

The subtitle to *On the Origin of Species* reveals the influence that the British agricultural practices of selective breeding and Malthusian

---

29. Ruse, *The Evolution-Creation Struggle*, 71.

30. Michael Ruse, *Darwin and Design* (Cambridge, MA: Harvard University Press, 2003), 99.

31. Janet Browne, *Charles Darwin: The Power of Place* (Princeton, NJ: Princeton University Press, 2002), 14–33.

32. Ibid., 33–42.

33. Ibid., 88.

population theory had on Darwin's thinking. That subtitle, *Or the Preservation of Favored Races in the Struggle for Life*, anticipates the main argument that Darwin lays out in the first four chapters of the book. Darwin's entire thesis relies on two very simple and irrefutable observations:

1. There is natural variation among individuals in any population of organisms, plants or animals, and many of these variations are heritable.[34]
2. In every population, more offspring are produced than ultimately survive; consequently, there is an inherent struggle for existence.[35]

For his readers, Darwin reviews many examples of heritable variation in both domestic and wild populations of organisms, focusing particularly on domestic pigeons, which have a high degree of variability in a wide variety of traits.[36] Many of those reading Darwin's manuscript would fully appreciate these facts due to the widespread popularity of breeding pigeons in Darwin's day.

Darwin's claim of geometric growth occurring in natural populations had already been established, in principle, by Malthus—all Darwin did was extend those arguments from human to natural, wild populations. There were many examples from the British colonialization experience, as Darwin pointed out, where an introduced species of plant or animal would reproduce so rapidly that an island or other invaded habitat could be quite literally overrun by the new species in a very short time.[37] Using theoretical calculations, Darwin showed that even very slow-breeding species such as the elephant would similarly increase in an uncontrolled manner unless there was some type of "check" imposed on the population by external factors.[38] Those external checks on the population precipitated the struggle for existence among individuals of the same species and between individuals of closely related species who shared the same

34. Darwin, *On the Origin of Species*, 2–45.
35. Ibid., 46–61.
36. Ibid., 13–21.
37. Ibid., 309–32.
38. Ibid., 49.

habitat. The natural variations present in the population would leave some individuals better equipped for the resultant competition than others. Darwin would use the term "natural selection" to explain the outcome of this struggle:

> If such (useful variations) do occur, can we doubt that individuals having any advantage, however slight, over others, would have the best chance of surviving and procreating their kind? On the other hand, we may feel sure that any variation in the least degree injurious would be rigidly destroyed. This preservation of favorable variations and the rejection of injurious variations, I call Natural Selection.[39]

Darwin chose the term natural selection specifically to make an analogy of what he was proposing with humankind's selection of desirable traits in domestic species. But according to Darwin it was the nonliving "conditions of life" such as temperature, rainfall, food, or wind, that would do the selecting of which "organic beings" survived and which ones did not.[40] These selective pressures acting on the individual organisms making up a population would cause the population to gradually change over time. We can now see Lyell's principles of uniformitarianism extending also to the living world. In his chapter titled "Natural Selection," Darwin offered his now-famous branching tree diagram to explain how these uniform processes operating over many generations could lead to the formation of many different species from a single founding population.[41]

In a little over one hundred pages, Darwin had, perhaps unknowingly, completely revolutionized the scientific field of biology. I think it is safe to say that *On the Origin of Species* is really what formed biology as a scientific discipline, giving it a theoretical framework, like what Newton had done for physics, from which future scientific explorations could emerge. The remainder of Darwin's great book provides the first glimpses of the vast body of data he had accumulated through his travels, private studies, and communications

39. Ibid., 62–63.
40. Ibid., 67.
41. Ibid., 93–94.

with fellow naturalists. These provide Darwin's evidence supporting natural selection as a causal process in the speciation of plants and animals. He also takes the time to effectively counter what he anticipated would be some of the major criticisms of his theory, such as the relative absence of transitional species in the fossil record or the occurrence of peculiar species in very harsh or extreme environments.[42] Though attacks on Darwin's theory have continued until this day, few can deny the persuasiveness of his reasoned, well-articulated case.

Darwin gave us a new way of viewing life on Earth. In the conclusion to *On the Origin of Species,* Darwin states:

> There is grandeur in this view of life, with its several powers, having been breathed into a few forms or into one; and that whilst this planet has gone cycling on according to the fixed law of gravity, from so simple a beginning endless forms most beautiful and most wonderful have been, and are being evolved.[43]

The study of the living world would never be the same. Evolutionary biologist Theodosius Dobzhansky perhaps said it best a hundred years later: "Nothing in biology makes sense except in the light of evolution."[44]

Collateral Damage

In June of 1860, less than one year after the publication of *On the Origin of Species*, a famous debate took place at the Oxford University Museum that presaged much of the acrimony that would erupt between science and religion over the next 150 years. On the side of religion was the popular bishop of Oxford, Samuel Wilberforce, who objected to Darwin's theory. Opposing him was the British morphologist Thomas Henry Huxley, an outspoken defender of evolution and self-proclaimed "Darwin's bulldog." In the popular version

---

42. Ibid., 136–64.

43. Ibid., 388.

44. Theodosius Dobzhansky, "Nothing in Biology Makes Sense Except in the Light of Evolution," *American Biology Teacher* 35 (1973): 125–29.

of this debate, Wilberforce is said to have asked Huxley whether he was related to a monkey on his grandmother's or grandfather's side, to which Huxley replied:

> A man has no reason to be ashamed of having an ape for a grandfather. If there were an ancestor whom I should feel shame in recalling, it would rather be a *man* [i.e., Wilberforce], a man of restless and versatile intellect, who not content with success in his own sphere of activity, plunges into scientific questions with which he has no real acquaintance, only to obscure them by an aimless rhetoric.[45]

Darwin himself was absent from the Oxford debate, suffering as he was with poor health, and personally preferring his quiet country life to large argumentative professional/social gatherings. Whatever was in fact said during the debate cannot be known for sure, but both sides claimed victory, cementing in the public mind the commonly held idea that religion, Christianity especially, and the science of Darwin were in permanent conflict with each other.[46]

Darwin struggled personally with the implications his theory held for the orthodox brand of Christianity prevalent in Victorian England of his time. He discussed his religious views at some length in his autobiography published many years after his death.[47] Although Darwin expresses admiration for the New Testament, he admits that the punishing God of the Old Testament sowed doubts for him throughout his life. But it was the suffering in the world, that is, the struggle for existence, which is the main theme of Darwin's work, that led him, by the end of his life, to declare himself agnostic. Darwin saw natural selection, not a beneficent God, as the primary driving force behind nature, and admitted that he "did not think much about the existence of a personal God until a considerably later period of my life."[48] I find similar sentiment among many of my scientist friends who consider themselves agnostic or atheist. For many

45. Thompson, *Before Darwin*, 274.
46. Ruse, *The Evolution–Creation Struggle*, 95–96.
47. Darwin, *Autobiography of Charles Darwin*, 71–80.
48. Ibid., 72.

people, it seems, a Darwinian understanding of the natural world is all that is needed. Other aspects of religious belief beyond biological origins just don't seem relevant to their lives.

Although Darwin never declared himself to be an atheist, many biologists and others since Darwin's time have been eager to claim that title, hailing Darwin's work as their primary motivation. As evolutionary biologist Richard Dawkins famously declared, "Darwin made it possible to be an intellectually fulfilled atheist."[49] Philosopher Daniel Dennett compares "Darwin's dangerous idea" to a universal acid:

> It eats through just about every traditional concept and leaves in its wake a revolutionized worldview, with most of the old landmarks still recognizable, but transformed in fundamental ways.[50]

Among those ideas or concepts that have been forever changed by Darwin, according to Dennett, is all religion and any thoughts of a creator God. Others in the scientific community have followed the lead of these new atheist authors. And I must say that if the only religious alternatives available were the providentialism of Victorian England or the biblical literalism of modern-day creationists, I would have to agree with Dawkins and Dennett. But these are by no means the only religious alternatives—not even close.

A quick look at the world's religions would show that for the most part they are not antagonistic to science. If anything, most religions are generally supportive of science and have historically sought to harmonize religious teachings with new understandings of the natural world gained through science.[51] Darwinian evolution has certainly been more challenging to integrate with religious views than fields like chemistry or physics, but to suggest that integration cannot be done is overly simplistic. In traditional Catholic theology,

---

49. Richard Dawkins, *The Blind Watchmaker* (New York: W. W. Norton, 1986), 6.

50. Daniel C. Dennett, *Darwin's Dangerous Idea: Evolution and the Meanings of Life* (New York: Simon & Schuster, 1995), 63.

51. John Hedley Brooke and Ronald L. Numbers, eds., *Science and Religion around the World* (Oxford: Oxford University Press, 2011).

resistance to Darwin had more to do with the place of humankind in creation than with the details of the evolutionary process. Even in Darwin's time there were many Catholic scholars who were supportive of evolutionary theory and considered that God could have aided the process in some way.[52] In more modern times, the Vatican has repeatedly warned against materialist metaphysical conclusions that might be drawn from Darwinism but is broadly supportive of the science of evolution.[53]

In recent Catholic theologies still emerging through the work of John Haught, Ilia Delio, Elizabeth Johnson, and others, Darwinian evolution plays a foundational role. The same can be said for much Protestant Christian thought, as in the works of Robert John Russell, Alister McGrath, and John Polkinghorne. Judaism has historically been relatively untroubled by Darwinian thought, with some exceptions.[54] Rabbi Jonathan Sacks objects to atheistic conclusions of meaninglessness stemming from some forms of Darwinism, but finds evolutionary science and the Jewish faith mutually supportive in the areas of ethical thought, biodiversity, and the interconnectedness of the natural world.[55] Finally, for the Dalai Lama, the leader of Tibetan Buddhism, there is no conflict with evolutionary theory at all, which he believes fits entirely within the first of the Four Noble Truths of the Buddha.[56]

From this quick survey it seems that for many religious believers, at a personal level, Darwinian evolution does not present any special problems for their belief in God; in some cases, it even enhances religious understanding. But there is no doubt that there is still a strong public perception that Darwinism is antagonistic to religious faith. Many parishioners in the Catholic parishes I have visited come into workshops thinking that there is an ongoing battle

52. Peter M. J. Hess and Paul L. Allen, *Catholicism and Science* (Westport, CT: Greenwood Press, 2008), 73–86.

53. Ibid., 117–23.

54. Jonathan Sacks, *The Great Partnership: Science, Religion, and the Search for Meaning* (New York: Schocken Books, 2011).

55. Ibid., 209–32.

56. His Holiness the Dalai Lama, *The Universe in a Single Atom: The Convergence of Science and Spirituality* (New York: Morgan Road Books, 2005), 105.

between science and religion over Darwin. However, this does not have to do with the science of biological evolution. I think it is safe to say that the longstanding creation-vs.-evolution struggle that started in an Oxford lecture hall long ago would not have persisted to this day were it not for a series of social movements that grew out of Darwin's scientific ideas.

Darwinism Gone Wrong

Darwin's theory of evolution by natural selection provided a scientific explanation for the great biological diversity that is observed in the natural world. By articulating this new idea to the scientific community, Darwin had revolutionized the field of biology. But Darwin's ideas did not remain confined to the disciplines of biological science for which they were developed. As so often happens in human history, revolutionary ideas developed in one area of human society can quickly spread to other realms of human culture and experience.

Herbert Spencer (1820–1903) was an English sociologist and philosopher who wrote on many topics during the mid- to late 1800s, including biology, psychology, economics, and ethics. It was Spencer who first described Darwin's theory as "survival of the fittest," a phrase with which Darwinian theory has been inexorably linked ever since.[57] Spencer used this characterization of Darwin's theory in his own book, *Principles of Biology*, a very influential work of the late-nineteenth century.[58] Spencer believed that human societies evolved from simple to complex cultural forms in a manner similar to the evolution of complex biological organisms. Spencer argued that for society to progress, we needed to learn from nature and allow competition to reign freely. In this way the strong parts of society would flourish while the weak would gradually fall by the wayside. By the 1870s, the application of principles of Darwinian evolution to human socioeconomic theory had become a political ideology that was known as *social Darwinism*.[59] Spencer's form of social Darwin-

---

57. Ruse, *Darwin and Design*, 20.

58. Ruse, *The Evolution–Creation Struggle*, 103–11.

59. Joseph Fisher, "The History of Land Holdings in Ireland," *Transactions of the Royal Historical Society* 5 (1877): 228–326.

ism had harsh consequences for the poor, sick, and marginalized members of society.

While Spencer argued against *any* role for government in socioeconomic policy, others inferred from Darwin's work that the state could become a selective agent in directing the advancement of society. Charles Darwin's younger half-cousin, Francis Galton, combined Spencer's progressive sociology with Darwin's ideas on biological variability and natural selection.[60] Through numerous statistical studies of human biological traits and abilities, Galton founded a new field of sociology, which he called *eugenics*.[61] Galton attempted to define positive human abilities or traits that could be identified in families or individuals. It was Francis Galton who first used the phrase "nature versus nurture," another concept often erroneously attributed to Darwin.[62] In Galton's view it was heredity (or nature) that won out over upbringing, such that the social position of the British upper class was the result of their superior genetic make-up. Galton wished to apply his thesis to the overall betterment of English society by encouraging or even mandating the marriage of "promising couples." Out of Galton's work, the Eugenics Education Society was formed in England in the early 1900s, with similar politically active organizations forming throughout Western Europe and the United States soon afterward.[63]

Galton's goal was simply to amplify what he saw as humanity's best characteristics as a means for improving society. But Galton's new science and the political movements it spawned would soon take a nasty turn for the worse. Beginning in the United States, marriage laws were passed that prevented people with serious physical or mental disabilities from marrying. By the early 1900s, Gregor Mendel's work on heredity had been discovered, and biologists were working to integrate the science of genetics with Darwinian theory.

---

60. Browne, *Charles Darwin: The Power of Place*, 286–93.

61. Francis Galton, *Inquiries into Human Faculty and Its Development* (London: J. M. Dent, 1883).

62. Browne, *Charles Darwin: The Power of Place*, 396–400.

63. Peter Bowler, *Evolution: The History of an Idea, 25th Anniversary Edition* (Berkeley: University of California Press, 2009), 308–13.

Eugenicists extrapolated those ideas to their progressive efforts to improve society. Soon all manifestations of human disease and misfortune, including mental illness, low intelligence, criminal behavior, and even poverty, were said to have a genetic basis.[64]

To eugenicists, many of society's problems could be reduced or even eliminated by preventing the transmission of defective genes to the next generation. Leading proponents of eugenics in the United States included the biologist Charles B. Davenport, who founded the Eugenics Record Office (ERO) in Cold Spring Harbor, New York, and Margaret Sanger, whose efforts to promote birth control would eventually lead to the formation of the Planned Parenthood Federation of America.[65] Davenport's ERO would eventually become the Cold Spring Harbor Laboratory, one of the leading nonprofit biological research centers in the world today. The Johnson Immigration Act, backed up by reports from the ERO, was passed in 1924 in order to restrict immigrants coming to the United States from eastern and southern Europe who were viewed as genetically "inferior."[66] By the 1930s at least thirty states had passed compulsory sterilization laws targeting undesirable individuals. Involuntary sterilization was conducted primarily on incarcerated prisoners or institutionalized mental patients, but in some places social workers could petition for the sterilization of normal citizens with certain physical or mental disabilities. Some eugenicists even favored euthanasia as a possible solution to eliminate the undesirable from the human gene pool, though at least in the United States this was never implemented.[67] However, state eugenics programs in the United States served as models for eugenic laws enacted in European countries, including Nazi Germany, where over 400,000 people were involuntarily sterilized with

---

64. Garland Allen, "Genetics, Eugenics and the Medicalization of Social Behavior: Lessons from the Past," *Endeavor* 23 (1999): 10–19.

65. Marilyn M. Singleton, "The 'Science' of Eugenics: America's Moral Detour," *Journal of American Physicians and Surgeons* 19 (2014): 122–25.

66. Allen and Baker, *Biology*, 159–60.

67. Singleton, "The 'Science' of Eugenics."

an additional 300,000 killed in euthanasia facilities.[68] The horrors of the Jewish Holocaust soon followed.

Following World War II, eugenics fell out of political favor once the crimes of the Nazis were revealed for the world to see. However, various eugenics laws remained on the books in the United States until as late as the 1960s.[69] The science and language of the eugenicists have now mostly disappeared from Western society, though if we listen, we can still hear the echoes in public debates on physician-assisted suicide and capital punishment, and in the anti-immigration rhetoric of some modern-day politicians. The eugenics laws of the past century are an extreme example of the misapplication of a scientific theory to an idealistically driven sociopolitical agenda. Neither Charles Darwin nor his cousin Francis Galton intended or could have possibly anticipated the lengths to which this politically motivated thinking ended up going. But in the public mind, the theory of evolution and Charles Darwin have become more or less permanently linked with flawed social Darwinist political agendas such as eugenics, *laissez-faire* economics, Marxism, and even the horrors of Nazi Germany.[70] It is therefore not all that surprising that the science of evolution, now conflated with broadly disliked social and political ideologies, would be opposed by some religious communities.

Creationism and Its Descendants

The Scopes Trial

In 1925, a Tennessee high-school biology teacher, John Scopes, was arrested and tried for teaching evolution in his classes. Scopes was accused of violating the Butler Act, a new state law prohibiting this practice in Tennessee public schools. Ironically, Scopes's biology curriculum was based on a State of Tennessee prescribed

68. Stefan Kuhl, *The Nazi Connection: Eugenics, American Racism, and German National Socialism* (New York: Oxford University Press, 2002), 53, 100–102.

69. Allen and Baker, *Biology*, 161–62.

70. Michael Ruse, Can a Darwinian Be a Christian? The Relationship between Science and Religion (Cambridge: Cambridge University Press, 2001), 170–76.

textbook, *A Civic Biology*, by New York educator George Hunter.[71] Perhaps unnoticed by the Tennessee officials responsible for textbook selection, *A Civic Biology* contained sections on Darwin and evolution as well as social Darwinist ideas on eugenics and "human improvement."[72] But the Butler Act specifically prohibited the teaching of any theory "that man has descended from a lower order of animals," which was seen to violate the story of creation as told in the Bible. So, the Tennessee law placed Scopes and other biology teachers in the state in a bind. Should they teach the objectionable parts of the textbook prescribed by the state, thus breaking the law, or should they omit those lessons? Scopes, in a deliberate attempt to challenge the new law and at the urging of town leaders, decided to teach the objectionable parts of the book.[73]

The legal case that played out in the Rhea County Courthouse in Dayton, Tennessee, as *The State of Tennessee v. John Thomas Scopes*, was an over-the-top display of grand political theater that quickly became known as the "Scopes Monkey Trial." Both sides of the case were represented by high-profile, nationally known attorneys; three-time presidential candidate William Jennings Bryan for the prosecution and noted criminal defense lawyer Clarence Darrow for the defense. Daily updates of the trial were broadcast nationally on the radio and received front-page coverage in major newspapers. The trial itself has been described as a publicity stunt orchestrated to bring attention to the small Tennessee city where it took place.[74] In the end, John Scopes was found guilty of teaching evolution and charged a fine of $100. The circus-like atmosphere of the Scopes trial and its proceedings are wonderfully portrayed in the 1960 Hollywood film *Inherit the Wind*, starring Spencer Tracy, Fredric March, and Gene Kelly. Fundamentalist Christian objection to the science of evolution since the time of the Scopes Monkey Trial has become

---

71. George William Hunter, *A Civic Biology: Presented in Problems* (New York: American Book Company, 1914).

72. Ibid., 261.

73. Eugenie C. Scott, *Evolution vs. Creationism* (Berkeley: University of California Press, 2009), 99–102.

74. Edward J. Larson, *Summer for the Gods: The Scopes Trial and America's Continuing Debate over Science and Religion* (New York: Basic Books, 2006).

known as *creationism*, a form of pseudoscience that is dismissed by scientists because of the lack of physical evidence and the complete failure of creationists to apply rigorous scientific methodology to their own claims.[75]

Laws and Specific Types of Creationism

Creationism has taken on a variety of forms in the United States since the time of the Scopes trial, but its main goal has always been to oppose the teaching of evolution in public schools. *Young-earth creationism,* based on the book *The Genesis Flood* by John Whitcomb and Henry Morris, insists on the literal interpretation of biblical scripture.[76] Therefore the Earth's age, as determined by counting back through the Hebrew lineages to the time of Adam and Eve, can be no more than about six thousand years. Young-earth creationism thus denies not just evolution; it denies virtually *all* science. It ignores the findings of geology and astronomy that date the Earth's age to about 4.5 billion years, as well as the methods of chemistry and physics on which these dates are based. The $27–million Creation Museum, which opened in Petersburg, Kentucky, in 2007, is a testament to the tenacity of this fundamentalist strain of American Protestantism.

After the Scopes trial, creationist laws restricting the teaching of evolution, patterned after Tennessee's Butler Act, were passed in Arkansas and Mississippi but failed in several other states.[77] They were infrequently enforced with legal actions but had a stultifying effect on American education. Biology textbooks used in the public schools across the country often avoided any mention of Darwin or evolution for fear of triggering local outrage, and consequently losing sales in the textbook marketplace.

The start of the space race in 1951 brought about far-reaching reform of American science policy, including a reevaluation of the

75. Allen and Baker, *Biology*, 168–80.

76. John C. Whitcomb and Henry M. Morris, *The Genesis Flood: The Biblical Record and Its Scientific Implications* (Phillipsburg, NJ: Presbyterian and Reformed Publishing, 1961).

77. Scott, *Evolution vs. Creationism*, 102–3.

content of high school science textbooks.[78] New textbooks seeking to modernize and update science education in all fields, even biology, were adopted, including in places with old anti-evolution laws. The last of these laws vanished in 1968 when a Little Rock high school biology teacher, Susan Epperson, sued the State of Arkansas for prohibiting her from teaching evolution in a case that went all the way to the US Supreme Court. In the case *Epperson v. Arkansas,* the Supreme Court ruled that the state law's primary purpose was to protect a particular religious dogma and was therefore in violation of the First Amendment of the US Constitution.[79]

With the repeal of anti-evolution laws in the United States, creationism itself evolved. *Scientific creationism,* based on a 1974 book of the same name by Henry Morris, seeks to provide physical evidence that supports the biblical accounts of creation and other events described in the Bible. In addition, scientific creationism, also known as *creation science*, seeks to undermine evolutionary theory by providing scientific evidence, such as a "lack of transitional forms" in the fossil record, that "proves" Darwin was wrong. By stripping away scriptural references and much of the overtly religious language, advocates presented this form of creationism as a scientific theory that should receive "equal time" or a "balanced" consideration along with Darwinian evolution in science classes.[80] Initiatives to pass equal-time laws began in many states and were eventually successful in Arkansas and Louisiana. However, these laws were also overturned as violations of the First Amendment of the US Constitution with the same reasoning that the Supreme Court had used previously, that is, that the laws were religiously motivated.

Intelligent Design

With creation science now out of favor, *Intelligent Design* would be the next "theory" to be proposed by creationists as a scientific alternative to evolution. Intelligent Design (ID) emerged as a "new

78. Ibid., 104–5.
79. Ibid., 225.
80. Ibid., 111–17.

scientific theory" in the biology textbook *Of Pandas and People*, published in 1989 by the creationists Percival Davis and Dean Kenyon. *Of Pandas and People* was originally conceived as a creation-science textbook entitled *Biology and Creation*.[81] However, after the court defeats of creation science, the authors somewhat shamelessly revised their manuscript by simply removing the words "creationism" and "creationists" and replacing them with the new language of "intelligent design" and "design proponents." Very few, if any, "design proponents" existed at the time *Of Pandas and People* was published. The Discovery Institute, a conservative think tank based in Seattle, Washington, provided financial and intellectual resources for the fledgling ID movement. Perhaps sensing that they needed to establish some expert theoretical credibility, ID gained the assistance of legal scholar Philip Johnson, author of *Darwin on Trial* (1991), and a handful of scientists such as mathematician William Dembski and biochemist Michael Behe. Though the scientific community largely ignored *Darwin on Trial,* it sold reasonably well and brought fame and fortune to its author, emboldening new "ID theorists" to enter the fray.[82] Out of nowhere, a new field of science was created.

In the strictest sense, ID is not creationism. ID does not rely on scriptural references, and many of the ID authors do not even identify their mysterious designer; the role of God in the creation of biological diversity is merely implied. Most ID advocates accept the scientific facts about the age of the universe, geology, and even the history of life as revealed by the fossil record. Their task is simply to refute Darwinian evolution as the primary driving force behind life's diversity and thereby create the impression that an alternative explanatory theory is justified. Michael Behe, a biochemist at Lehigh University and author of the bestselling *Darwin's Black Box: The Biochemical Challenge to Evolution*, is a great case in point.

81. Kenneth Miller, *Only a Theory: Evolution and the Battle for America's Soul* (New York: Penguin Books, 2008), 113–17.

82. Scott, *Evolution vs. Creationism*, 122–23.

Behe begins his book by declaring that "the natives are restless."[83] He describes the field of evolutionary biology as a science in disarray, with many disputes over the interpretation of data and the reliability of the scientific evidence for evolution. Out of all this confusion come conflicting new ideas and a search for new mechanisms. Never mind that debate and disagreement about data and the generation of new hypotheses are a hallmark of any healthy field of science. Having created an illusion of scientific doubt and uneasiness, Behe begins his attack by going after what he sees as the weakest link in evolutionary theory. To directly quote Darwin himself:

> If it can be demonstrated that any complex organ existed which could not have possibly been formed by numerous, successive, slight modifications, my theory would absolutely break down.[84]

Behe was all too happy to take up the challenge. According to Behe, the science of biochemistry has now broken open the cell, also known as Darwin's black box, to reveal a treasure trove of "irreducibly complex" systems that, by Darwin's own admission, would seem to invalidate his theory. Using the analogy of a mousetrap, each of these biochemical systems consists of several essential functional parts, and the removal (or change) of any one of them could easily cause the whole system to fail. We can see this in the human blood-clotting system, where a single mutation in one or another of the numerous clotting factors involved results in the heritable bleeding disorder hemophilia. In the cell, the functioning pieces of these irreducibly complex systems are enzyme proteins, each of which is encoded for by genes. For an irreducibly complex system to evolve gradually, according to Behe, the DNA comprising each of the many genes for these proteins would have to mutate in lockstep over many generations, which would be a mathematical impossibility.[85] Behe cites the blood-clotting system and four other "irreducibly complex"

---

83. Michael Behe, *Darwin's Black Box: The Biochemical Challenge to Evolution* (New York: Free Press, 1996), 26.

84. Darwin, *On the Origin of Species*, 150.

85. Behe, *Darwin's Black Box*, 74–97.

biochemical systems as the proof that destroys Darwinian theory. Anti-evolutionists could rejoice! Creationists armed with ID theory promoted as a scientific alternative to evolution quickly launched a new round of "equal time" initiatives in communities around the United States, some of which succeeded.[86]

In October 2004, in the small central Pennsylvania town of Dover, science teachers were required to read a disclaimer to all their classes at the start of the unit on evolution that offered an "alternative" explanation to Darwin. The book *Of Pandas and People* was offered as a supplement to the standard textbook to present the alternative "scientific theory" of ID.[87] A school parent group, led by Tammy Kitzmiller, with support provided by the American Civil Liberties Union, sued the school board to rescind the mandate. The biology textbook used in the Dover Area science curriculum at the time was *Biology: The Living Science*, coauthored by Kenneth Miller of Brown University and Joseph Levine of Boston College. As it turned out, Professor Miller had also written about intelligent design.[88]

In *Finding Darwin's God*, Miller used examples from University of California biochemist Russell Doolittle's published work to explain how the "irreducibly complex" blood-clotting cascade referenced by Michael Behe might have evolved in vertebrates. The blood-clotting factors are all serine proteases, a family of digestive enzymes that break proteins down into smaller fragments. They are normally used in the digestive cavity to break down food, or inside cells where they assist in the processing of cellular signals. Miller suggested that a mistargeting of a pancreatic protease to the blood, in a vertebrate ancestor of the distant past, may have begun the evolution of the clotting system. From that point forward, a relatively small number of gene duplications over many millions of years could have bought about the complex system we see today. This demonstrates not only how a complex biochemical amplification circuit can develop over

86. Scott, *Evolution vs. Creationism*, 146–64.

87. Ibid., 147.

88. Kenneth Miller, *Finding Darwin's God: A Scientist's Search for Common Ground between God and Evolution* (New York: HarperCollins, 1999).

evolutionary time but also how the system itself originated from something else, that is, a digestive enzyme, that had nothing to do with blood clotting in the first place.[89]

In fact, Miller showed how each of Behe's "irreducibly complex" systems could be derived from scientifically plausible genetic changes that would not require simultaneous mutations.[90] Thus, although Behe's book was hailed by ID advocates as a scientific breakthrough, no new facts were presented. Finally, *Darwin's Black Box* reveals the Achilles heel of all ID arguments: the mistake of making absolutist claims. Behe claimed that no publication in the history of science has ever described "how molecular evolution of any real, complex biochemical system either did occur or even might have occurred."[91] The very same year in which *Darwin's Black Box* was published, a Darwinian explanation for the origin of the Krebs cycle, certainly one of the most important and complex of all biochemical pathways, was published.[92] Science is always progressing. Just because some phenomenon in the natural world has not yet been explained, that does not mean that it never will be. ID arguments based on such reasoning are doomed to failure.

Likewise, anti-evolutionist efforts to insert ID into school science curricula would ultimately fail. In a flashback to the Scopes Monkey Trial of a bygone era, the case of *Kitzmiller v. Dover Area School Board,* held in the United States District Court in Harrisburg, Pennsylvania, beginning in September 2005, was dubbed by media outlets as the "Dover Panda Trial." The proceedings featured Kenneth Miller as a lead witness for the prosecution and Michael Behe as the lead witness for the defense.[93] The twenty-one–day "Panda Trial" attracted much of the same newspaper and broadcast attention that had been present at the "Monkey Trial" eighty years before, though

89. Ibid., 152–58.

90. Ibid., 129–64.

91. Behe, *Darwin's Black Box*, 185.

92. Enrique Melendez-Hevia, Thomas G. Waddell, and Marta Cascante, "The Puzzle of the Krebs Cycle: Assembling the Pieces of Chemically Feasible Reactions, and Opportunism in the Design of Metabolic Pathways during Evolution," *Journal of Molecular Evolution* 43 (1996): 293–303.

93. Scott, *Evolution vs. Creationism*, 146–51.

perhaps with a bit less hoopla. At the end of the trial, District Court judge John E. Jones, who himself had been appointed to the bench by a conservative US president, found in favor of the plaintiffs on all counts. The judge ruled that ID was not a science because (1) by allowing for supernatural causation, ID did not follow the scientific method; (2) ID did not subject itself to peer scrutiny as do other sciences; and (3) ID was widely rejected by the larger scientific community.[94] The defendants had not even consulted with scientists or their own science teachers before adopting the ID policy. Further, Judge Jones found that ID was primarily a religious view—a simple relabeling of Christian creationism—and therefore the Dover school board's actions were in violation of the First Amendment of the US Constitution.

Lasting Effects on Science Education

While fleeting creationist political victories have not impeded the maturation and growth of evolutionary biology as a field of science, they have adversely affected science education in the United States and around the world. For decades after the Scopes Trial, high school biology textbooks made little or no reference to evolution. Even after the reintroduction of Darwin into school textbooks in the 1960s, many teachers avoided teaching the subject, a trend that continues in some places even to this day.[95] Although creation science and ID have lost repeatedly in US courtrooms, they have scored public relations victories in the United States and abroad, where increasing numbers of the global community express doubts about Darwin and evolution.[96] This not only affects the public's knowledge about human origins and our connections to the natural world, it also means that there are generations of our global brothers and sisters who have a gross misunderstanding of science. Approximately 10 percent of children in the United States attend private schools, to which the various court cases litigated over the years do not apply.

94. Ibid., 151–53.

95. Ibid., 103.

96. Ronald Numbers, *The Creationists: From Scientific Creationism to Intelligent Design*, exp. ed. (Cambridge, MA: Harvard University Press, 2006), 396–430.

Private schools, many with church affiliations, may follow any curriculum they choose. This creates a significant market for creation science or ID textbooks, which publishers are all too eager to satisfy. I teach at a Catholic university, and over the years have met many students who attended private Catholic high schools. Only about half of these students were taught anything about evolution in their high school science classes, and some of those who were, learned about Darwin along with ID via the discredited "teach the controversy" strategy of the Discovery Institute.[97] That's a shame!

However well meaning creationists and ID advocates might be in their own minds, by undermining science education, their efforts have had far-reaching public policy effects. It seems likely that the same guarded ignorance or denial that many people believe to be okay for the science of evolution is okay for other areas of science as well. In a Pew Research Poll conducted in 2014, 35 percent of US adults still completely disregarded evolution, 32 percent distrusted public health vaccines, 41 percent did not think global human population growth is a problem, and a full 50 percent denied the role played by humans in global climate change.[98] This kind of scientific ignorance cannot continue if humankind is to deal effectively with the issues confronting our world. If religious opponents of science would only consider that the history of life on Earth is far more interesting and religiously compelling than it would be if a designing God had orchestrated every last detail—after all, it is on an Earth where life is free to create itself that miracles can happen.

Wonderful Life

The Burgess Shale in British Columbia, Canada, is a rock formation containing an abundance of fossils dating to Middle Cambrian times, about 508 million years ago, when this area was a muddy ocean bottom. It was discovered in 1909 by Charles Doolittle Walcott, a paleontologist and secretary of the Smithsonian Institute in Washing-

97. Scott, *Evolution vs. Creationism*, 159–63.

98. Cary Funk and Becka A. Alper, *Religion and Science* (Pew Research Center, www.pewresearch.org, 2015).

ton, DC. While on a recreational outing with his wife, Helena, in the Canadian Rockies, Walcott came across a slab of rock containing an abundance of fossilized creatures, the likes of which he had never seen before.[99] They returned to the site the next day with their children in tow and found the source of the rock slab in a shale formation farther up the slope of a hill. The Walcott family and a small team from the Smithsonian returned to the quarry site each summer for several years and excavated thousands of fossils, which were sent back to Washington for later study and cataloging. Walcott classified the fossils he had found among known animal groups, but the significance of his finds were not revealed in full until decades after his death in 1927. In the 1960s, Simon Conway Morris, a student of paleontologist Harry Whittington at Cambridge University, began going through the Smithsonian's collection drawers as a follow up to the Whittington team's own collection trip to British Columbia. Not only were there examples of all our modern animal phyla present, but a plethora of previously unknown animal types as well.[100]

In his book *Wonderful Life*, Stephen Jay Gould writes extensively and lovingly of the Whittington team's reclassification of the Burgess fossil fauna. The Burgess samples are unique among Cambrian fossils in that many of the animal's soft body parts were preserved, a rarity in fossils of this age. Gould's explanation for the sudden appearance of so many forms of life in these mid-Cambrian rocks was that they must be descended from a soft-bodied animal ancestor of the Early Cambrian that diversified very rapidly into the Burgess fauna.[101] Walcott, in contrast, had placed the Burgess fauna into a few known taxonomic groups that he thought descended gradually through the Early Cambrian in Darwinian fashion.[102] To Gould, the lesson that is learned from the Burgess fauna is the importance of *contingency* in evolutionary biology.[103] Many of the Burgess animal

---

99. Stephen Jay Gould, *Wonderful Life: The Burgess Shale and the Nature of History* (New York: W. W. Norton, 1989), 70–78.

100. Ibid., 79–239.

101. Ibid., 45–52.

102. Ibid., 257–63.

103. Ibid., 288–89.

groups are found nowhere since the Cambrian. Gould proposes that from the time of the Cambrian onward, rapid diversification as well as periodic decimations left Earth with the few forms that eventually evolved into our modern-day animals.

The title of Gould's book comes from the famous Frank Capra film *It's a Wonderful Life*, in which George Bailey, a down-on-his-luck family man from an obscure town in upstate New York visits a parallel world in which he had never been born. George, to his great joy, finds that his life has had great meaning and impact after all. The parallel world is far different and meaner than his own. In other words, the lives of everyone in George's world are contingent on George having played a positive role in them. Gould applied the message of this beloved Christmas holiday film to the Burgess shale and the history of life on Earth:

> Replay the tape a million times from a Burgess beginning and I doubt if anything like *Homo sapiens* would ever evolve again. Indeed it is a wonderful life.[104]

Darwin pointed to the sudden appearance of Cambrian (called Silurian in Darwin's time) animals like trilobites in the oldest rocks containing fossils as a potential problem for his theory. But he attributed this observation to what he called the "imperfection" of the fossil record.[105] Darwin thought that there must have been ancestral versions of these organisms that were just not preserved as fossils or had not yet been discovered. Walcott's interpretation of the Burgess shale was consistent with Darwin's view. For Gould, the sudden explosion of animals in the Cambrian was the result of very rapid diversification from one or a few unknown lineages that date to Precambrian times. To Gould the sudden burst of diversification seen in the Cambrian differed from slow gradual Darwinian change, but he still saw these forms as descending from common ancestors.

Stephen C. Meyer of the Discovery Institute in Seattle, Washington, has a far different explanation. Meyer agrees with Darwin that

104. Ibid., 259.

105. Darwin, *On the Origin of Species*, 242–45.

the Cambrian explosion is a problem for Darwinian evolution. He calls this "Darwin's Doubt," and considers it the fatal flaw of Darwinism.[106] The discoveries of Early Cambrian fossils dating to 518 million years ago in the Mt. Maotianshan shales near Chengjiang, China, show an even more diverse assemblage of organisms than the Burgess shale. According to Meyer, this is a "top-down" problem for Darwinism, in which fewer groups should be found in older rocks. Meyer concludes from his extensive discussion of the fossil record that the Cambrian explosion as revealed in the Burgess and Maotianshan shales are the sure signs of an Intelligent Designer.[107] But recent findings indicate that we do not need to infer supernatural causes for the Cambrian explosion. There was likely a natural environmental trigger.

There are fossils even older than the Cambrian found in the Ediacara Hills of South Australia by Australian geologist and fossil collector Reginald Sprigg in 1949.[108] The sediments that formed these rocks accumulated around 575 million years ago during the last stages of the Precambrian, which is now called the Ediacaran period in honor of these fossils. Because these were soft-bodied animals, the remains of the Ediacarans are not well preserved, and the fossils consist mostly of impressions left on the ocean floor; but over one hundred different forms have now been identified.[109]

DNA analysis of genes that are common to all animals living today trace all modern phyla to an evolutionary divergence that happened as long as 750 million years ago.[110] These "molecular clock" studies have been criticized by Stephen Meyer and others due to inconsistencies between some of the clock dates and the fossil record for known groups.[111] But refinements of methodologies have resulted in better

---

106. Stephen C. Meyer, *Darwin's Doubt: The Explosive Origin of Animal Life and the Case for Intelligent Design* (New York: HarperCollins, 2013), 6.

107. Ibid., 353–81.

108. Peter Ward and Joe Kirschvink, *A New History of Life: The Radical New Discoveries about the Origins and Evolution of Life on Earth* (New York: Bloomsbury Press, 2015), 108.

109. Benton, *The History of Life*, 50–51.

110. Douglas H. Erwin et al., "The Cambrian Conundrum: Early Divergence and Later Ecological Success in the Early History of Animals," *Science* 334 (2011): 1091–97.

111. Meyer, *Darwin's Doubt*, 102–13.

agreement between the clocks and the fossil record and confirm that the earliest divergence of animal groups probably occurred at least 100 million years before the Cambrian.[112] Fossils and molecular biology now both suggest that a diversity of animal types was likely present at the start of the Cambrian explosion. All that was needed was for something to light the fuse.

Erik Sperling and his research team at Harvard University have determined from the analysis of a large collection of iron mineral data from Cambrian and Precambrian rocks that oxygen levels in the Precambrian ocean were very low, less than 1 percent of what they are now, until just before the start of the Cambrian.[113] After examining the species composition of modern living ocean communities in a range of oxygen conditions, Sperling has proposed that a slight rise in ocean oxygen levels, perhaps to no more than 10 percent of our current levels, may have been enough to shift some animals to more active predatory lifestyles.[114] This, in turn, would have pressured soft-bodied prey organisms to become more active either by burrowing into the sediment or swimming up into the water column. The result would have been a biological "arms race" through the Cambrian period as the diversifying collection of animals acquired a variety of adaptations for survival under these new living conditions.[115] Claws, teeth, shells, body armor, and other adaptations all appear in the fossil record at this time. By the end of the Cambrian period, easily recognizable ancestors of most modern phyla, including our own, *Chordata*, are represented in the fossil record.

There are many aspects of Sperling's Cambrian oxygenation hypothesis that remain to be tested, but they are testable. This is unlike the ID proposals of Stephen Meyer and Michael Behe. These

---

112. John A. Cunningham, Alexander G. Liu, Stefan Bengtson, and Philip C. J. Donoghue, "The Origin of Animals: Can Molecular Clocks and the Fossil Record Be Reconciled?" *BioEssays* 39 (2016): 1–12.

113. Erik A. Sperling et al., "Statistical Analysis of Iron Geochemical Data Suggests Limited Late Proterozoic Oxygenation," *Nature* 523 (2015): 451–54.

114. Erik A. Sperling et al., "Oxygen, Ecology, and the Cambrian Radiation of Animals," *PNAS USA* 110 (2013): 13446–51.

115. Douglas Fox, "What Sparked the Cambrian Explosion?" *Nature* 530 (2016): 268–71.

types of proposals are sometimes called "God of the gaps" explanations.[116] Natural phenomena that are, as of yet, unexplainable by contemporary science, namely, Darwin's black box (Behe) or the Cambrian conundrum (Meyer), are given as examples of God's action in the world. The problem is that as soon as these mysteries of nature find scientific explanations, the place for God gets smaller and smaller. Creationists and ID advocates seek to uphold the importance of God and religious belief in the drama of the universe, and, as a practicing Roman Catholic myself, I applaud that ideal. But they are going about it in the wrong way. They are, in fact, diminishing God. I believe that God is present in all aspects of nature if we know how to look and how to listen. This requires us to imagine a new theology *for* evolution, not *instead of* evolution. That is exactly what theologians like John Haught and Ilia Delio are trying to provide for us.[117]

While there is very much that remains unknown to us about Precambrian life, we know a whole lot more about post-Cambrian life. There have been many excellent histories of the last 500 million years of life on Earth that have been written since Darwin's time. My personal favorites are *Life: An Unauthorized Biography* by Richard Fortey, which tells life's story in chronological order leading inevitably to the emergence of humans; and *The Ancestor's Tale* by Richard Dawkins, written in reverse order in the manner of Geoffrey Chaucer's medieval epic *The Canterbury Tales*. Much of our knowledge of evolutionary history is dependent on a type of organ system that was absent during life's earliest history. This organ system first burst on the scene during the arms race of Cambrian explosion and has written life's history in the gradually accumulating sediments of the past 500 million years ever since. Our witness to the history of complex animal life from the Cambrian period to the present day is the skeletal system.

---

116. Thomas Dixon, *Science and Religion: A Very Short Introduction* (Oxford: Oxford University Press, 2008), 44–46.

117. John F. Haught, *Resting on the Future: Catholic Theology for an Unfinished Universe* (New York: Bloomsbury, 2015); Ilia Delio, *Christ in Evolution* (Maryknoll, NY: Orbis Books, 2008).

These Old Bones

In his book *Life Ascending,* biochemist Nick Lane describes the "ten great inventions of evolution."[118] These inventions include the origins of life, DNA, photosynthesis, the eukaryotic cell, and sex, all of which we considered in chapter 5. To these, Lane adds movement, sight, warm bloodedness, consciousness, and finally death. I agree with Lane on the importance of all of these evolutionary innovations. But to Lane's list I would add an eleventh invention that has a similar magnitude of importance as the others: the process of *biomineralization.* Biomineralization is the process by which living organisms produce the inorganic minerals that interface with proteins and other biological molecules to become bones, shells, teeth, and other hard structures of animal skeletons.

From their beginnings in the Cambrian, skeletal tissues have evolved to provide the scaffolding that supports the biomass of a living organism on land, making large body size for animals possible. Bones provide the attachment points for muscle tissue so that contraction can result in movement of complex animal life through their complex environment so that they can find food, defend themselves from predators, and find mates with which to procreate. In vertebrates, bones provide protective coverings to sensitive internal organs such as the brain, in which—in at least one vertebrate species, *Homo sapiens*—consciousness emerged. It is the bones, teeth, and shells of animals, long dead, that persist in the fossil record and provided the first scientific clues to the dramatic history of life on our planet. Over Earth's history, biomineralization has altered the chemistry of the oceans and given rise to large geological structures like coral reefs, which in turn support a plethora of marine creatures. Biomineralization is thus a critical link between the nonliving inorganic world of water, rocks, and minerals and the biological wonders of creation.

The process of biomineralization involves the selective extraction and accumulation of chemical elements from the environment and

118. Nick Lane, *Life Ascending: The Ten Great Inventions of Evolution* (New York: W. W. Norton, 2009).

the transport of these elements to internal sites, where they are precipitated out of solution as inorganic deposits. There are over sixty different types of inorganic minerals that are produced by living organisms.[119] Evolution did not invent the minerals formed by plants and animals. These minerals can also be formed in nonliving aquatic systems under the right conditions. What evolution invented is the cellular processes that are able to control the timing and location of the inorganic precipitation process. Common cellular mechanisms for controlling the production of minerals include (1) creation of a cellular or extracellular microenvironment in which anions and cations are concentrated to produce supersaturated solutions out of which the mineral can precipitate; (2) the secretion of a protein or other biological molecule that attracts and binds mineral ions in particular conformation, which then nucleates the growth of crystals; or (3) the production or removal of crystal growth inhibitors in the locations where crystallization occurs. Most biomineralization systems use some combination of these general mechanisms.[120]

The oldest biological silicate minerals date to approximately 740 million years ago, and the oldest known biological carbonates date to about 650 million years ago.[121] The very old age of these fossils, predating the Cambrian explosion, suggests that the ability to control the production of inorganic minerals evolved very early in animal history. However, genetic analysis shows that in the various animal phyla in which biomineralization occurs, the process seems to have developed after the Precambrian divergence of the main animal groups. Thus, biomineralization seems to have been invented by evolution fourteen or more times, and the similarities we see are the result of convergent evolutionary processes.[122]

The various skeletal structures emerging in the Cambrian period were of two main types: *exoskeletons*, such as the protective shells

119. Stephen Mann, *Biomineralization: Principles and Concepts in Bioinorganic Materials Chemistry* (Oxford: Oxford University Press, 2001), 7–24.

120. Ibid., 25–37.

121. Andrew Knoll, "Biomineralization and Evolutionary History," *Reviews in Mineralogy and Geochemistry* 54 (2003): 329–56.

122. Duncan J. E. Murdock and Philip C. J. Donoghue, "Evolutionary Origins of Animal Skeletal Biomineralization," *Cells Tissues Organs* 194 (2011): 98–102.

of crustaceans and molluscs; and *endoskeletons*, like the interior bones of fish and other vertebrates. In fish, endoskeletons developed originally as a soft skeletal tissue composed largely of cartilage. Some Cambrian fish, called *ostracoderms*, also developed a mineralized exoskeleton consisting of bony scales covering the body surface. Ostracoderm scales protected these small jawless fish from the crushing claws and tooth plates of the nimbler arthropod predators, such as the ubiquitous trilobites of the Cambrian seas. By the beginning of the Ordovician period 485 million years ago, fish developed jaws from their gill arches, and the bony scales became modified into the formidable offensive weapons called teeth. Some species of fish, like sharks and rays, continued along their evolutionary path with a cartilaginous endoskeleton. But in other lineages the cartilage endoskeleton became mineralized, giving rise to the rigid skeletal structure called bone.[123]

Bone is a composite material, made up of an organic matrix consisting largely of the protein collagen, into which the calcium phosphate mineral hydroxyapatite is precipitated by bone cells. A collagen fibril is composed of three long protein chains that are wrapped tightly around each other, forming a triple helical structure. In cartilage, collagen fibrils align end to end and parallel with one another and become cross-linked to other fibrils. A collagen fiber is thus a rope containing hundreds or even thousands of cross-linked individual fibrils, which together have tremendous tensile strength. Bone formation begins with the production of a cartilage template secreted by *chondrocytes*. As the chondrocytes become surrounded by the dense collagen matrix, they become enlarged and die, releasing tiny spherical globules called matrix vesicles, which are derived from the cell membranes.[124] It is within the matrix vesicles that the first hydroxyapatite mineral crystals form. Once seeded by the matrix vesicles, the mineralization process spreads out into and

---

123. Brian K. Hall, *Bones and Cartilage: Developmental and Evolutionary Skeletal Biology*, 2nd ed. (London: Academic Press, 2015).

124. Roy E. Wuthier, "A Review of the Primary Mechanism of Endochondral Calcification with Special Emphasis on the Role of Cells, Mitochondria and Matrix Vesicles," *Clinical Orthopaedics and Related Research* 169 (1982): 219–42.

among the collagen fibers of the matrix, transforming the soft cartilage into a hard tissue. The mineralized cartilage is soon invaded by *osteoblasts* and *osteoclasts*, which remodel it into bone.

When the foundations of large buildings or bridges are constructed, heavy steel rebar is positioned within a mold into which the liquid concrete mixture is poured. As the mixture dries and the mold is removed, the concrete is able to withstand rotational and side-to-side motion due to resistance provided by the internal parallel arrays of rebar. The concrete also has great compressive strength and can bear the weight of the final structure. Similarly, bone is able to withstand the rotational and side-to-side tensions caused by muscular contractions, while simultaneously protecting the internal structures and supporting the body weight of even the largest land animals. In an aquatic animal, the body weight is largely supported by the water that surrounds it. Great white sharks weighing up to 1,900 kg have a soft cartilaginous skeleton. Their only hard tissues are the teeth. Such a creature would collapse under its own body weight on land. Without the structural support of an internal mineralized skeleton, animals would never have been able to take the first tentative steps in life's next great adventure—land! We will discuss the development of land animals, including humans, in the next and final chapter.

7

Humans

> Then God said: Let the earth bring forth every kind of living creature: tame animals, crawling things and every kind of wild animal. And so it happened. God made every kind of tame animal, every kind of wild animal, and every kind of thing that crawls on the ground. God saw that it was good. Then God said: Let us make human beings in our image, after our likeness. Let them have dominion over the fish of the sea, the birds of the air, the tame animals, all the wild animals, and all the creatures that crawl on the earth. God created mankind in his image; in the image of God he created them; male and female he created them. . . . God looked at everything he had made, and found it very good. Evening came, and morning followed—the sixth day. (Gen 1:24–27, 31)

The Bible's sixth day of creation corresponds to roughly 500 million years of evolutionary history, about one-ninth of Earth's total history. During the Cambrian period, the Earth was very warm, the result of an atmosphere rich in greenhouse gases such as carbon dioxide.[1] But during the Ordovician period, 488 million years ago, things started to change. The first land plants started to colonize seashores and banks of lakes and streams. Prior to this time the Earth's landmasses were bleak and barren places. The first land plants were rather sim-

1. Peter Ward and Joe Kirschvink, *A New History of Life: The Radical New Discoveries about the Origins and Evolution of Life on Earth* (New York: Bloomsbury Press, 2015), 124–25.

ple, the ancestors of today's mosses and liverworts.[2] They could live only in very moist environments where the cells of the plant body could absorb nutrients directly from water. Over time, plants started developing a vascular system for transporting water and nutrients through their tissues, roots systems, and tough cell walls that provided structural support. This allowed plants to colonize areas further inland. While the land became green, the animal phyla established in the Cambrian explosion expanded and diversified. Their larger body sizes and more active metabolisms were supported by increasing atmospheric oxygen levels, a by-product of plant photosynthesis.[3] But by the dawning of the Devonian period, 420 million years ago, all animal life was still in the oceans. The next 60 million years saw a dramatic diversification of fish. Some remained heavily armored like their Cambrian ancestors, while others developed into peculiar looking, lobe-finned fishes like the deep-sea *Coelacanth*, and still others became sleek and muscular, the ancestors of today's bony fishes and the cartilaginous sharks and rays.[4] These animals lived among the extensive coral reefs that filled the shallow seas surrounding landmasses. Others began to adapt to fresh water, working their ways up rivers to find lakes, ponds, and streams to colonize.

By the end of the Devonian, vast forests had spread across the land. The coal forests of the subsequent Carboniferous period (360–300 million years ago) removed copious amounts of carbon dioxide from the atmosphere and turned it into biomass, releasing even more oxygen into the atmosphere.[5] As generation after generation of Carboniferous ferns and trees died and fell to the forest floor, huge deposits of decaying organic matter provided valuable food resources to any animals that were able to exploit them. The first animals to take advantage of the newly abundant plant resources on land were invertebrates: worms, millipedes, and the earliest ancestors of the insects.[6]

---

2. Michael J. Benton, *The History of Life: A Very Short Introduction* (Oxford: Oxford University Press, 2008), 69–76.
3. Ward and Kirschvink, *A New History of Life*, 157–61.
4. Richard Fortey, *Life: A Natural History of the First Four Billion Years of Life on Earth* (New York: Alfred A. Knopf, 1998), 136–65.
5. Ward and Kirschvink, *A New History of Life*, 190–202.
6. Benton, *The History of Life*, 69–79.

The rapid generation time of these organisms was well suited to the rapid exploitation of new resources. High atmospheric oxygen levels supported still-higher metabolic rates and a great diversity of arthropods, as insects, spiders, and scorpions filled the conifer forests.[7] Now, in addition to the carbohydrates and oils produced by plant photosynthesis, abundant sources of animal protein could be found on land for any fish brave enough to venture out of the water. Our understanding of how ancient fish emerged from the Devonian seas to become land animals comes not simply from comparative anatomical studies or finding "missing links" in the fossil record; these were the tools that Darwin used. Evolutionary biology today includes a vast array of new sciences unknown in Darwin's time. In the more than 150 years since *On the Origin of Species* was published, the science of biology evolved dramatically.

The Secrets of Inheritance

Very early on in *On the Origin of Species,* Darwin admits that "the laws governing inheritance are quite unknown."[8] To me it is a tribute to Darwin's skill as a scientist that he formulated his ideas in the absence of any clear knowledge of how inheritance, a process central to understanding evolution, actually works. In Darwin's time it was most commonly thought that the various traits of mother and father were "blended" or averaged out as they were passed on to the next generation. One of the biggest problems with the blended inheritance idea was that it could not explain how a particular unique characteristic could completely disappear from one generation and then reappear in a subsequent one. Unbeknown to Darwin and the rest of his scientific community, the principles behind biological inheritance had already been discovered by one of their contemporaries, an obscure Austrian monk named Gregor Mendel.

Johann Mendel was born in 1822 into a German farm family that lived and worked in the border region of the Austrian Empire, an

7. Ward and Kirschvinck, *A New History of Life*, 190–202.

8. Charles Darwin, *On the Origin of Species* (London: Folio Society, 2006), 8. Reprint of first edition published in 1859 by John Murray, London.

area that is now the Czech Republic. He studied physics at the nearby University of Olomouc and at the age of twenty entered St. Thomas Abbey in Brno to become an Augustinian priest, taking the name of Gregor. His abbot, Fr. C. F. Napp, sent him to the University of Vienna to continue his studies; and by the time he returned to St. Thomas Abbey he had developed an interest in plant heredity from his botany professor, Franz Unger.[9] Mendel started his experiments in pea cultivation in 1854, and by 1856, Fr. Napp, who also had an interest in science, had a new greenhouse built to encourage Mendel's studies.[10] Mendel's formal experiments with pea crossings (interbreeding) took place between 1856 and 1863. He selected seven independent, easily identifiable traits, such as pod color and seed shape, which he followed and counted after each of his crossings.

Probably the best known of the hereditary principles Mendel discovered during his seven-year study would eventually become known as his "law of dominance." If two pea plants, one from a lineage with green seeds and one from a lineage with yellow seeds, were crossed, all the offspring of this first, or $F_{1,}$ generation would have green seeds. If individuals from this F_1 generation were then crossed, yellow seeds would reappear in the second, or $F_{2,}$ generation, in a predictable 3 green to 1 yellow ratio.[11] Mendel concluded that the two variants in seed color were due to hereditary units that he called "factors," in which one "form," in this case green seeds, was "dominant" over the "recessive" yellow form. Mendel's "factors" are now called genes, and the various "forms" for each trait are now called alleles; but his language of dominant and recessive traits is still used today. Two other rules that Mendel defined are the "law of segregation," which states that each gamete (the egg or sperm) receives one allele for each gene from the parent, and the "law of independent assortment," which describes how the genes sort during gamete formation.[12] Using these three hereditary principles, Mendel was able to show that one could

9. Robin Marantz Henig, *The Monk in the Garden: The Lost and Found Genius of Gregor Mendel, the Father of Genetics* (New York: Houghton Mifflin, 2000), 56–59.

10. Ibid., 89–93.

11. Ibid., 91.

12. Ibid., 188–93.

accurately predict the proportions of traits in future generations by knowing what traits are present in the original parent plants.

Widespread fame eluded Mendel during his lifetime. He presented his studies in pea genetics over two lectures in 1865 to a small gathering of scientists of the Brno Society for the Study of Natural Sciences.[13] The work was subsequently published in German in 1866 in a volume of the society's proceedings, with the title *Experiments in Plant Hybridization*.[14] The larger scientific community took almost no notice. In 1868, Mendel was elected as the new abbot of St. Thomas, promptly ending his scientific career. He was now consumed with various administrative and political duties, including a dispute with the local government over monastery taxation.[15] Mendel did some additional scientific studies with hawkweed, mice, and honeybees during his lifetime, but they were never published. These studies and all of Mendel's original pea-plant data were lost when his papers were burned by his successor at St. Thomas after his death in 1884 at the age of sixty-one.[16] Gregor Mendel lived and died in obscurity.

Mendel's groundbreaking work in genetics remained on the dusty shelves of European academic libraries for thirty-five years until rediscovered in 1900 by two rival European biologists, Hugo de Vries of Holland and Carl Correns of Germany.[17] Correns and de Vries independently confirmed Mendel's experiments, and the field of genetics was launched, eighteen years after Darwin's death. It is known that Mendel read Darwin's *On the Origin of Species* after it was translated into German, but the two never corresponded.[18] An unopened reprint of Mendel's paper, likely sent by the monk to the famous Charles Darwin, was found in Darwin's library after his death.[19] But Darwin never mentioned Mendel in any of his works or publica-

13. Ibid., 133–42.

14. Gregor J. Mendel, "Versuche über Pflanzenhybriden," *Verhandlungen des naturforschenden Vereines in Brünn*, Bd. IV für das Jahr, 1865 Abhandlungen: 3–47.

15. Henig, *Monk in the Garden*, 165.

16. Ibid., 171–72.

17. Ibid., 183–92.

18. Ibid., 124–25.

19. Ibid., 143.

tions. It is interesting to speculate about how the fields of genetics and evolutionary biology might have progressed if the famous naturalist Charles Darwin had ever become acquainted with the work of this obscure Austrian monk.[20]

Biology Grows Up

Mendel's formal university training had been primarily in mathematics and physics, so he brought a physicist's rigor for quantitative data to his study of pea plants. Once his work was rediscovered in 1900, biologists understood the mathematical patterns of inheritance. Biology had become a quantitative science with its own sets of laws and principles like those that existed in the traditional "hard" sciences like chemistry and physics. With a firm theoretical basis now established by Darwin and quantitative rigor provided by Mendel, biology was growing up. The next big step forward was taken by Thomas Hunt Morgan of Columbia University in New York, who developed an animal model for genetics research, the ubiquitous fruit fly, *Drosophila melanogaster*.[21]

Between 1910 and 1920, Morgan with his students discovered that he could create mutations in fruit flies by treating them with various chemical or radioactive agents. Many of these mutations turned out to be heritable and followed Mendelian inheritance patterns. However, Morgan found that not all characteristics followed established Mendelian patterns. For example, a gene for white eye color was linked to the sex chromosome and did not produce expected patterns in the F_1 and F_2 generations. When a white-eyed female was crossed to a red-eyed, wild-type male, *all* the male offspring would have white eyes while *all* the females would have red eyes.[22] By carefully counting thousands upon thousands of flies, Morgan and his colleagues found other genetic linkages and established the math-

20. P. Lorenzano, "What Would Have Happened if Darwin Had Known Mendel (or Mendel's Work)?" *History and Philosophy of the Life Sciences* 33 (2011): 3–49.

21. John A. Moore, *Science as a Way of Knowing: The Foundations of Modern Biology* (Cambridge, MA: Harvard University Press, 1993), 328–59.

22. Ilona Miko, "Thomas Hunt Morgan and Sex Linkage," *Nature Education* 1 (2000): 143–46.

ematical basis for these inheritance patterns. He also found that on rare occasions, inheritance patterns could change as a result of a chromosomal behavior, called *cross over*, in which portions of adjacent chromosomes were exchanged during the sorting process that occurs during sperm and egg formation. By counting the frequency of these cross-over events, Morgan's team was able to estimate the relative distance separating genes on the *Drosophila* chromosomes. Using this mathematical precision to determine the positions of linked *Drosophila* genes, one of Morgan's students, Alfred Sturtevant, produced the first genetic map.[23]

The power of the *Drosophila* model was in the very short generation time for the flies; less than two weeks. Mendel, with his pea plants, could complete only one or two crossings per growing season. In the laboratory, Morgan could complete hundreds of crossings in a single year. Since each female fruit fly could lay up to four hundred eggs, Morgan's model also brought the statistical power of large data sets to his analysis. Research in the field of genetics exploded, with departments of genetics being established at universities around the world. Many researchers continued to work with *Drosophila*, but other animal models such as the mouse *Mus musculus*, the Norwegian rat *Rattus norvegicus*, and others were soon added to geneticists' toolboxes. The principles of genetic inheritance that Morgan established were also applied to the study of human health and disease. With Darwin's theory of natural selection as the foundation and Mendelian genetics as an experimental lever, a conceptual revolution in the biological sciences had been launched. For his lifetime of accomplishments in bringing Mendelian genetics into the mainstream of modern science, Thomas Hunt Morgan was awarded the Nobel Prize in medicine in 1933.[24]

The revolution that would become known as the "modern synthesis" or sometimes the "Neo-Darwinian synthesis" swept quickly

---

23. Alfred H. Sturtevant, "The Linear Arrangement of Six Sex-linked Factors in Drosophila, as Shown by Their Mode of Association," *Journal of Experimental Zoology* 14 (1913): 43–59.

24. Garland E. Allen, *Thomas Hunt Morgan: The Man and His Science* (Princeton, NJ: Princeton University Press, 1978).

through biology. It transformed the field into a quantitative scientific discipline. Over a thirty-year period, the study of patterns of genetic inheritance and their influence on biological evolution gave rise to many new subdisciplines, including developmental biology, population genetics, and molecular biology.[25] The culmination of this conceptual revolution was marked with the awarding of the 1962 Nobel Prize in Medicine to James Watson, Francis Crick, and Maurice Wilkins for the discovery of the structure of the genetic molecule, DNA, in 1953. Francis Crick, an English biophysicist, and American geneticist James Watson combined forces at Cambridge University to do what can best be described as theoretical biology. Watson and Crick did no direct experimentation or physical observation themselves. They relied on data in the biochemical literature on the chemical composition of DNA and on X-ray diffraction data furnished by Maurice Wilkins and Rosalind Franklin at King's College, which revealed the general shape and size of the molecule. Using this data and a large, three-dimensional metal sculpture, Watson and Crick produced the now famous *double-helix* model of DNA.[26] It is a reflection of the times that Rosalind Franklin, who was as directly involved in this discovery as her three male colleagues, was left off the Nobel platform.

Over the next several decades, thousands of biologists and biochemists throughout the world, working with Watson and Crick's model of DNA, deciphered how the genetic code is organized, the cellular process by which the code is translated into proteins, and, finally, how mutations or other changes in the DNA sequence result in the natural variations that are observed in living beings. New discoveries in the fields of genetics, molecular biology, and developmental biology continue to be made each and every year. A whole new industry, biotechnology, was eventually born out of this work. Our modern scientific framework for understanding the biological world was now complete.

The molecular basis of genetic variation is a chemical property

25. Moore, *Science as a Way of Knowing*, 360–83.

26. James D. Watson, *The Double Helix* (New York: Atheneum Press, 1968).

of DNA. It provides the raw material on which natural selection, operating over hundreds of millions of years, has produced the great abundance and diversity of life forms that have populated and are populating our Earth. Scientific work, in many different fields of biology over the past century, has confirmed the validity of Darwin's theory of natural selection many times over. The convergence of traditional morphological, paleontological, and geological studies with still-emerging genetic and molecular techniques have given science a solid understanding of life's evolutionary history, from the Devonian fishes to modern humans.

Let's Go for a Walk

The earliest four-legged vertebrates, or tetrapods, probably lived and fed in shallow aquatic areas and moved out onto land only sporadically to feed, perhaps to breed, or even to escape predation while gulping air. The first definitive tetrapods known are amphibians whose fossilized bones are found in Late Devonian rocks formed 360 million years ago.[27] The bodies of these animals are decidedly "fish-like," and the limbs contain the same bones found in the limbs of all tetrapods living today. But for many years, a "missing link" in the fossil record between fish and amphibians was not known. Recall from chapter 6 that the absence of transitional forms in the fossil record is a primary creationist or intelligent-design critique of evolutionary theory.[28] The trouble with relying on the absence of data for your argument is that data, in this case a true "missing link," can eventually be found. And so, in 2006, a transitional fish fossil named *Tiktaalik* was found in Devonian rocks in Canada.[29] *Tiktaalik* had scales and gills like any fish but also had functional wrist bones at the base of its fins, which the animal could use to prop itself up on the substrate. We also know, from our new molecular toolbox, that

27. Benton, *The History of Life*, 79–82.

28. Stephen C. Meyer, *Darwin's Doubt: The Explosive Origin of Animal Life and the Case for Intelligent Design* (New York: HarperCollins Publishers, 2013), 34–39.

29. Edward B. Daeschler, Neil H. Shubin, and Farish A. Jenkins, "A Devonian Tetrapod-Like Fish and the Evolution of the Tetrapod Body Plan," *Nature* 440 (2006): 757–63.

the same homeotic genes (called *HOX genes*) that control fin development in fishes also control limb development in all tetrapods, including humans.[30] So our genetic and paleontological data confirm each other and, there is now little doubt that land vertebrates are descended from Devonian fishes.

Whatever the initial impetus for moving out onto the land was, early tetrapods found an abundance of food in the Carboniferous forests and quickly diversified on land, giving rise to at least forty different animal families.[31] These animals ranged in size, habitat, and lifestyle. Initially, they were primarily predatory, feeding on worms, insects, fish, or other tetrapods; but over time, as gastrointestinal tracts developed, herbivory became a dominant way of life for some groups. The high oxygen levels present in the atmosphere and in the oceans during this time could support larger and metabolically more active animals. The internal, mineralized skeletons of the tetrapods provided the structural body support needed for adapting to a life out of the water.[32] Another product of biomineralization, the eggshell, was part of an evolutionary adaptation that freed animals, once and for all, from an amphibious life dependent on water for reproduction.

A typical bird egg contains a series of membranes that surround the primary *oocyte*, or egg cell, which, once fertilized, will develop into a new individual. The oocyte contains the maternal DNA, the cellular machinery necessary for cell division and early development, and a nutrient supply called the yolk. The *amniotic membranes* surround and maintain a fluid-filled environment around the developing embryo. The outermost membrane, the shell membrane, secretes a protein-rich matrix in which calcium carbonate crystals are precipitated, producing the hard, protective shell. The hardened shell is porous enough to allow respiratory gases to be exchanged between the embryo and its outside environment, and it also protects against

30. Kyriel M. Pineault and Deneen M. Wellik, "Hox Genes and Limb Musculoskeletal Development," *Current Osteoporosis Reports* 12 (2014): 420–27.

31. Ward and Kirschvinck, *A New History of Life*, 196–208.

32. Benton, *The History of Life*, 83–84.

dehydration. Animals were thus able to travel great distances from water sources and nest on dry land. This kind of egg, an *amniotic egg*, evolved in a group of tetrapods called reptiles over 300 million years ago.[33] The first reptile that we know of, *Hylonomus*, was a lizard, 10–20 cm in size, of the Carboniferous coal forests that likely fed on millipedes and insects. *Hylonomus* fossils have been found in fossilized, hollow tree trunks where the animal may have sheltered during floods or nested.[34] Reptiles were no longer tied to water bodies for reproduction; they could now make a home anywhere on the single enormous supercontinent of Pangea, which contained all the landmass on Earth.

At the beginning of the Permian period, 300 million years ago, the tropical rainforest ecosystems that had dominated Pangea during the Carboniferous collapsed as the climate became cooler and drier.[35] Rivers and inland lakes dried up. But because their eggs provided them with reproduction independent of water, the ancestral amniotes were able to occupy and thrive in all parts of the drying supercontinent. The ancestral lineage of amniotic reptiles split into several groups, including the *synapsids* and *diapsids*. The synapsids, which include the "mammal-like reptiles," came to dominate Pangea throughout the Permian period. Although most of them were initially rather small in size, their descendants ranged widely in size and body styles. The armored, herbivorous *Scutosaurus* and the saber-toothed *Inostrancevia* that preyed upon them were larger than modern-day hippos and rhinos.[36] The other main group of amniotes, the diapsids, included the crocodile-like *Archosaurs*, the ancestor of all modern-day reptiles, snakes, and turtles. In many ways, the diversity and abundance of animal life inhabiting Pangea and the great ocean around it 252 million years ago was as great if not greater than what we find in the world today. But then disaster struck!

---

33. Ibid.

34. George R. McGhee Jr., *When the Invasion of Land Failed: The Legacy of the Devonian Extinctions* (New York: Columbia University Press, 2014), 254–55.

35. Jim Baggott, *Origins: The Scientific Story of Creation* (Oxford: Oxford University Press, 2015), 293–96.

36. Benton, *The History of Life*, 109–12.

Apocalypse and Opportunity

Biological extinction occurs when no living, reproducing members of a species remains. Extinctions happens all the time as one species is gradually replaced by another over thousands or millions of years. But since the beginning of the Cambrian period 542 million years ago, geologists have identified five *mass-extinction events.* A mass-extinction event is a large-scale disappearance of an abnormally large number of species in a comparatively short period of time (in geological terms).[37] The reasons for these extinction events are presumably due to global ecological disruptions of some type. The exact causes of these events are the subject of much scientific investigation and speculation. The greatest of all mass extinctions occurred at the end of the Permian period, 251 million years ago, and brought the Paleozoic (ancient animal life) era to a dramatic close. In the end-Permian extinction event, also called "the Great Dying," 96 percent of all marine animal species and 80 percent of all land animal species disappeared over a period of less than a million years.[38] Evidence suggests that the immediate cause of the Permian extinction was a runaway cycle of global warming set up by disruption of the Earth's carbon cycle.[39] But the trigger for the event is not known for certain. The timing of the end-Permian extinction coincides with a series of massive eruptions from a super volcano called the Siberian Traps. Another possibility is global, large-scale release of the toxic gas hydrogen sulfide from anoxic ocean waters. Whatever the ultimate cause, evidence suggests that the worst of these toxic conditions lasted around 60,000 years.[40] The devastating effect on Permian species was near total. Life on Earth was at the brink of annihilation.

In the oceans, the dominant trilobites were entirely gone, but a few species of molluscs, sea urchins, and fishes remained, along with isolated fragments of coral reefs. On land, the giant clubmosses

---

37. Elizabeth Kolbert, *The Sixth Extinction: An Unnatural History* (New York: Henry Holt, 2014), 15–17.

38. Benton, *The History of Life*, 101–2.

39. Ward and Kirschvinck, *A New History of Life*, 211–24.

40. Seth D. Burgess, "High-Precision Timeline for Earth's Most Severe Extinction," *PNAS USA* 111 (2014): 3316–21.

and horsetails that dominated the Permian forests were largely destroyed, but a few seed ferns and early gymnosperms remained. Very few of the land tetrapods survived the Permian apocalypse. But in some remote corners of the Pangean super continent, perhaps a secluded valley, ravine, or cave, and in a few protected, near-shore bays or lakes, life found a way. The survivors included a few species of *Archosaurs* and a handful of synapsid herbivores such as *Lystrosaurus. Lystrosaurus* was a pig-sized creature with two canine teeth and a bony beak that allowed it to snap off plant stems for food.[41] Insects were devastated, though overall they fared better than the larger animals. However these remnants of the Paleozoic era were able to survive, whether by a particular fortuitous adaptation or just by being at the right place at the right time, they were the seeds of Earth's next great biological boom, the Mesozoic era, also known as the Age of the Dinosaurs.

Life's recovery from the Great Dying was slow at first, but eventually a new diversity of plants and animals spread over the face of the Earth. The biggest evolutionary breakthroughs of the Triassic period were the first dinosaurs, which descended from the surviving Permian *Archosaurs.*[42] These archosaurs gave rise not only to the dinosaurs and flying pterosaurs but their modern-day relatives, the crocodiles, turtles, and birds. By the end of the Triassic period, 200 million years ago, all the major groups of dinosaurs had appeared.[43] For the next 140 million years, which include the Jurassic and Cretaceous periods, the dinosaurs ruled the Earth. This lineage of reptiles was better adapted to the warm, dry conditions prevalent in Pangea during the Triassic period than were the mammal-like reptiles who had dominated the forests of the Permian period.[44] Hence the dinosaurs now would become the dominant herbivores and predators of Pangea.

The dinosaurs survived another large-scale extinction event at the end of the Triassic period as the supercontinent Pangea began break-

41. Benton, *The History of Life*, 111–12.

42. Baggott, Origins, 298–304.

43. Benton, *The History of Life*, 132–35.

44. Michael Benton, *The Dinosaurs Rediscovered: How a Scientific Revolution Is Rewriting History* (London: Thames & Hudson, 2019), 39–51.

ing up.[45] The Atlantic Ocean started to open, and the landmasses that would become Eurasia and North America drifted north, away from Gondwanaland, which would eventually become South America, Africa, and Antarctica. The complexities of the emerging coastlines and new geographic configurations of the landmasses created a wide range of new habitats and ecologies to be exploited by the diversifying populations of dinosaurs. Some of them grew to enormous sizes, like the giant sauropods *Apatosaurus* and *Argentinosaurus* and the super-predator *Tyrannosaurus rex*.[46] The great body weights of these gargantuan beasts were supported by the robust skeletons that we now see as casts in museum displays. A visit to the Earth at the end of the Cretaceous period, 65 million years ago, would have been awe inspiring but also a terrifying experience for humans. Life had never been so abundant, so diverse, and . . . so large! And then in a blinding flash, the dinosaurs vanished.

Theodicy

As we have seen in chapter 6, Darwin struggled personally with the legacy of extinction, pain, and suffering that he saw in the history of life on Earth, so much so that by the end of his life he considered himself an agnostic. In his autobiography, Darwin restates a very old theological question:

> A being so powerful and so full of knowledge as a God who could create the universe, is to our finite minds omnipotent and omniscient, and it revolts our understanding to suppose that his benevolence is not unbounded, for what advantage can there be in the sufferings of millions of animals throughout almost endless time?[47]

In other words, how can we account for the presence of a good and loving God who allows so much suffering to go on in the world? The

---

45. Steve Brusatte, *The Rise and Fall of the Dinosaurs* (New York: William Morrow, 2018), 85–99.

46. Benton, *The History of Life*, 136–44.

47. Charles Darwin, *The Autobiography of Charles Darwin*, ed. Nora Barlow (New York: W. W. Norton, 1958), 75.

existence of suffering and evil in the world is the problem of theodicy.[48] How much more would Darwin's concern be amplified had he known anything about the mass extinctions that occurred at the end of the Permian and Cretaceous periods?

But in the view of a growing number of theologians, Darwinism also provides an answer to the problem of theodicy, and, in this way, Darwin has provided a "gift to theology."[49] According to Catholic theologian John Haught, Darwinism dispels the notion of the deliberate design of all living creatures once and for all. This lifts an intractable theological burden. Freed from the responsibility for "design," God can also not be held responsible for the various misfortunes and suffering that all living things must eventually endure. God did not design those either. No longer do we need to account for such events as all being a "part of God's plan." Further, from a trinitarian Christian context, God, in the person of Jesus, who suffered and died on the cross, suffers *with* the natural world, not apart from it. Haught suggests that "Christians have discerned in the 'Christ-event' the decisive self-emptying or *kenosis* of God."[50] Elizabeth Johnson adds, "The *kenotic* position perceives that God voluntarily self-limits divine power in order to participate voluntarily in the life of the world."[51] God's voluntary participation includes the suffering of the world. This is reminiscent of St. Paul saying, "We know that all creation is groaning in labor pains even until now" (Rom 8:22).

God enters freely into the suffering of nature and joins with all creatures in the process of evolution. From a Franciscan perspective, the God of love who suffers with the world is a humble God.[52] Ilia Delio combines the idea of the humility of God with the progressive evolutionary vision of Teilhard de Chardin. Teilhard was motivated in part by his battlefield experiences of the evils of World War I to

---

48. John F. Haught, *God after Darwin: A Theology of Evolution* (Boulder, CO: Westview Press, 2000), 45.

49. Ibid., 45–56.

50. Ibid., 110.

51. Elizabeth Johnson, *Ask the Beasts: Darwin and the God of Love* (London: Bloomsbury Publishing, 2014), 162.

52. Ilia Delio, *The Humility of God: A Franciscan Perspective* (Cincinnati, OH: Franciscan Media, 2005), 89–103.

use the sweep of evolutionary progress as perhaps a way of bringing order and harmony out of chaos and loss.[53] From this perspective, each human person makes the choice of joining with God or against God in the creative process, and it is resistance to this mystery that is at the root of evil. Whether one agrees with a progressive view of evolution or not, a new solution to the problem of theodicy emerges from the integration of Darwinian science and contemporary Christian thought. Not all theologians will likely agree with these new perspectives, but the conversation and our understanding of God have been moved forward—perhaps to a point where we might find a new answer on how to respond to the ongoing extinctions in our world and the human responsibility for them.

And the Meek Shall Inherit the Earth

Since Darwin's time, the fate of the giant creatures that we call the dinosaurs was the object of much speculation. Possible reasons included a global cooling of the climate brought on by heavy snow, or perhaps a period of tremendous volcanic upheavals. In the mid-1970s, Walter Alvarez, a young geologist studying the origins of the Apennine Mountains in Italy, came across a thin layer of clay between layers of limestone straddling the transition between the Cretaceous period and the younger, Tertiary period. Alvarez's father, Luis, who was a Nobel Prize–winning physics professor at the University of California, arranged for the analysis of the clay layer and found it to be highly enriched in the element iridium.[54] Iridium, which is very rare on Earth's surface but is abundant in meteorite dust, falls to Earth at a slow steady rate either in larger meteorites that we see burning up in our atmosphere as shooting stars or, very occasionally, in meteors that impact the Earth's surface. Excited by the implications of this finding, Walter traveled to several other locations around the world where Late Cretaceous limestones were exposed and found the same iridium-rich layer of sediment he had

53. Ilia Delio, *Christ in Evolution* (Maryknoll, NY: Orbis Books, 2008), 141–43.

54. Walter Alvarez, *T. Rex and the Crater of Doom* (Princeton, NJ: Princeton University Press, 1991), 63–70.

found in Italy. To Walter and Luis Alvarez, the best explanation for this finding was an impact, 65 million years ago, by a comet or asteroid. This could have caused a global cataclysm that annihilated the dinosaurs and many other life forms that existed on Earth at this time. The Alvarezes published their impact hypothesis in the journal *Science*,[55] triggering a decade-long debate in the geological community and a search for the impact site. Finally, in 1991, using the old survey records of a Mexican petroleum company, the impact site was located just off the coast of the present-day Yucatan peninsula near the town of Chicxulub.[56] Beneath the waters of the Gulf of Mexico, buried under millions of years of sediment, lies an impact crater 200 km across and initially as deep as 40 km.

Alvarez estimates that the force of the impact explosion was roughly equivalent to that of 100 million hydrogen bombs.[57] The environmental consequences of this collision are almost unimaginable. Alvarez suggests that a giant fireball flung molten debris thousands of kilometers in every direction while injecting thousands of metric tons of dust high into the atmosphere, heating the air like an oven. A great firestorm then swept through the forests of North and South America, raising the temperature of the atmosphere to several hundred degrees and incinerating almost everything in its path. At the same time, a tsunami, perhaps a thousand kilometers high, swept along the coasts of the world, devastating the shorelines and low-lying areas. Enormous quantities of seawater were vaporized and reacted with sulfates from the rock and nitrogen from the air to form acids, which bathed the devastated surface of the Earth in an acid rain that may have lasted for weeks. Much of Earth's animal and plant life, especially in the present-day Americas, perished within hours. As the ejected dust and firestorm soot spread around the globe, the Earth was plunged into a long period of total darkness

---

55. Luis W. Alvarez, Walter Alvarez, Frank Asaro, and Helen V. Michel, "Extraterrestrial Cause for the Cretaceous-Tertiary Extinction," *Science* 208 (1980): 1095–1108.

56. Alan R. Hildebrand et al., "Chicxulub Crater: A Possible Cretaceous/Tertiary Boundary Impact Crater on the Yucatán Peninsula, Mexico," *Geology* 19 (1991): 867–71.

57. Alvarez, *T. Rex and the Crater of Doom*, 8.

that shut down photosynthesis. Globally, food chains collapsed. Any large animals that survived the initial destruction would soon succumb to starvation the world over.

As the dust from the last day of the Cretaceous period began to settle and sunlight returned, photosynthesis could begin to recover. But the comet impact had vaporized massive limestone deposits in the Gulf of Mexico, releasing trapped carbon dioxide into the atmosphere. This would have set up a greenhouse effect, making much of the Earth's surface uninhabitable for many years, until the planktonic food webs in the seas and the forests and grasslands on land could recover. By then the dinosaurs, large marine reptiles, and almost all bird life were extinct. In the seas, the abundant populations of ammonites and many fishes were extinct.[58] Life on Earth would never be the same, but it would go on. Hidden deep in burrows and caves, evolving in the shadows of the dinosaurs for well over 100 million years, the heirs to this new world would finally emerge.

The earliest mammals evolved from reptiles of the Triassic period around 200 million years ago, long before the Cretaceous extinction event.[59] They were very small in size and likely looked like lizards. During the Jurassic period, while dinosaurs were becoming much larger and more diverse, the three major modern groups of mammals appeared. They are the egg-laying monotremes (echidnas and platypus), the marsupials (kangaroos, koalas, possums, and wombats), and placental mammals (everything else). The earliest mammals were likely small nocturnal insectivores.[60] Mammals are warm-blooded and have fur for insulation, so they were able to move about during nights or on colder days when the dinosaurs were much less active. During times when dinosaurs were most active or during cold periods, the tiny mammals could remain in underground burrows or other secluded hiding spaces where they could continue to nurture their young and/or hibernate

58. Benton, *The History of Life*, 144–45.

59. Zhe-Xi Luo, "Transformation and Diversification of Early Mammal Evolution," *Nature* 450 (2007): 1011–19.

60. Benton, *The History of Life*, 135–36.

for extended periods. It is these various mammalian adaptations that enabled them to survive the apocalypse that swept the dinosaurs from the face of the Earth.[61]

The Cenozoic era, also known as the Age of Mammals, began 65 million years ago on the day the Mesozoic era ended. The first 10 million years or so of this era, called the Paleocene epoch, was essentially a time of recovery from the Cretaceous catastrophe. The Paleocene saw a rapid diversification of both plants and animals.[62] Flowering plants, the angiosperms, became the dominant form of plant on Earth and evolved side by side with animals in a mutually interdependent way. The colorful and aromatic flowers of angiosperms and the nutritious fruits that they produce provided a rich food source for animals. In turn, animal contact with the plants provided a mechanism for the spread of pollen and the dispersal of seeds to new areas. With the dinosaurs gone, rapid niche exploitation and the co-evolution of plants and animals during the Paleocene resulted in a recovery of the world's jungles and other land habitats. The diversification of mammalian life during the Paleocene was as spectacular as the diversification of reptiles during the early years of the Mesozoic. Today there are twenty-one distinct orders of mammals, ranging from aardvarks and armadillos to whales and dolphins, and most of them appeared during this rapid diversification period. One of the more recent species to emerge from the ape lineage would quickly become the single-most dominant creature ever to live on Earth. This is a species that not only responds to climate change or other ecological catastrophes; it also causes them.

Human Evolution

When I was in graduate school, living in Columbia, South Carolina, there was a local artist who was commissioned to paint murals on many of the city's buildings. On one, the Taylor Street Pharmacy, he painted a young woman in a gymnastic pose whose long,

61. Olaf R. P. Bininda-Emonds et al., "The Delayed Rise of Present-Day Mammals," *Nature* 446 (2007): 507–12.

62. Ward and Kirschvinck, *A New History of Life*, 307–19.

curled hair gave rise to strands of light that became a rainbow covering the long side of the building. Across the top of the mural was the inscription "Wellness of Body, Mind, and Spirit." As I walked past the pharmacy each day on my way to the University of South Carolina campus, those three words, "body, mind, and spirit," became deeply embedded together in my own psyche. To me, they came to mean the real essence of humanity. In my experience, you can't really talk about one of these human characteristics without talking about the others. We might talk about the evolution of the human body over geological epochs or the development of a human mind during a lifetime, but without consideration of the spirit, the picture is incomplete.

How did our species, *Homo sapiens,* come to be who we are today, that is, human in body, mind, and spirit? One traditional explanation, the one to which many religious believers adhere, is the familiar tale found in the first chapter of the book of Genesis. This story was first written down by an ancient people who lived long ago. It was certainly told for an audience that had a very different understanding of the natural world than we have today, but this should not be a problem. As long ago as 400 CE, St. Augustine of Hippo argued that we should not insist on a literal reading of scripture if new information comes to light that was not available to ancient peoples.[63] Science has revealed that the species *H. sapiens* emerged on Earth as all species do—gradually over many years, through the process Darwin called evolution by natural selection. The "modern synthesis" of Darwinian natural selection, genetics, and molecular biology has opened a window on the natural world that was not available to the philosophers, scholars, and theologians of centuries past. It is through the window of evolution that biologists view the world in order to build on Darwin's theory. According to Pope John Paul II,

> [Darwin's theory] has been progressively accepted by researchers following a series of discoveries in various fields of knowl-

63. Peter M. J. Hess and Paul L. Allen, *Catholicism and Science* (Westport, CT: Greenwood Press, 2008), 6–12.

> edge. This convergence, neither sought nor fabricated, of the results of work that was conducted independently is a significant argument in favor of this theory.[64]

In other words, Pope John Paul II said that we must take the science of evolution seriously if we are to understand our biological origins. What we learn about our biological origins might, in turn, bring us to a deeper religious sense of humanity—body, mind, and spirit.

Body

In 1871, Charles Darwin published a follow-up work to *On the Origin of Species* entitled *The Descent of Man*, in which he applied his theory of natural selection to the investigation of human origins.[65] Darwin did not propose that humans descended from apes, as the popular caricatures portray, but rather that we shared a common ancestor with the great apes that are found today in the forests of Africa. There are obviously many differences between humans and modern apes—body size, brain size, behavior patterns, and civilization—to name just a few. But Darwin proposed that what started our ancestors down the evolutionary road to becoming human was becoming bipedal, that is, walking on two legs. Modern science has largely confirmed Darwin's hypothesis and has revealed a whole lot more.

The earliest ancestors of the primates were most likely squirrel-like creatures that spent most of their lives in forest canopies of what is now the Eurasian landmass, feeding on insects.[66] From these origins, these ancestral animals spread west to North America and south to Africa, where they gave rise to the first monkeys around 35 million years ago. By around 25 million years ago, Earth had entered a cooling period, and the tropical forests began to thin out. Some groups of monkeys spent more time on the ground along the edges of the forests. Over time, these animals gave rise to the first apes.[67] Between six

---

64. John Paul II, "Evolution and the Living God," in *Science and Theology: The New Consonance*, ed. Ted Peters (Boulder, CO: Westview Press, 1997), 149–52.

65. Charles Darwin, *The Descent of Man: And Selection in Relation to Sex* (London: Folio Society, 2008), reprint of the rev. 2nd ed. published in 1877.

66. Baggott, *Origins*, 313–20.

67. Iyad Zalmout et al., "New Oligocene Primate from Saudi Arabia and the Divergence of Apes from Old World Monkeys," *Nature* 466 (2010): 360–64.

and eight million years ago lived the last common ancestor between *hominins* (the tribal name given to the human evolutionary lineage) and our nearest primate cousins, the chimpanzees. These creatures lived an arboreal existence in tropical African forests, subsisting mostly on fruits, much as modern chimpanzees do today.[68]

Around five million years ago, Earth's climate again changed. Earth entered a period of cooling, and the African rainforests started receding, giving way to more open woodlands and eventually grasslands. Around the edges of the retreating forests, food became more seasonal and difficult to find. Ancient hominins had to travel farther to find food. It turns out that if you start with a basic primate body plan, a bipedal gait is a more efficient way of traveling than on all fours.[69] Although bipedal hominins were slower than creatures who could run on all fours, their heads were elevated, affording them a longer line of sight on open grasslands. Thus, predators could be avoided, even though they could not necessarily be outrun. The transition of hominins from arboreal living to full bipedalism likely did not happen all at once, but in fits and starts. One can imagine hominin populations relying initially on short dashes between the covering trees, and then gradually evolving into organisms that spent longer and longer times in the open as our ancestors adapted to the gradual disappearance of the forests. Eventually, the trees were no longer needed for cover and food. The hominin forelimbs, already adapted for grasping tree branches, could now become useful not only for carrying food but for grasping sticks and rocks to be used in food gathering and/or bodily defense.

The remains of our oldest fully bipedal ancestor, *Australopithecus afarensis,* dating to about 3.5 million years ago, were discovered in Ethiopia in the 1970s in an area called the East African Rift Valley. This find, nicknamed *Lucy* after the popular Beatles' song "Lucy in the Sky with Diamonds," is probably the most famous of early hominins, but several similar species of around this age have also been identified.[70] The oldest recognized member of our human genus,

---

68. Daniel Lieberman, *The Story of the Human Body: Evolution, Health, and Disease* (New York: Pantheon Books, 2013), 28–31.

69. Ibid., 39–47.

70. Baggott, *Origins*, 322.

Homo habilis, meaning "handy man" for the species' use of simple tools, was found in the Olduvai Gorge area of the African Rift Valley in the 1960s by Louis and Mary Leakey.[71] The remains of other archaic human species have been found in Africa, the Middle East, Europe, Asia, and the islands of Indonesia.[72] A long-standing model of human evolution held that we began as one of these ancient species over one million years ago in Africa and gradually spread to other parts of the world, with the various dispersed groups evolving together into modern *H. sapiens.* According to this *multiregional model,* low levels of gene flow between the dispersed groups kept the evolving humans a single coherent species throughout our history, despite the development of regional racial differences.[73] Over time, each of these ancestral species was thought to give rise to the next in a long linear sequence eventually leading to *H. sapiens* around 200,000 years ago. The famous cartoon of an ape-like creature gradually standing up and transforming into a human in some ways characterizes this simple model, but it turns out to be incorrect. The story of human evolution now seems much more complicated and far more intriguing than the linear multiregional model.

In common usage, the word "human" refers to a member of our species *H. sapiens.* In contrast, anthropologists will often mean "human" to include any member of our genus *Homo,* including all now-extinct species. This language might include modifiers like "modern" to refer to *H. sapiens* and "archaic" to refer any of the extinct *Homo* species.[74] I will use the word "human" in its most inclusive sense to refer to all members of our genus, unless noted otherwise. Recent evidence suggests that there was not a single human radiation out of Africa but likely many, and by different species of humans. *Homo sapiens* was just the most recent migrant. Also, not all human species started out in Africa (though they had ancestors

71. Bernard Wood, *Human Evolution: A Very Short Introduction* (Oxford: Oxford University Press, 2005), 79–82.

72. Lieberman, *The Story of the Human Body,* 108.

73. Franz Weidenreich, "Facts and Speculations concerning the Origin of *Homo sapiens,*" *American Anthropologist* 49 (1947):187–203.

74. Chris Stringer, *Lone Survivors: How We Came to Be the Only Humans on Earth* (New York: St. Martin's Griffin, 2012).

there), and at various times these different species had contact with each other. The first African migrant, *Homo ergaster*, appears to have been an African contemporary of the Leakeys' *H. habilis.*[75] *Homo ergaster* moved from Africa out across the Arabian Peninsula and had spread as far as the Caucasus Mountains in Turkey by about 1.8 million years ago. [76] In the mountains of Turkey, the story of *H. ergaster*, so far as we know, came to an end. We do not know why the species did not go any farther. But an African descendent of *H. ergaster*, named *Homo erectus*, or "upright man," would go on to become the most long-lived of all human species. *Homo erectus*, with a more upright posture, larger brain, and body size than any of its predecessors, would thrive throughout Africa and Asia perhaps until as recently as 35,000 years ago.[77]

Groups of *H. erectus* are thought to have left Africa around 1.7 million years ago and spread through Asia and Indonesia.[78] In Asia, *H. erectus* fossils have been given names like "Peking Man" or "Java Man" after the locations in which they have been found.[79] It was Teilhard de Chardin's work with a team of archaeologists at the famous Peking Man site at Zhoukoudian Cave in China that inspired his theological writings on human evolution.[80] *Homo erectus* made use of fire, as had *H. ergaster*, but was more adept at using tools than any of its predecessors had been. Descendants of the Asian populations of *H. erectus* include *Homo soloensis* ("Solo Man"), found in Java, and *Homo floresiensis*, nicknamed "the hobbits" for their small size. *Homo floresiensis*, as far as is currently known, lived exclusively on the remote Indonesian island of Flores from around 180,000 years ago until as recently as 12,000 years ago.[81] Very recently, another Pacific island descendent of *H. erectus* was discovered in the

---

75. Baggott, *Origins*, 326–27.
76. Wood, Human *Evolution*, 79–86.
77. Ibid., 90–93.
78. Stringer, *Lone Survivors*, 26.
79. Ibid., 5–35.
80. Ursula King, *Spirit of Fire: The Life and Vision of Teilhard de Chardin* (Maryknoll, NY: Orbis Books, 1996), 126–33.
81. M. J. Morwood et al., "Archaeology and Age of a New Hominin from Flores in Eastern Indonesia," *Nature* 431 (2004): 1087–91.

Philippines.[82] A European descendent of *H. erectus* found in Spain, *Homo antecessor,* dated at around 800,000 years ago, suggests that for a time, *H. erectus* and its descendants may have been quite widespread on the Eurasian continent.[83]

A species distinctly different from, though possibly descended from *H. erectus,* appeared in Africa around 700,000 years ago. This species had a larger brain and reduced jaws and teeth, possibly due to more systematic use of cooking fire. For an African species, it has a rather unusual name, *Homo heidelburgensis,* because the first fossil of its type was found far from Africa in Germany.[84] The wide geographic distribution of *H. heidelburgensis* fossils indicates that a third migration of a human species out of Africa had taken place somewhere around 400,000 years ago.[85] *Homo heidelburgensis* was the immediate forebear of our own species, *H. sapiens,* in Africa and at least two distinctly non-African human species.[86] European populations of *H. heidelburgensis* gave rise to the Neanderthals (*Homo neanderthalis*), which thrived throughout western and central Europe from 300,000 to 30,000 years ago, and the Denisovans (*Homo denisova*), which occupied eastern Asia and Indonesia at approximately the same time.

The third significant descendent of *H. heidelburgensis,* the modern human *H. sapiens,* emerged first in Africa approximately 200,000 years ago.[87] There is evidence that some *H. sapiens* migrated from east Africa and spread throughout the Middle East around 100,000 years ago.[88] For reasons unknown, the migration stopped, but *H. sapiens* did expand throughout Africa, with the population reaching over one million individuals by about 90,000 years ago.[89] Between 80,000

---

82. Florent Detroit et al., "A New Species of *Homo* from the Late Pleistocene of the Philippines," *Nature* 568 (2019): 181–86.

83. Baggott, *Origins*, 331.

84. Wood, *Human Evolution*, 93.

85. Ibid., 86–93.

86. Baggott, *Origins*, 332–34.

87. Stringer, *Lone Survivors*, 206.

88. Saioa Lopez, Lucy van Dorp, and Garrett Hellenthal, "Human Dispersal out of Africa: A Lasting Debate," *Evolutionary Bioinformatics* 11, no. S2 (2016): 57–68.

89. Stanley H. Ambrose, "Late Pleistocene Human Population Bottlenecks, Volcanic

and 70,000 years ago, the African population declined sharply, falling to as low as a few thousand individuals in what appears to be a near-extinction event for our species. The reason for *H. sapiens*'s near-extinction is uncertain, but it has been suggested that it could be linked to a worldwide change in climate triggered by the massive volcanic eruption of Mount Tobo in Sumatra. According to this "genetic bottleneck" theory, changes to the African homeland of our ancestors included an extended drought and disruption of the monsoon patterns on which central African rainforests depend.[90] A genetic bottleneck is an evolutionary concept that has been observed in many different animal and plant species after a near die-off or the separation of a small group from a larger population. Genetic changes that arise through mutation in the small group can pass quickly through the entire population, leading to a period of rapid differentiation of new characteristics.

The actual number of *H. sapiens* migrations out of Africa is still uncertain,[91] but by 60,000 years ago human populations in Africa had largely recovered, and by 45,000 years ago a major migration of *H. sapiens* out of Africa had begun.[92] This migration was wildly successful. By 40,000 years ago, our species inhabited Australia and Indonesia, and by 25,000 years ago, *H. sapiens* was in all parts of Europe. Asian migrations included the area of Beringia in eastern Siberia, where an intercontinental land-bridge facilitated the crossing of *H. sapiens* into North America. By 12,000 years ago, modern humans had occupied all parts of the world, from the African rainforests of our ancestors to the southernmost tip of South America and all places in between. In a span of perhaps 50,000 years from our near extinction in central Africa to the colonization of South America, we had become the most prolific and successful of all human species. But our great evolutionary success seems to have come at the expense of our sibling species.

Winter, and Differentiation of Modern Humans," *Journal of Human Evolution* 34 (1998): 623–51.

90. Ambrose, "Late Pleistocene Human Population Bottlenecks," 623–51.

91. Lopez et al., "Human Dispersal out of Africa," 57–68.

92. Wood, *Human Evolution*, 109–10.

Mind

If a starship full of explorers from another world visited Earth some 50,000 years ago, around the time our species' successful "out of Africa" migration began, they would have found at least six human species inhabiting different parts of the world. These would have included the three sibling species *H. neanderthalis, H. denisova,* and *H. sapiens* living in Europe, Asia, and Africa respectively. They also could have encountered the long-lived *H. erectus* populations of southern Asia and their Indonesian offshoots, *H. soloensis* and the diminutive *H. floresiensis.* It is not far-fetched to suppose that there may have been other human species about whom we do not yet know. As I finish this book, *H. luzonensis* from the Philippine Islands has just been added to the list.[93] Returning to Earth today, the explorers would find only one human species remaining, namely, us. So, what happened?

We do know that as the geographic range of *H. sapiens* expanded, the range of other species contracted. This has been detailed quite convincingly for the Neanderthals of western Europe. European caves occupied originally by Neanderthals were later occupied by modern humans.[94] At some sites there is evidence of alternating occupation of caves by Neanderthals and modern humans, with the last layer of fossils belonging to humans. This indicates that around 45,000 years ago, Neanderthals and modern humans occupied the same parts of Europe.[95] The youngest Neanderthal remains from the Iberian Peninsula of modern Spain and Portugal are aged at about 35,000 years. After this time, the Neanderthals appear to have become extinct, replaced in all parts of Europe by the new arrivals, *H. sapiens.*[96] Similarly, the extinction of *H. floresiensis* corresponds closely with the arrival of our species on the remote, hobbit-home world of Flores.[97]

---

93. Detroit et al., "A New Species of *Homo*," 181–86.

94. Dimitra Papagianni and Michael A. Morse, *The Neanderthals Rediscovered* (London: Thames & Hudson, 2015), 154–65.

95. Ibid., 176

96. Ibid.

97. Thomas Sutikna et al., "Revised Stratigraphy and Chronology of *Homo floresiensis* at Luong Bua in Indonesia," *Nature* 532 (2016): 366–69.

It cannot be said with certainty if *H. sapiens* directly caused the extinction of our sibling species or simply occupied their niches as the dwindling archaic humans succumbed to other factors. But we do know that our species had some contact with the other humans, as interbreeding of the species is known to have occurred.[98] Native Europeans today have a 2 to 4 percent Neanderthal component in their DNA.[99] Aboriginal Australians and natives of Melanesia have 4 to 6 percent Denisovan DNA.[100] Whether these interspecific interactions were violent or peaceful can only be speculation. We do not know whether *H. sapiens* overcame the other human species we encountered through a series of interspecific tribal wars, assimilation, and interbreeding of the newcomers with the indigenous populations, or by being better competitors for limited food and other resources. Quite possibly it was some combination of these. But the eventual fate of our sibling species was the same as has been experienced by so many species—plants, insects, mammals, birds, etc.—within a very short time of encountering *H. sapiens* for the first time: extinction.

There is a popular childhood mental experiment called "Who would win in a fight?" Batman or Superman? X-Men or Power Rangers? Tyrannosaurus rex or Velociraptor? We might also venture: *H. sapiens* or *H. neanderthalis*? We know from fossil evidence that *H. neanderthalis* had a more robust physical build than the original *H. sapiens* of 100,000 years ago. Fossilized skulls show that *H. neanderthalis* also had a larger brain size.[101] Neanderthals were skilled in the manufacture and use of stone tools and weapons.[102] Neanderthal prowess in hunting the large game of Europe probably made them

98. Julia Galway-Witham and Chris Stringer, "How Did *Homo sapiens* Evolve?" *Science* 360 (2018): 1296–98.

99. Richard E. Green et al., "A Draft Sequence of the Neanderthal Genome," *Science* 328 (2010): 710–22; Kay Prufer et al., "The Complete Genome Sequence of a Neanderthal from the Altai Mountains," *Nature* 505 (2014): 43–49.

100. Matthias Meyer et al., "A High-Coverage Genome Sequence from an Archaic Denisovan Individual," *Science* 338 (2012): 222–26.

101. Baggott, *Origins*, 332–34.

102. Papagianni and Morse, *Neanderthals Rediscovered*, 83–91.

better warriors than our ancestors.[103] It thus seems likely that one on one, our ancient African ancestors would be no match for our neighbors to the north. We also know that if the first *H. sapiens* incursion into Neanderthal territory occurred 100,000 years ago, as some evidence suggests, it did not go so well. *Homo sapiens* populations contracted back into our African homeland, perhaps repulsed by a physically superior species. In Africa, our species appears to have suffered a near-extinction event, but those that survived gave rise to a new population that was somehow different. *Homo sapiens* swept out of Africa a second time and quickly populated the Earth, replacing every other human group we came into contact with. What changed?

Careful analysis of Neanderthal and *H. sapiens* skulls from 30,000 to 40,000 years ago shows that the brains of *H. sapiens* were smaller overall than Neanderthals, but our temporal lobes were 20 percent larger.[104] The temporal lobe of the human brain is where the language centers are located. Just underlying the temporal lobe is the hippocampus, where learning and memory functions originate. So, the current thinking is that somewhere between 100,000 and 50,000 years ago, African *H. sapiens* developed complex language that led to better communication skills, allowing for better coordination among larger groups of humans.[105] By then, a band of modern *H. sapiens* coming up against a group of Neanderthals might still lose the first round of a hostile interaction but would be able to come up with and coordinate changing strategies that would lead to success in subsequent encounters.[106] These more modern *H. sapiens* also traded with other groups of *H. sapiens*, suggesting more than just tribal cooperation. Cave paintings and artifacts from 30,000 years ago indicate storytelling and imaginative thinking.[107] These *H. sapiens* were well on their way to becoming us. The cognitive revolution had begun, and with it would eventually come the great human civilizations of

---

103. Ibid., 151–53.

104. Lieberman, *The Story of the Human Body*, 137–41.

105. Yuval Noah Harari, *Sapiens: A Brief History of Humankind* (New York: HarperCollins, 2015), 119–32.

106. Ibid., 34–36.

107. Ibid., 20–25.

history. A computer modeling study with an enculturated *H. sapiens* population encountering a Neanderthal population of similar size predicted that competitive exclusion of the Neanderthals would result.[108] If Neanderthals had developed complex language and thought sooner, the outcomes might have been different.

When I am discussing human evolution with church or other religious groups it is usually about this time in the story that a hand goes up in the back of the room and I know the question that is coming. "What about Adam and Eve?" a thoughtful voice calls out, garnering the affirming nods of many in the audience. In the late 1980s a study was done using newly developed DNA technology to sequence and compare mitochondrial DNA (mtDNA) from a broad cross-section of the global human population.[109] In humans, mitochondria, which contain some DNA, are present in all of our cells but are derived entirely from mitochondria present in the ovum (egg). Our mtDNA comes only from our mothers. The thinking was that if mtDNA from a large number of living humans was sampled, variations in the DNA sequence could be used to trace the timing and location of our most recent maternal common ancestor, in other words, "Eve," if one uses a religious context. Reports of the "finding of Eve" made news headlines around the world.[110] Subsequent studies were done using the Y-chromosome to trace the human male lineage to "Adam."[111]

The original "mitochondrial Eve" and "Y-chromosome Adam" studies confirmed a sub-Sahara African location as the home for our human ancestors, but disagreed significantly on the date. Subsequent analysis and refinement of methodologies have arrived at a

108. William Gilpin, Marcus W. Feldman, and Kenishi Aoki, "An Ecocultural Model Predicts Neanderthal Extinction through Competition with Modern Humans," *PNAS USA* 113 (2016): 2134–39.

109. Rebecca Cann, Mark Stoneking, and Allan C. Wilson, "Mitochondrial DNA and Human Evolution," *Nature* 325 (1987): 31–36.

110. Stringer, *Lone Survivors*, 3.

111. Fulvo Cruciani et al., "A Revised Root for the Human Y-chromosome Phylogenetic Tree: The Origin of Patrilineal Diversity in Africa," *American Journal of Human Genetics* 88 (2011): 814–18.

time of 135,000 years ago for Eve and 142,000 years ago for Adam.[112] These calculations are for the origination of an unbroken lineage of male or female offspring leading back to *H. sapiens*'s most recent common ancestor. This calculation does not necessarily mean that there was a single Adam and a single Eve, biologically. We know that there were many other human males and females living at the time. We also know there were other human species. So how do we reconcile our biological origins with our beloved and foundational religious narratives?

Spirit

The biblical story of the first man and woman, Adam and Eve, as recorded in Genesis, emerged from the mists of prehistory and the oral traditions of the Hebrew people around 5,000 years ago. By that time there were a number of thriving human civilizations firmly established (Mesopotamian, Greek, Egyptian, Chinese), each with its own stories. Telling stories requires language, and *H. sapiens*'s development of language, it seems, coincided with the development of our temporal lobe. Interestingly, modern neuroscience shows that the temporal lobe is also involved in religious and spiritual experiences.[113] Could it be that the development of language and the capacities of the temporal lobe also gave ancient humans the capacity to become aware of God for the first time and, through language, to begin to share those experiences with others?

In *The Descent of Man*, Charles Darwin suggested that it was spiritual practices and religion that set humankind apart from all other creatures, and he speculated on how these might have arisen:

> As soon as the important faculties of the imagination, wonder and curiosity, together with some power of reasoning, had become partially developed, man would naturally crave to understand what was passing around him and would have vaguely speculated on his own existence.[114]

---

112. Stringer, *Lone Survivors*, 180–81.

113. Andrew Newberg, Eugene D'Aquili, and Vince Rause, *Why God Won't Go Away: Brain Science and the Biology of Belief* (New York: Ballantine Books, 2002).

114. Darwin, *The Descent of Man*, 98.

Rituals and belief systems are deep-seated in our evolutionary past, as can be seen in the cave paintings, carvings, jewelry, and burial practices of our ancient ancestors as long as 100,000 years ago.[115] These observations and the ubiquitous practice of religions among modern peoples have led many to suggest that perhaps religious belief and practice gave some sort of evolutionary advantage to our human ancestors. In 1975, E. O. Wilson coined the term *sociobiology* to apply biological principles to the study of the social behavior of living organisms, including humans.[116] Wilson suggested that human religious and ethical behaviors were favored by natural selection working on groups of humans over time to enhance cooperative and mutually beneficial interactions. More recently, religions have been viewed as a product or even a "by-product" of our cognitive evolution.[117] For example, according to a recent theory from E. Fuller Torrey, the critical steps in the cognitive development of early humans were: first, the development of self-awareness, and an awareness of the thoughts of others; followed by an "autobiographical memory," which is the ability to project oneself forward and backward in time.[118] Once these cognitive abilities developed, they became involved in the worship of ancestors, nature spirits, and eventually gods as our species progressed over time.

It is noticeable that many biologically based theories of religion often have an implicit materialistic assumption underlying them.[119] It's as if to say that if the biological basis of religion can be explained in naturalistic terms, then any supernatural agency of God can be ruled out. But it seems to me that this type of approach serves only to confirm the philosophical commitments of the authors. Just because

---

115. Chris Stringer, *The Origin of Our Species* (New York: Penguin Books, 2011), 129–37.

116. Edward O. Wilson, *Sociobiology: The New Synthesis* (Cambridge, MA: Belknap Press, 1975), 4.

117. E. Fuller Torrey, *Evolving Brains, Emerging Gods: Early Humans and the Origins of Religion* (New York: Columbia University Press, 2017), 218–23.

118. Ibid., 203–06.

119. Richard Dawkins, *The God Delusion* (New York: Houghton Mifflin, 2006); Pascal Boyer, *Religion Explained: The Evolutionary Origins of Religious Thought* (New York: Basic Books, 2001), 375.

we can explain how and why something might have developed, we cannot necessarily predict to what purpose this trait, ability, or characteristic might be applied in the future. As we discussed in chapter 6, the protease enzymes of the blood-clotting cascade likely evolved from an accidental mistargeting of digestive enzymes to the bloodstream. The serine proteases, from an initial purpose of digesting dietary protein, later became adapted and elaborated as a solution to the problem of blood clotting. By the same argument, why could a suite of evolving cognitive abilities, developed originally because they enhanced certain survival skills of individuals in the wild, not be used for communication with a transcendent spirit or a creator God? In order to rule out this possibility, a precommitment to a materialist interpretation is required. As helpful as biologically based theories are in helping us to understand how we came to be who we are as a species, it is not helpful to overextend the methods of science and insist that they show "why there almost certainly is no God."[120] And it rules out the possibility that human experiences and relationship with God might be an ongoing part of the evolution of our species. Here is where the methods of theologians, ethicists, and social theorists just might be more helpful than traditional science.

Every Sunday, Roman Catholics profess that "We believe in one God, creator of heaven and earth," during the recitation of the Nicene Creed. Many Christians believe that God is eternal and unchanging. If God is eternal and unchanging, then it must be that it is our perception and our understanding of God that has actually evolved. Even a superficial reading of the Christian Bible reveals enormous differences between the vengeful, punishing God of the Old Testament and the God of love and forgiveness in the New. In his volumes on the Old and New Testaments, the popular Franciscan spirituality author Richard Rohr argues that it is not God, but rather our perceptions of God that have changed.[121] God has revealed Godself gradually over time as our human capacity to understand God

---

120. Dawkins, *The God Delusion*, 111–59.

121. Richard Rohr and Joseph Martos, *The Great Themes of Scripture: Old Testament* (Cincinnati, OH: Franciscan Media, 1987); Richard Rohr and Joseph Martos, *The Great Themes of Scripture: New Testament* (Cincinnati, OH: Franciscan Media, 1988).

has increased through the actions of the Holy Spirit. Our capacity to understand and respond to God's call did not stop with the New Testament but has continued to evolve. Some human conventions and practices, such as slavery, that were commonplace and accepted even in Jesus's time, are considered reprehensible by most religions today. The cognitive revolution triggered by our capacity to communicate was perhaps driven by, and has led to, an ongoing spiritual revolution. As a spiritual species, humans desire an ever-deepening relationship and understanding of God, to which God calls us. Our perceptions of God, physical reality, and one another have changed dramatically over human history and continue to change today. These changing perceptions continually expand the ways in which God reveals Godself to us.

Becoming Human

In the "Principle and Foundation" at the beginning of his *Spiritual Exercises,* St. Ignatius of Loyola states that "human beings are created to praise, reverence and serve God our Lord, and by means of doing this save our souls."[122] Contemporary Catholic theology, based heavily on the work of Jesuit theologian Karl Rahner, views the creation of the human person described by Ignatius as an ongoing process. What's more, each human person's "creation" is unique and personal:

> The phrase "the human person is created" must be read as a statement in the present tense. I have not been created once and for all in the past, but I am now the created one, my being created is something that is constantly taking place. Hence it must be said that I am the creature, now, uniquely. I am the one known to myself, the one who is directly the sole creature that has this characteristic of being immediately known, the characteristic which allows me to reach everything else.[123]

122. George E. Ganns, SJ, *The Spiritual Exercises of St. Ignatius: A Translation and Commentary* (Chicago: Loyola Press, 1992), 32.

123. Karl Rahner, *The Priesthood*, trans. Edward Quinn (New York: Seabury Press, 1973), 20–21.

Roman Catholics and most other Christians believe that each human person has a personal relationship with God. It is through our personal relationship and participation with God that we create not only ourselves but our evolving world.

Pierre Teilhard de Chardin, the French Jesuit we discussed in chapter 3, believed that humans were continuing to evolve, physically, mentally, and spiritually—guided by God toward some ultimate endpoint that he called the Omega Point. Although most modern biologists argue against directionality in the process of evolution, Teilhard's most important insight about evolution was that creation is an ongoing process. It is not something that happened long ago, and here we are today. Creation is happening today and every day, just as it was happening yesterday and all the yesterdays before that. In his book *Spirit of the Liturgy*, Joseph Ratzinger (Pope Emeritus Benedict XVI) writes:

> The cosmos is not a kind of closed building, a stationary container in which history may by chance take place. It is itself movement, from its one beginning to its one end. In a sense, creation *is* history. For example, against the background of the modern evolutionary world view, Teilhard de Chardin depicted the cosmos as a process of ascent, a series of unions. From very simple beginnings the path leads to ever greater and more complex unities, in which multiplicity is not abolished but merged into a growing synthesis, leading to the "Noosphere" in which spirit and its understanding embrace the whole and are blended into a kind of living organism.[124]

Teilhard believed that this series of unions would lead humanity ever closer to God. He also believed that our purpose, as humans, was to participate with God in God's ongoing creation. This is a profoundly optimistic view and one that today's world could surely learn from. Pope Emeritus Benedict XVI sees the vision of Teilhard de Chardin in the Catholic Mass, the liturgy that is celebrated every

124. Cardinal Joseph Ratzinger, *The Spirit of the Liturgy* (San Francisco: Ignatius Press, 2018), 42–43.

Sunday and each day of the week. This is a vision for the church that is open-ended and moving forward. This is not a backward-looking or static vision of the church. It is a vision that welcomes exploration for the faithful, similar to the vision of exploration shared by scientists. The solutions for which Pope Francis pleads, for the sake of our planet, in *Laudato si,'* require such a vision. Let's not be blind to it. Science and religion, together, can lead the way. For in the words of Pope John Paul II while discussing the intersection of science and religion, "We know, in fact, that truth cannot contradict truth."[125]

---

125. Pope John Paul II, "Evolution and the Living God," *Science and Theology: The New Consonance* (Boulder, CO: Westview Press, 1998), 149–52.

Index

Adam and Eve, 225, 226
adenosine triphosphate (ATP), 134, 135, 139, 143, 144
Age of Mammals, 213, 214
Age of the Dinosaurs, 208, 209
Albertus Magnus, 61
Alexander the Great, 87, 88, 89
Almagest (Ptolemy), 89, 90
Alvarez, Luis, 211, 212
Alvarez, Walter, 211, 212
amniotic egg, 206
animals and humans, origins of, in book of Genesis, 196
anthropic principle, 109–10
  weaker (WAP) and stronger (SAP), 110
Anthropocene era (Age of Man), 16
Apatosaurus, 209
archaea, 141, 143, 145, 146, 158
Archosaurs, 206, 208
Arecibo radio telescope, 154
Argentinosaurus, 209
Aristotle
  model of cosmos, 88–89
  and university curriculum, 59
asexual reproduction, 148
astrobiology, 151
atoms, 123
Augustine of Hippo, 94, 215
Australopithecus afarensis, 217
autotrophs, 144
Ayala, Francisco, 28
Bacon, Roger, 61
bacteria, 135, 139–43, 148. *See also* prokaryotes
Barbour, Ian, typologies of science and religion, 5–14, 45
Bardon, Louis, 78
Behe, Michael, 3, 181, 182–84, 190, 191
belief, in religion and science, 35–37
Bellarmine, Robert, 95, 98
Benedict XVI, Pope, on preservation of the environment, 16
Bergoglio, Jorge Mario. *See* Francis, Pope
Bergson, Henri, influence on Teilhard de Chardin, 68
Bhaskar, Roy, and critical realism, 45
Bible, literal interpretation of, 5, 179, 180
Big Bang, 100–109, 112, 114, 116, 117, 123, 124
binary fission, 148
biochemistry, 129, 130
biomineralization, 192, 193
bipedal hominins, 217
black hole, 102, 108, 112
body, human, evolution of, 216–21
bone formation, 194, 195
Boule, Marcellin, 68, 69
Bouyssonie, Jean and Amédée, 78
Boyer, Pascal, 29
brains, of *H. sapiens* and *H. neanderthalis*, 224

"brights," 65
Bryan, William Jennings, 178
Burgess fossil fauna, and evolution, 187–89
Bush, President George W., and hES cell research, 10, 11
Butler Act, 177, 178, 179

Cambrian conundrum, 189–91
Cambrian explosion, 159
Cambrian oxygenation hypothesis, 190
capital punishment, 177
carbon, chemistry of, 129, 130
Carter, Brandon, and anthropic principle, 110
Catholic Church
  on environmental crisis, 17
  and evolution, 172, 173
  and hES cell research, 10
  opposition to theology of Teilhard de Chardin, 70, 71
Catholic theologians, and Darwinian evolution, 173. *See also* Delio, Ilia; Haught, John; Johnson, Elizabeth; Küng, Hans; Mooney, Christopher; Rahner, Karl; Teilhard de Chardin, Pierre
Catling, David, 156
Cech, Thomas, 137
cells, composition of, 136
chloroplasts, 145, 146
chromosomes, human, 147
Clavius, Christopher, 91
climate change deniers, 18, 151
Cold Springs Harbor Laboratory, 176
Collins, Francis, 8, 51, 52
Columbus, Christopher, 89
conflict typology, 5–6, 21, 22
consciousness, 74, 75, 76
  inevitability of, 77–79
conservation of energy, law of, 134
constants, 109
consumer economy, 18
contingency, in evolutionary biology, 187, 188
Copernicanism, as contrary to church teaching, 95
Copernicus, Nicolaus, heliocentric cosmology of, 90, 91
Correns, Carl, 200
Cosmic Egg (primeval atom), 104
Cosmic Microwave Background (CMB) radiation, 106, 107
cosmological constant, 102
cosmos, models of, 88–100
Council of Trent, and interpretation of scripture, 94
Coyne, George, 8
creation, 83
  in book of Genesis, 87
  of human person as ongoing, 229, 230
Creation Museum, 179
creation science. *See* scientific creationism
creationism, 31, 177–86
  effect on science education, 185–86
  and science textbooks, 179, 180
Crick, Francis, 203
critical realism, 43–46, 52
cross-over inheritance pattern, 202
Crusades, 30
Cuvier, Georges, and immutability of species, 164
cytoskeleton, 145

Dalai Lama, and evolutionary theory, 173
dark energy, 115
dark matter, 115
Darrow, Clarence, 178

Darwin, Charles, 46
and evolution, 13, 14, 159–77
exploration in Galapagos Islands, 162, 163
and laws of inheritance, 198
and natural selection, 165–67
and origins of life, 130, 131, 139
religious views of, 171, 172
voyage on HMS *Beagle*, 160–65
Darwin, Erasmus, 159, 163
Darwin, Robert, 159, 160
Darwin on Trial (Johnson), 181
Darwinism
Christian responses to, 14–19
and problem of theodicy, 210, 211
Darwin's Black Box (Behe), 3, 181, 182, 184
Darwin's black box, 182
Darwin's Doubt, 189
Darwin's Theory. *See* natural selection
Davenport, Charles B., 176
Davies, Paul, 110, 111, 155
Davis, Percival, 31, 181
Dawkins, Richard, 3, 29, 53, 54, 55, 62, 65, 172, 191
death of God, 65
Delio, Ilia, 72, 173, 191, 210
Dembski, William, 3, 181
Dennett, Daniel, 65, 72, 172
Dennin, Michael, on fullness of reality, 20
developmental biology, and science and religion, 9, 10
dialogue typology, 8–12, 22, 23
diapsids, 206
Dicke, Robert, 107
dinosaurs, mass extinction of, 208, 209, 211–13
Discovery Institute, 3, 53, 55, 181, 186, 188
DNA
discovery of structure of, 203
double-helix model of, 203
human, 15, 58
Dobzhansky, Theodosius, 170
Doolittle, Russell, 183
Doppler effect, 103
and detection of planets, 152
Drake, Frank, 154, 155
Drake equation, 155, 156

Earth, formation of, 126, 127
Ecklund, Elaine, 62, 63
Eddington, Arthur, 103, 104
Ediacaran fossils, 189
education
discipline-centered, 60
effects of creationism and intelligent design on, 185–86
educational system, 59, 60, 61, 63, 64, 65
egg shell, and evolutionary adaptation, 205, 206
Einstein, Albert, 14, 46, 99, 112, 113
and theory of relativity, 101–2
electromagnetic force, 109
elements, 123
primary, 124
empirical observation, 37, 38
endoplasmic reticulum, 145
endoskeletons, 194, 205
entropy, 134
Epperson, Susan, 180
Epperson v. Arkansas, 179
eugenics, 175, 176, 177
Eugenics Education Society, 175
Eugenics Records Office (ERO), 176
eukaryotes, 140, 141, 145–48, 155, 158
euthanasia, and eugenics, 176, 177
evangelical Christians, and evolutionary biology, 30, 31

evolution, 83
  Catholic teaching on, 14, 15, 16
  and evangelical Christianity, 30, 31
  great inventions of, 192
  human, 214–31
  as ongoing process, 72, 73, 75
  Pius XII's neutral stance on, 7
  and science and religion, 12–14
  scientific alternatives to, 181–84
  and the skeletal system, 192–95
  theistic, 76, 77
  wars, 12, 13
  See also Darwin, Charles
evolutionary biology, and integration typology, 12–14
exoplanets, 152
exoskeletons, 193
extinction
  biological, 207–9
  of human sibling species, 222–25
Extrasolar Planets Encyclopedia, 152
extremophiles, 140, 141

faith, in God and science, 32
faith and reason, 31–33
FitzRoy, Robert, 161
four fundamental forces, 109, 110
Francis, Pope
  on continuing creation, 231
  on the environment, 17–19, 55
  and integration typology, 23
  on interdependence of humans and nature, 150
Francis of Assisi, St., 17, 18
Franklin, Rosalind, 203
fruit fly, genetic research on, 201–2
Fulbright, Jeannie, 31
fundamentalism, 63
  and literal reading of Bible, 39

Gaia hypothesis, 149
Galapagos Islands, explorations of Charles Darwin, 162, 163
Galilei, Galileo. *See* Galileo
Galilei, Giulia, 92
Galilei, Vincenzo, 91
Galileo
  astronomical studies of, 92, 93
  and Copernican model of universe, 94, 95, 96
  model of cosmos, 91–98
Galileo Affair, 95–98
Galton, Francis, and eugenics, 175, 177
Gandhi, Mahatma, on truth and humility, 56
general relativity, theory of, 102, 112
genes, dominant and recessive, 199
genetic inheritance, principles of, 198–204
genetics, and evolutionary theory, 15
Gilbert, Walter, 137
Glimcher, Melvin, 47, 48
God
  belief in, 29, 62, 173, 174
  in cosmic story, 118–21
  denial of, 24
  development in understanding of, 45, 46
  hidden everywhere, 106, 118
  presence in all, 58
  self-revelation of, 228, 229
  suffering of, 16, 210
God of the gaps explanations, 191
Goldilocks enigma, 110–12, 118
Golgi complex, 145
Goodenough, Ursula, 28, 37
Gould, Stephen J., 7, 71, 72, 187, 188
gravitational force, 109
graviton particle, 114
Great Dying, 207, 208
Great Oxygenation Event, 144
Greene, Brian, 111, 114, 115, 117, 118

Gregory XIII, Pope, calendar revision of, 91
Griffiths, Paul, 66

habitable zone (HZ), 153
Haldane, J. B. S., 131, 132
Harris, Sam, 42, 52, 53, 55
Harrison, Harry, 76
Haught, John, 13, 72, 173, 191, 210
Hawking, Stephen, 112–15, 117
Hazen, Robert, 133
Henslow, John Stevens, 160
heritable variation, 168
Herschel, John, 160
hES cells. *See* human embryonic stem cells
heterotrophs, 144
Hidden Reality, of multiverse, 118
history of cosmos, place of humankind in, 73, 74, 75
Hitchens, Christopher, 3, 72
HMS *Beagle*, 160–65
Holocaust, 177
Homo antecessor, 220
Homo denisova, 220, 222
Homo erectus, 69, 73, 219, 220, 222
Homo ergaster, 219
Homo floresiensis (the hobbits), 73, 219, 222
Homo habilis, 218, 219
Homo heidelburgensis, 220
Homo luzonensis, 222
Homo neanderthalis, 220, 222, 223
Homo sapiens, 17, 37, 73, 75, 79, 150, 188, 192, 215, 218, 220–26
- and development of complex language and thought, 222–26
- migration out of Africa, 220, 221

Homo soloensis, 219, 222
Hooker, Joseph, 131, 167
Hoyle, Fred, 105
Hubble, Edwin, 103, 104, 108
Hubble's Law, 104
human embryonic stem cells (hES cells), 9, 10, 11, 12
Human Genome Project, 52, 61
Humani generis (Pius XII), 7, 70
Humanist Manifesto, 28
humankind
- creation in book of Genesis, 215
- emergence of, 83
- ongoing creation of, 229, 230

humankind and physical world, interdependence, 148–51
humility, 26–31
- in *Humanist Manifesto*, 28
- among humanists, 28
- in science and religion, 54–56
- in world's religions, 27

Hunter, George, 178
Hutton, James, 161
Huxley, Sir Julian, 71, 73
Huxley, Thomas Henry, proponent of Darwin's theory, 170, 171
hydrothermal vent microbes, 142
Hylonomus, 206

Ignatius of Loyola, 41, 229
Imitation of Christ (Thomas à Kempis), 26
immigration, and eugenics, 176, 177
independence typology, 7–8, 22
induced pluripotent stem cells (iPSC), 10, 11
Inherit the Wind, 178
inheritance, biological, 198–202
Inostrancevia, 208
integration typology, 12–14, 23, 24
intelligent design, 53, 54, 119, 180–85
- and creationism, 181
- effect on science education, 185–86

iPSC. *See* induced pluripotent stem cells

iridium, as evidence of global cataclysm, 211, 212

John Paul II, Pope
 on Darwinian theory, 14, 15
 on hES cell research, 9, 10
 on science and religion, 8
 on science of evolution, 215, 216
Johnson Immigration Act, 176
Johnson, Elizabeth, 13, 16, 72, 173, 210
Johnson, Philip, 181
Jones, John E., 185
Judaism, and Darwinian evolution, 173

Kenyon, Dean, 31, 181
Kepler, Johannes, 94
Kepler-186f, 153
Kepler space telescope, 152
King, Ursula, 68, 69
Kitzmiller, Tammy, 183
Kitzmiller v. Dover Area School Board. *See* Panda Trial
knowledge
 and belief, 33–37
 provisional nature of, 45
Koch, Robert, 140
Krebs cycle, Darwinian explanation for, 184
Kuhn, Thomas, on paradigm shifts, 46
Küng, Hans, and paradigm shifts in theology, 50

Lamarck, Jean Baptiste, 163, 164
Lamarckian evolution, 163, 164
land animals, emergence from ancient fish, 197, 198
land vertebrates, descent from Devonian fishes, 204, 205
Lane, Nick, 138, 139, 192
language, development of, 222–26
Large Hadron Collider (CERN), 116
last universal common ancestor (LUCA), 139–42
 home of, 142
Laudato si' (Pope Francis), 17, 18, 19, 23, 55, 231
law of dominance, 199
law of independent assortment, 199
law of segregation, 199
laws of motion (Newton), 99, 100
Lawson, Nicholas, 162
Leakey, Louis and Mary, 218
Lemaître, Georges-Henri
 and Big Bang singularity, 103, 107
 cosmological model of, 103–6
Levine, Joseph, 183
life
 abiotic origins, 130–39, 149
 emergence of, 83
 extraterrestrial, 151–57
 multicellular, 9, 140, 141, 147, 158, 159
 origin in the seas, 158
 origins in book of Genesis, 122
 requirements for, 135, 136
life energy, 142, 143
Linnaeus, Carolus, classification system of, 163
liposomes, 136, 137
Lorenz, Konrad, 79
Lovelock, James, 148, 149, 150
LUCA. *See* last universal common ancestor
Lyell, Charles, 161, 162, 164, 167, 169
lysosomes, 145
Lystrosaurus, 208

Malthus, Robert, 166
Malthusian catastrophe, 166
mammals, evolution from reptiles, 213, 214

Margulis, Lynn, 145, 146, 148, 149, 150, 154
marriage laws, and social Darwinism, 175
Mars
  life on, 148
  water flow on, 154
Mars Exploration Rover Vehicles, 153, 154
Martin, William, 141
mass-extinction events, 16, 207
matrix vesicles, paradigm shift in research on, 47, 48, 49
Mayor, Michel, 152
McGrath, Alister, 173
Medici, Cosimo, 93
Mendel, Gregor (Johann), 5, 175
  and biological inheritance, 198–201
Meyer, Stephen C., 3, 54, 188, 189–91
  and Darwin's Doubt, 188, 189
Miller, Kenneth, 13, 183, 184
Miller, Stanley, 132
mitochondria, 145, 146
mitochondrial Eve, 225
molecules, formation of, 125
Mooney, Christopher, 72
Morgan, Thomas Hunt, 201, 202
Morris, Henry, 179, 180
Morris, Simon Conway, 187
  and inevitability of conscousness, 77, 78
M-theory, 114, 115, 117, 118
multiverse(s), 111–12, 114, 116, 118, 119

Napp, C. F., 199
natural selection, 13, 14, 46, 166–70
natural theologians, 160
natural theology, 39
nature
  and Catholic sacramentality, 80
  versus nurture, 175
  study of, and worship of God, 61
Nazi Germany, and eugenics, 176, 177
Neanderthals, 68, 78, 79, 220, 222–25
  and religious rituals, 78, 79
Neo-Darwinian synthesis, 202, 203
new atheists, 3, 42, 52, 72, 65, 66, 172
Newton, Isaac, 5, 8, 14
  view of universe, 99, 100
  work in physics, 98–100
NOMA. *See* non-overlapping magisteria
non-overlapping magisteria (NOMA), 7, 71, 72

Obama, President Barack, 51, 52
ocean, formation of, 127
Of Pandas and People (Davis and Kenyon), 31, 181, 183
Old Man (Neanderthal), 78
Omega and Christ, 74, 75, 76
Omega Point, 74, 230
On the Origin of Species by Means of Natural Selection (Darwin), 13, 131, 167–70, 198, 200, 216
Oparin, Alexander, 131, 132
organelles, 145, 146
organic chemistry, 129
Oxford debate, over evolution, 170, 171
oxygenic photosynthesis, 143, 144

Paley, William, 160
Panda Trial, 184, 185
paradigm shifts, 46–51
  in science, 47–49, 51
  in theology, 50–51, 72–73
Paris Accord, 18, 151
particle types (quarks, gluons, leptons), 116, 117
Pasteur, Louis, 130, 131, 140

pasteurization, 130
Paul V, Pope, 95
Peacocke, Arthur, 13
on creator God in cosmic story, 119, 120
Peebles, James, 107
"Peking Man," 69, 219
Penzias, Arno, 107
photosynthesis, 142, 143
physician-assisted suicide, 177
"Piltdown Man Hoax," 71
Pioneer Voyager exploration satellites, 154
Pius XI, Pope, 105
Pius XII, Pope
on evolution and evolutionism, 7, 70
and new cosmology, 105, 110
Planck's constant, 109
planets
Earth-life, 153
with intelligent life, 155, 156
Planned Parenthood Foundation of America, 176
Plato, 20, 88
Polkinghorne, John, 173
Pontifical Academy of Sciences, 105, 106
population theory, 166, 168, 169
prokaryotes, 139, 140, 145, 146, 148, 154, 158. *See also* bacteria
Protestant theologians, and Darwinian evolution, 173
protocells, 138
Ptolemy, Claudius, model of cosmos, 89–91

quadrivium, 59
Queloz, Didier, 152

Rahner, Karl, on ongoing creation of human person, 229, 230
Randall, Lisa, on philosophical implications of multiverse, 118, 119, 121
Ratzinger, Joseph (Pope Benedict XVI), on continuing creation, 230, 231
reality
eleven dimensions of, 24
nature of, 19–25
physical and spiritual, 20–25
reason, and religious belief, 32
recombination, 147
relativity, theory of, 46, 99
religion
biological basis, 227, 228
decline of, 65, 66
in evolutionary past, 226, 227
myths of, 29, 30
on other worlds, 156
religious conflict, 30
religious experience, 38
negative, 62, 63
respiration, 144
revelation, and religious experience, 38, 39
ribosomes, 145
ribozymes, 137, 138
RNA world hypothesis, 137, 138
Rohr, Richard, 228
on paradigm shift in religion, 50, 51
Ruse, Michael, 53
Russell, Robert John, 173

Sacks, Jonathan, 173
Sagan, Carl, 154, 155
Sanger, Margaret, 176
science
focus on, in education, 60, 61
as secular religion, 53
science and religion
Barbour's typologies of, 5–14
warfare mindset, 4, 5, 6

scientific creationism, 180
scientific knowledge, 33, 34, 35
scientific materialism, 5, 24, 25, 62
scientists
  humility before natural world, 37
  religious beliefs of, 62, 63
  view of reality, 28, 29, 30
Scopes, John, 177, 178
Scopes Monkey Trial (1925), 53, 177–79, 184, 185
scripture, senses of, 39, 40
Scutosaurus, 206
Search for Extraterrestrial Intelligence (SETI), 154, 155
selective breeding, 165
self-reflectiveness, 74
self-replication, 135
Septuagint, 88
serial endosymbiosis theory (SET), 146, 148
Sermon on the Mount, on humility, 26
sexual reproduction, 147, 148
skeletal system, and evolution, 192–95
slime (prebiotic soup), and origins of life, 131–34, 137
smokers, black and white, 132, 133, 138, 141
social Darwinism, 174–77
solar system, formation of, 125, 126
special relativity, theory of, 102
Spencer, Herbert, and survival of the fittest, 174, 175
Sperling, Erik, 190
spiritual direction, 41, 42
Spiritual Exercises (Ignatius of Loyola), 41, 229
spiritual experience, 40–43
spirituality, 40–43
spontaneous generation, 130, 163
Sprigg, Reginald, 189
Standard Model, 112, 113
stardust, elemental, 124, 125
stars, birth of, 101, 102, 124
State of Tennessee v. John Thomas Scopes. See Scopes Monkey Trial
steady-state hypothesis, 105, 106
stem cell research, 9–12
Stenger, Victor, 3
sterilization laws, and eugenics, 176
string theory, 24, 25, 113–16
stromatolites, 142
strong nuclear force, 109
struggle for existence, 166, 167
Sturtevant, Alfred, 202
suffering, God's voluntary participation in, 210
sun, 102, 108
  formation of, 125, 126
supernovae, 102, 124
survival of the fittest, 174
Sutherland, John, 133, 139
symbiosis, 145, 146
synapsids, 206

Tacey, David, 42, 66
  on spiritual revolution, 50
Taylor, Charles, 65, 66
Teilhard de Chardin, Pierre, 210
  on continuing human evolution, 230
  controversy surrounding, 70, 71, 72
  early life, 67, 68
  and evolution, 68–70
  and human consciousness, 74, 75, 76
  on Spirit of God in physical matter, 58
  as theologian, 70–72, 72–79
  and vertebrate paleontology, 68–70

telescope, invention and early development of, 92, 98
Teresa of Avila, on humility, 27
theodicy, 209–11
theology, of evolution, 76, 77
theory of everything, 112–15, 117, 118
thermodynamics, 134–35
Thomas à Kempis, 26
Thomas Aquinas
  on humility, 27
  and knowledge and belief, 36
Thompson, James, and human embryonic stem cells, 9
Tiktaalik, transitional fish fossil, 204
Torrey, E. Fuller, 227
transdifferentiation, and stem cell research, 11
Transiting Exoplanet Survey Satellite (TESS), 152
transmutation of species, 163, 164
trilobites, 159, 188, 194, 207
trivium, 59
Trump, President Donald, denial of climate change, 18, 151
Tyrannosaurus rex, 209

Unger, Franz, 199
uniformitarianism, 161, 164, 169
universal gravitation (Newton), 99, 101
universe
  creation of, 101, 102
  expanding, 103, 104, 124
university, curriculum, 59, 60, 64, 65
Urban VIII, Pope (Maffeo Barberini), 95, 96, 97, 98
Urey, Harold, 132

Very Large Array facility, 154
voice of God, in nature, 79, 80, 81
Vries, Hugo de, 200

Walcott, Charles Doolittle, 186–88
Wallace, Alfred Russell, 167
water
  chemistry of, 127–29
  and life on Earth, 128
  living, 128, 129
  as symbol of God's spirit, 128
Watson, James, 203
weak nuclear force, 109
Wedgwood, Emma, 165
Wedgwood, Josiah, 161
Wells, H. G., 140
Whitcomb, John, 179
White, Andrew Dickson, 89
Wilberforce, Samuel, opponent of Darwin's theory, 170, 171
Wilkins, Maurice, 203
Wilson, E. O., 22, 79, 227
Wilson, Robert, 107
Witten, Edward, 114
Woese, Carl, 140, 141
world religions, as supportive of science, 172, 173
Wright, Robert, 45
Wuthier, Roy, 47, 48

Y-chromosome Adam, 225, 226
young-earth creationism, 179